PEARSON EDEXCEL INTERNATIONAL A LEVEL

STATISTICS 1

Student Book

Series Editors: Joe Skrakowski and Harry Smith

Authors: Greg Attwood, Ian Bettison, Alan Clegg, Ali Datoo, Gill Dyer, Jane Dyer, Keith Gallick, Susan Hooker, Michael Jennings, John Kinoulty, Mohammed Ladak, Jean Littlewood, Bronwen Moran, James Nicholson, Su Nicholson, Laurence Pateman, Keith Pledger, Joe Skrakowski, Harry Smith

Published by Pearson Education Limited, 80 Strand, London, WC2R 0RL.

www.pearson.com/international-schools

Copies of official specifications for all Pearson qualifications may be found on the website: https://qualifications.pearson.com

Text © Pearson Education Limited 2019
Edited by Eric Pradel
Typeset by Tech-Set Ltd, Gateshead, UK
Original illustrations © Pearson Education Limited 2019
Illustrated by © Tech-Set Ltd, Gateshead, UK
Cover design by © Pearson Education Limited 2019

Cover images: *Front*: **Getty Images:** Werner Van Steen
Inside front cover: **Shutterstock.com:** Dmitry Lobanov

First published 2019

22
10 9

British Library Cataloguing in Publication Data
A catalogue record for this book is available from the British Library

ISBN 978 1 292245 14 0

Printed in Slovakia by Neografia

Acknowledgements
(Key: b-bottom; c-centre; l-left; r-right; t-top)

Images:
The authors and publisher would like to thank the following individuals and organisations for permission to reproduce photographs:

Alamy Stock Photo: Mark Levy 1, Cosmo Condina Stock Market 124; **Getty Images:** Billie Weiss/Boston Red Sox 54; **Shutterstock.com:** ifong 29, Anette Holmberg 95, Jeremy Richards 151, Stephen Marques 3, istidesign 3, Ecuadorpostales 5

Endorsement Statement
In order to ensure that this resource offers high-quality support for the associated Pearson qualification, it has been through a review process by the awarding body. This process confirms that this resource fully covers the teaching and learning content of the specification or part of a specification at which it is aimed. It also confirms that it demonstrates an appropriate balance between the development of subject skills, knowledge and understanding, in addition to preparation for assessment.

Endorsement does not cover any guidance on assessment activities or processes (e.g. practice questions or advice on how to answer assessment questions) included in the resource, nor does it prescribe any particular approach to the teaching or delivery of a related course.

While the publishers have made every attempt to ensure that advice on the qualification and its assessment is accurate, the official specification and associated assessment guidance materials are the only authoritative source of information and should always be referred to for definitive guidance.

Pearson examiners have not contributed to any sections in this resource relevant to examination papers for which they have responsibility.

Examiners will not use endorsed resources as a source of material for any assessment set by Pearson. Endorsement of a resource does not mean that the resource is required to achieve this Pearson qualification, nor does it mean that it is the only suitable material available to support the qualification, and any resource lists produced by the awarding body shall include this and other appropriate resources.

ABOUT THIS BOOK

The following three themes have been fully integrated throughout the Pearson Edexcel International Advanced Level in Mathematics series, so they can be applied alongside your learning.

1. Mathematical argument, language and proof

- Rigorous and consistent approach throughout
- Notation boxes explain key mathematical language and symbols

2. Mathematical problem-solving

- Hundreds of problem-solving questions, fully integrated into the main exercises
- Problem-solving boxes provide tips and strategies
- Challenge questions provide extra stretch

The Mathematical Problem-Solving Cycle

specify the problem → collect information → process and represent information → interpret results → specify the problem

3. Transferable skills

- Transferable skills are embedded throughout this book, in the exercises and in some examples
- These skills are signposted to show students which skills they are using and developing

Finding your way around the book

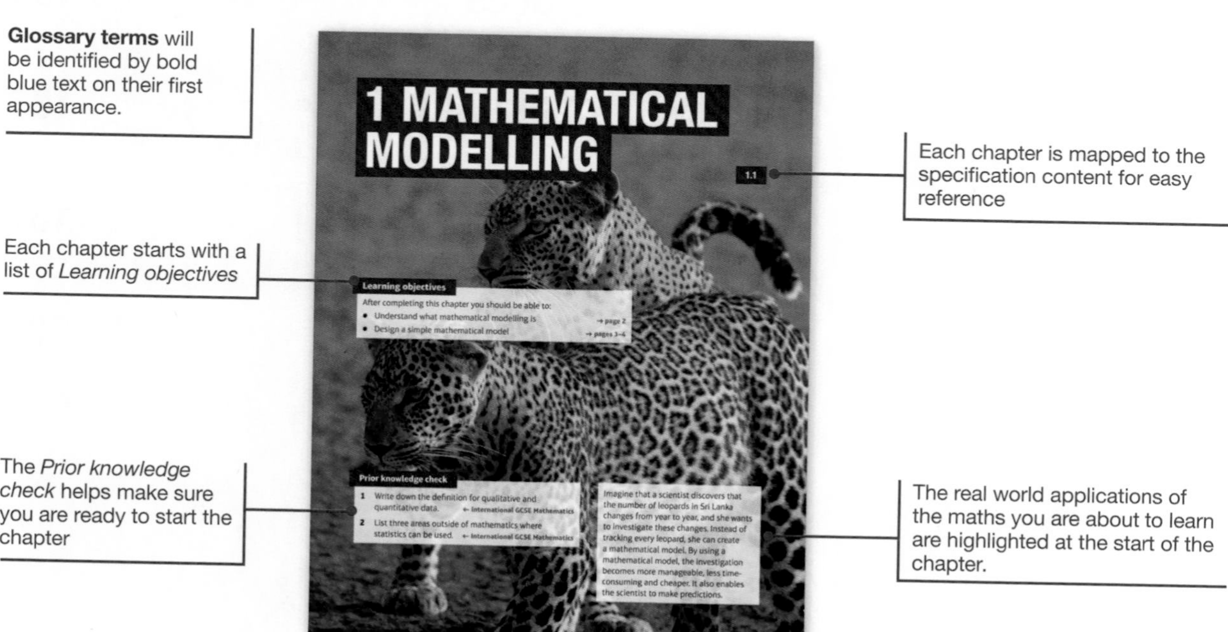

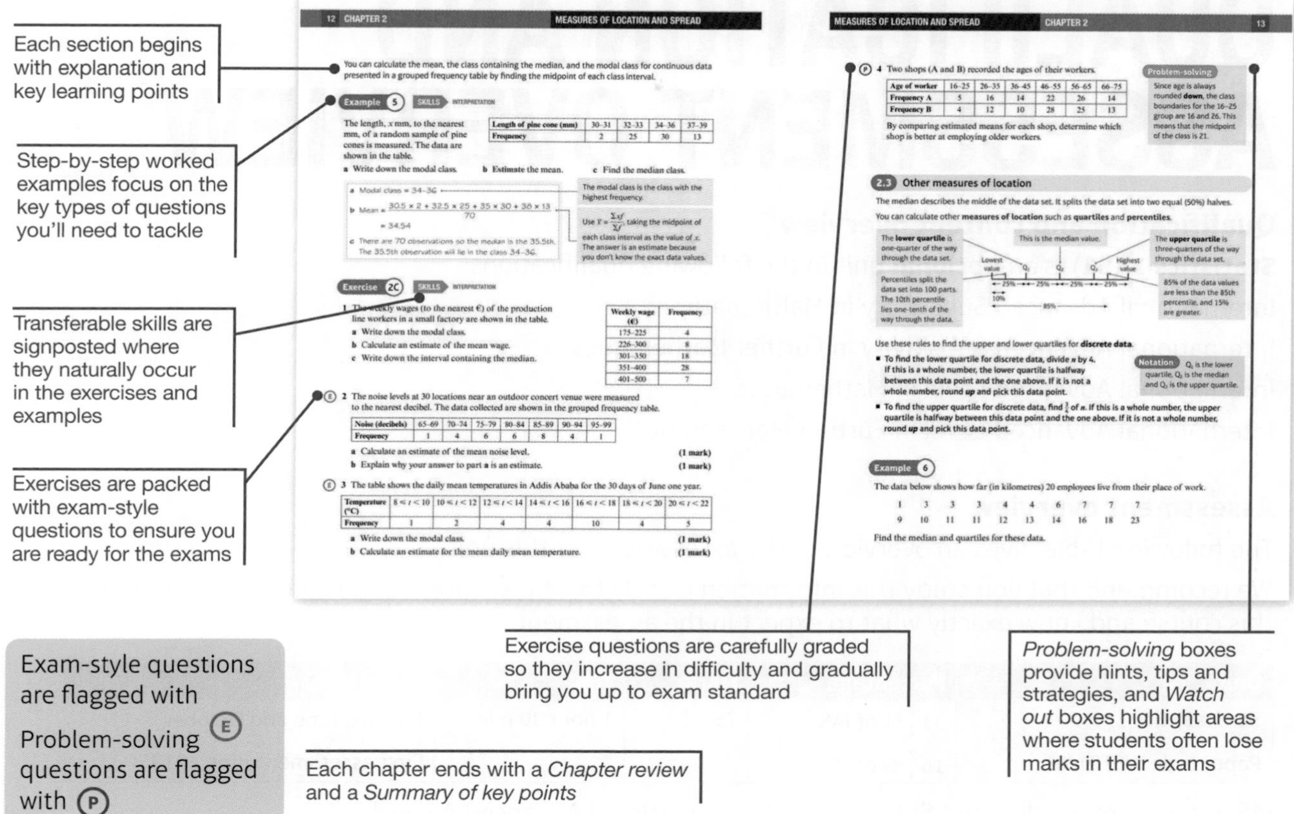

Each section begins with explanation and key learning points

Step-by-step worked examples focus on the key types of questions you'll need to tackle

Transferable skills are signposted where they naturally occur in the exercises and examples

Exercises are packed with exam-style questions to ensure you are ready for the exams

Exam-style questions are flagged with (E)

Problem-solving questions are flagged with (P)

Exercise questions are carefully graded so they increase in difficulty and gradually bring you up to exam standard

Problem-solving boxes provide hints, tips and strategies, and *Watch out* boxes highlight areas where students often lose marks in their exams

Each chapter ends with a *Chapter review* and a *Summary of key points*

After every few chapters, a *Review exercise* helps you consolidate your learning with lots of exam-style questions

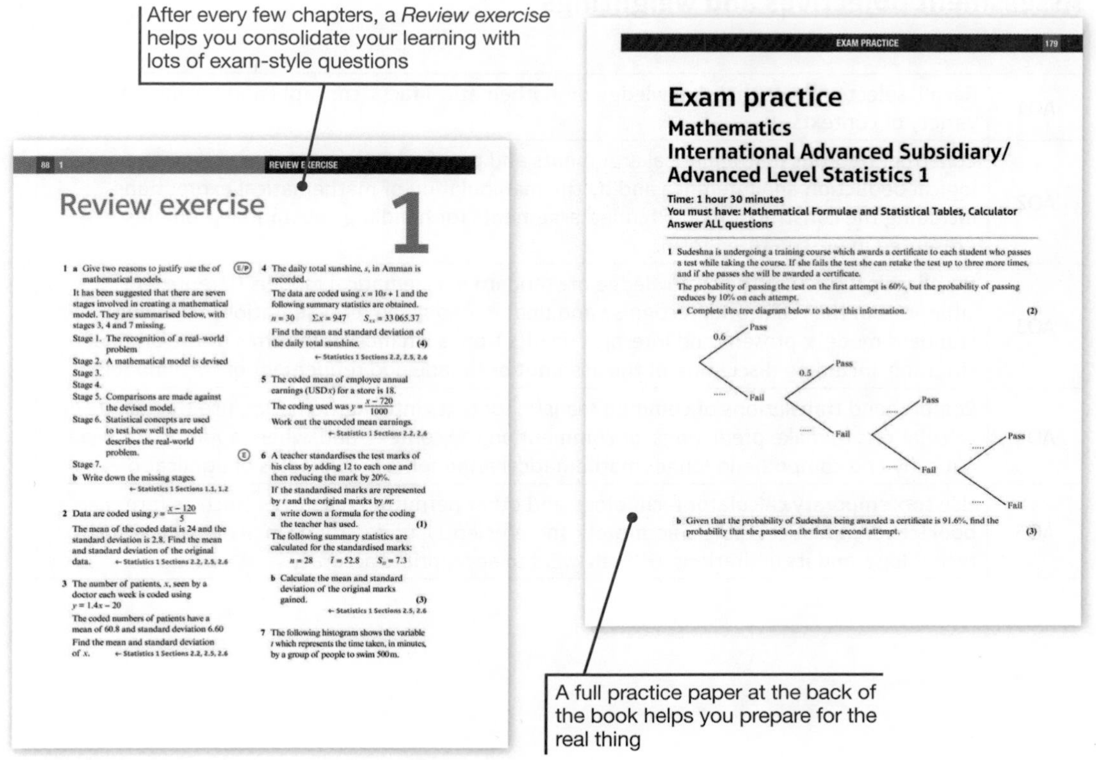

A full practice paper at the back of the book helps you prepare for the real thing

QUALIFICATION AND ASSESSMENT OVERVIEW

Qualification and content overview

Statistics 1 (S1) is an **optional** unit in the following qualifications:

International Advanced Subsidiary in Mathematics

International Advanced Subsidiary in Further Mathematics

International Advanced Level in Mathematics

International Advanced Level in Further Mathematics

Assessment overview

The following table gives an overview of the assessment for this unit.

We recommend that you study this information closely to help ensure that you are fully prepared for this course and know exactly what to expect in the assessment.

Unit	Percentage	Mark	Time	Availability
S1: Statistics 1 Paper code WST01/01	$33\frac{1}{3}$% of IAS $16\frac{2}{3}$% of IAL	75	1 hour 30 min	January, June and October First assessment June 2019

IAS: International Advanced Subsidiary, IAL: International Advanced A Level.

Assessment objectives and weightings

		Minimum weighting in IAS and IAL
AO1	Recall, select and use their knowledge of mathematical facts, concepts and techniques in a variety of contexts.	30%
AO2	Construct rigorous mathematical arguments and proofs through use of precise statements, logical deduction and inference and by the manipulation of mathematical expressions, including the construction of extended arguments for handling substantial problems presented in unstructured form.	30%
AO3	Recall, select and use their knowledge of standard mathematical models to represent situations in the real world; recognise and understand given representations involving standard models; present and interpret results from such models in terms of the original situation, including discussion of the assumptions made and refinement of such models.	10%
AO4	Comprehend translations of common realistic contexts into mathematics; use the results of calculations to make predictions, or comment on the context; and, where appropriate, read critically and comprehend longer mathematical arguments or examples of applications.	5%
AO5	Use contemporary calculator technology and other permitted resources (such as formulae booklets or statistical tables) accurately and efficiently; understand when not to use such technology, and its limitations. Give answers to appropriate accuracy.	5%

Relationship of assessment objectives to units

	Assessment objective				
S1	**AO1**	**AO2**	**AO3**	**AO4**	**AO5**
Marks out of 75	20–25	20–25	15–20	5–10	5–10
%	$26\frac{2}{3}$–$33\frac{1}{3}$	$26\frac{2}{3}$–$33\frac{1}{3}$	20–$26\frac{2}{3}$	$6\frac{2}{3}$–$13\frac{1}{3}$	$6\frac{2}{3}$–$13\frac{1}{3}$

Calculators

Students may use a calculator in assessments for these qualifications. Centres are responsible for making sure that calculators used by their students meet the requirements given in the table below.

Students are expected to have available a calculator with at least the following keys: +, −, ×, ÷, π, x^2, $\sqrt{x}$, $\frac{1}{x}$, x^y, ln x, e^x, $x!$, sine, cosine and tangent and their inverses in degrees and decimals of a degree, and in radians; memory.

Prohibitions

Calculators with any of the following facilities are prohibited in all examinations:

- databanks
- retrieval of text or formulae
- built-in symbolic algebra manipulations
- symbolic differentiation and/or integration
- language translators
- communication with other machines or the internet

Extra online content

Whenever you see an *Online* box, it means that there is extra online content available to support you.

SolutionBank

SolutionBank provides worked solutions for questions in the book. Download the solutions as a PDF or quickly find the solution you need online.

Use of technology

Explore topics in more detail, visualise problems and consolidate your understanding. Use pre-made GeoGebra activities or Casio resources for a graphic calculator.

Online Find the point of intersection graphically using technology.

GeoGebra

GeoGebra-powered interactives

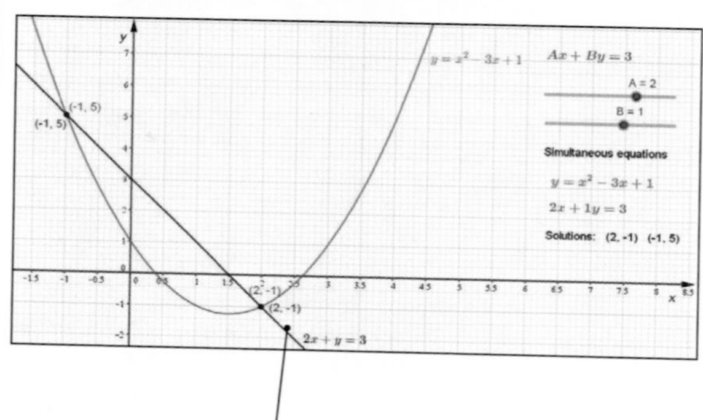

Interact with the mathematics you are learning using GeoGebra's easy-to-use tools

CASIO®

Graphic calculator interactives

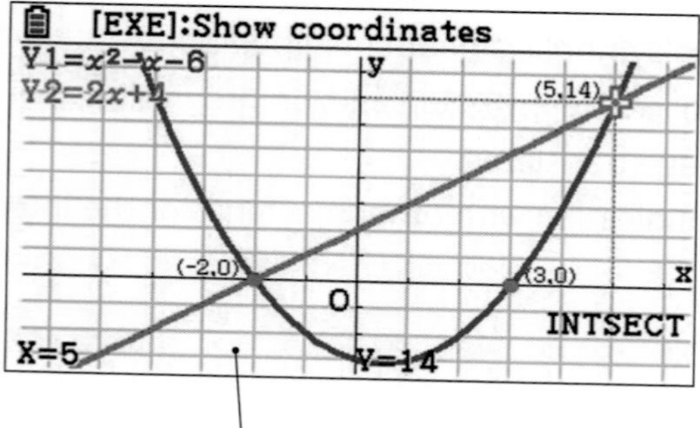

Explore the mathematics you are learning and gain confidence in using a graphic calculator

Calculator tutorials

Our helpful video tutorials will guide you through how to use your calculator in the exams. They cover both Casio's scientific and colour graphic calculators.

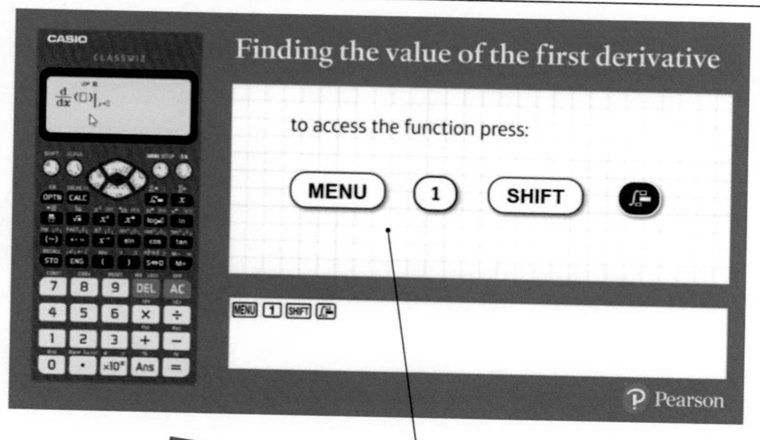

Step-by-step guide with audio instructions on exactly which buttons to press and what should appear on your calculator's screen

Online Work out each coefficient quickly using the ${}^nC_r$ and power functions on your calculator.

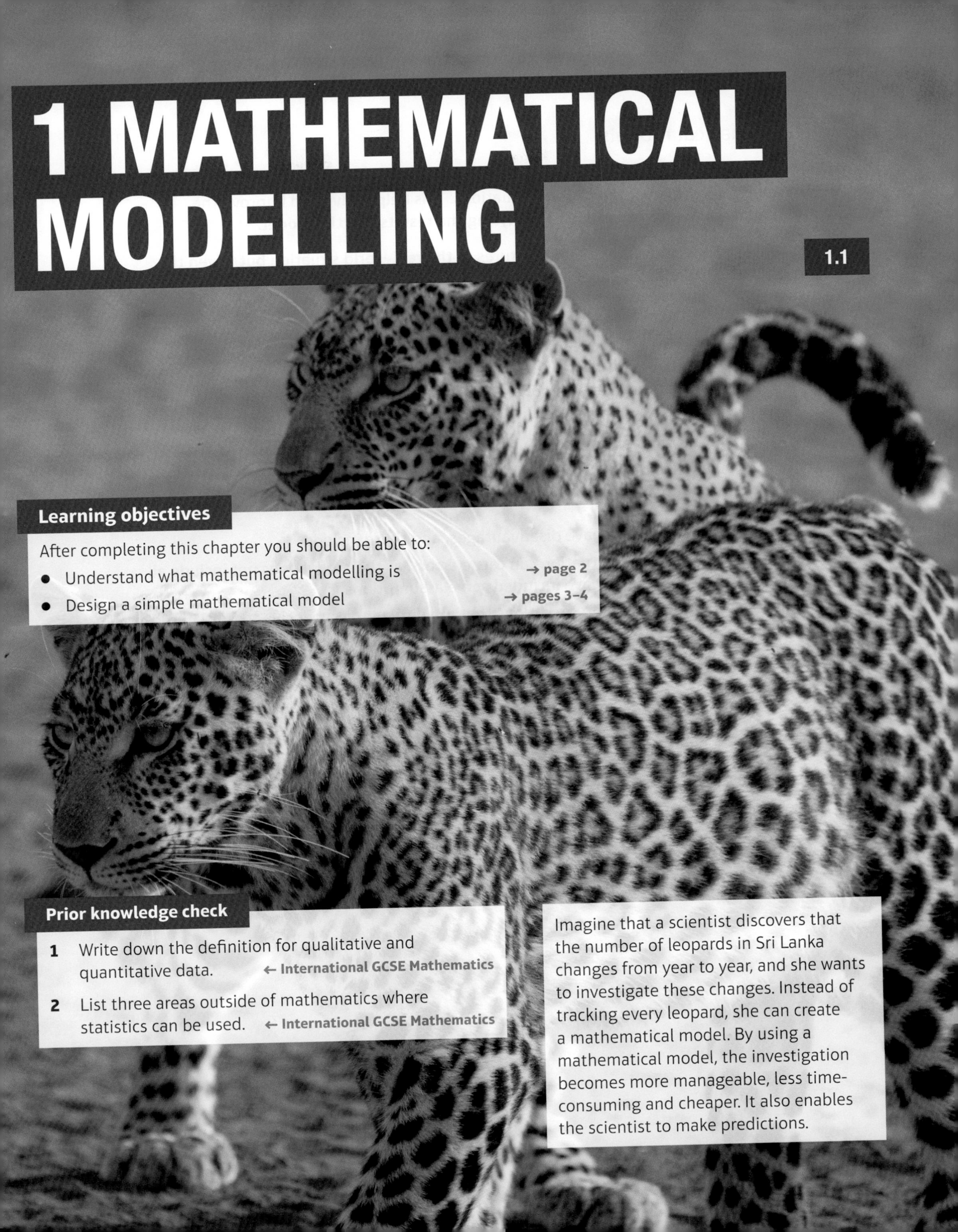

1 MATHEMATICAL MODELLING

1.1

Learning objectives

After completing this chapter you should be able to:

- Understand what mathematical modelling is → page 2
- Design a simple mathematical model → pages 3–4

Prior knowledge check

1. Write down the definition for qualitative and quantitative data. ← International GCSE Mathematics
2. List three areas outside of mathematics where statistics can be used. ← International GCSE Mathematics

Imagine that a scientist discovers that the number of leopards in Sri Lanka changes from year to year, and she wants to investigate these changes. Instead of tracking every leopard, she can create a mathematical model. By using a mathematical model, the investigation becomes more manageable, less time-consuming and cheaper. It also enables the scientist to make predictions.

1.1 Mathematical models

A **mathematical model** is a **simplification** of a real-world situation. It can be used to make **predictions** and forecasts about real-world situations. This helps solve and improve the understanding of real-world situations by analysing the results and the **model**.

The model will aim to include all the main features of the real-world situation but, given the difficulties of the real world, the model may have to be based on certain assumptions. As a result, these assumptions will need to be taken into consideration when analysing the results.

There are many advantages of mathematical models, and these include (but are not limited to):

- they are relatively quick and easy to produce
- they are usually a much more cost-effective way of analysing the real-world situation
- they enable predictions to be made
- they help improve the understanding of our world
- they help show how certain changes in **variables** will affect the outcomes
- they help simplify complex situations.

However, mathematical models do have disadvantages, and these include:

- simplification of the real-world situation can cause errors, as the model does not include all aspects of the problem and may have included some assumptions
- the model may work only in certain conditions that are difficult or expensive to fulfil in the real world.

SKILLS ANALYSIS

Give two advantages and disadvantages of using a mathematical model:

Advantages	Disadvantages
They are relatively quick and easy to produce	Simplification of a real-world situation may cause errors as the model is too simplistic
They help enable predictions to be made	The model may work only in certain conditions

1.2 Designing a model

The process of designing a model generally involves seven stages, outlined below.

Stage 1: The recognition of a real-world problem

Stage 2: A mathematical model is devised

Stage 3: Model used to make predictions about the behaviour of the real-world problem

Stage 4: Experimental data are collected from the real world

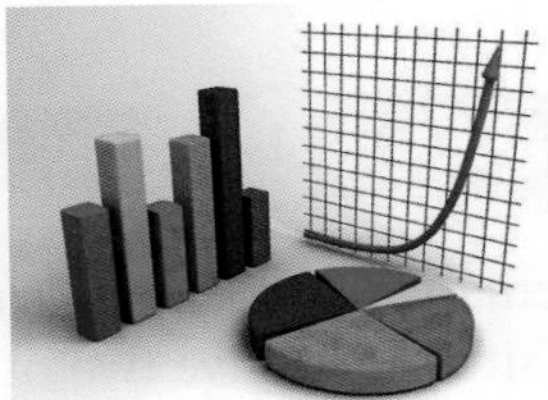

Stage 5: Comparisons are made against the devised model

Stage 6: Statistical concepts are used to test how well the model describes the real-world problem

Stage 7: Model is **refined**

Example 2

SKILLS EXECUTIVE FUNCTION

A scientist is investigating the population of owls and notices that the population varies year to year. Give a summary of the stages that are needed to create a mathematical model for this population variation.

1 Some assumptions need to be made to ensure the model is manageable. Birth and death rates of owls should be included, but food supply and environment changes should not.

2 Plan a mathematical model which will include diagrams.

3 Use this model to predict the population of the owls over a period of years.

4 Include and collect fresh data that match the conditions of the predicted values. You may also use historical data from the previous years.

5 Analyse the data using techniques you will meet in this course to compare the predicted data with the experimental data.

6 Use statistical tests that will provide an objective means of deciding if the differences between the model's predictions and experimental data are within acceptable limits.

If the predicted values do not match the experimental data closely enough, then the model can be refined. This will involve repeating and refining steps 2–6. This model is then constantly refined making the model more and more accurate.

Exercise 1A

SKILLS ANALYSIS; EXECUTIVE FUNCTION

1 Briefly explain the role of statistical tests in the process of mathematical modelling.

2 Describe how to refine the process of designing a mathematical model.

3 It is generally accepted that there are seven stages involved in creating a mathematical model. They are summarised below. Write down the missing stages.

Stage 1:

Stage 2: A mathematical model is devised

Stage 3: Model used to make predictions

Stage 4:

Stage 5: Comparisons are made against the devised model

Stage 6:

Stage 7: Model is refined

Chapter review 1

SKILLS ANALYSIS; EXECUTIVE FUNCTION

1 Mathematical models can simplify real-world problems and are a quick way to describe a real-world situation. Give two other reasons why mathematical models are used.

2 Give two advantages and two disadvantages of the use of mathematical models.

3 Explain how mathematical modelling can be used to investigate climate change.

4 A statistician is investigating population growth in Southeast Asia. Give a summary of the stages that are needed to create a mathematical model for this investigation.

Summary of key points

1 A mathematical model is a simplification of a real-world situation.

2 It is generally accepted that there are seven stages involved in creating a mathematical model.

- Stage 1: The recognition of a real-world problem
- Stage 2: A mathematical model is devised
- Stage 3: Model used to make predictions
- Stage 4: Experimental data collected
- Stage 5: Comparisons are made against the devised model
- Stage 6: Statistical concepts are used to test how well the model describes the real-world problem
- Stage 7: Model is refined

3 There are advantages and disadvantages to mathematical models. Some of these are:

Advantages	Disadvantages
They are relatively quick and easy to produce	Simplification of a real-world situation may cause errors as the model is too simplistic
They help enable predictions to be made	The model may work only in certain conditions

2 MEASURES OF LOCATION AND SPREAD

2.2
2.3

Learning objectives

After completing this chapter you should be able to:

- Recognise different types of data → pages 6–8
- Calculate measures of central tendency such as the mean, median and mode → pages 9–12
- Calculate measures of location such as percentiles → pages 13–15
- Calculate measures of spread such as range, interquartile range and interpercentile range → pages 16–17
- Calculate variance and standard deviation → pages 18–21
- Understand and use coding → pages 21–25

Prior knowledge check

1 Calculate the mean, mode and median of the following data:
10, 12, 38, 23, 38, 23, 21, 27, 38 ← International GCSE Mathematics

2 A train runs for 3 hours at a speed of 65 km per hour, and for the next 2 hours at a speed of 55 km per hour. Find the mean speed of the train for the 5 hour journey. ← International GCSE Mathematics

3 Find the mean, median, mode and range of the data shown in this frequency table.

Number of peas in a pod	3	4	5	6	7
Frequency	4	7	11	18	6

← International GCSE Mathematics

Wildlife biologists use statistics such as mean wingspan and standard deviation to compare populations of endangered birds in different habitats.

2.1 Types of data

In statistics, we collect observations or measurements of some variables. These observations are known as data. Variables associated with non-numerical data are **qualitative variables**, and variables associated with numerical data are **quantitative variables**. The flowchart below shows different types of data in more detail.

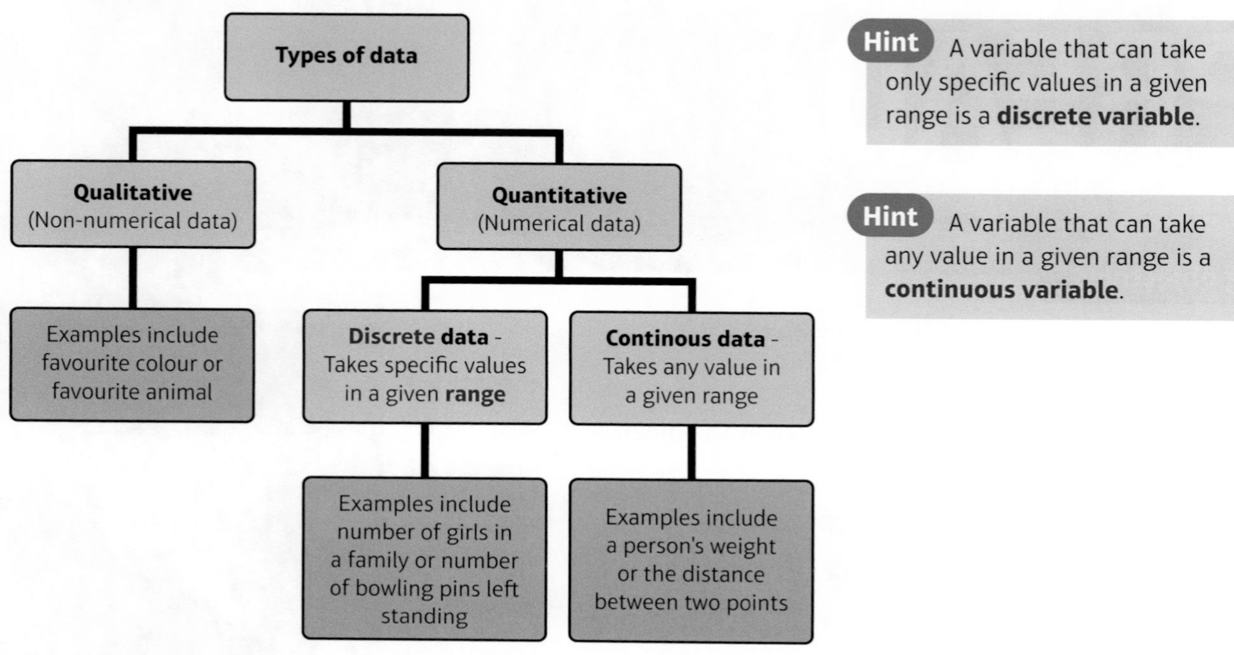

Hint A variable that can take only specific values in a given range is a **discrete variable**.

Hint A variable that can take any value in a given range is a **continuous variable**.

Example 1

State whether each of the following variables is continuous or discrete.

a Sprint times for a 100 m race

b Length

c Number of 10 cent coins in a bag

d Number of boys in a family

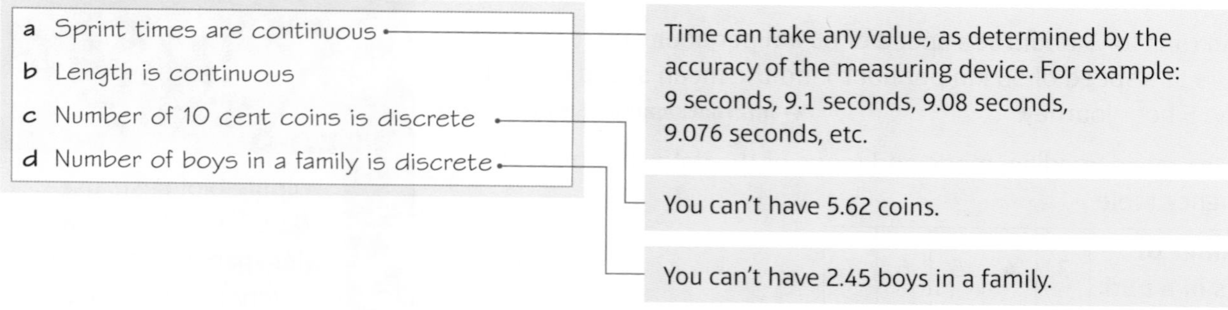

Large amounts of discrete data can be written as a frequency table or as grouped data. For example, the table below shows the number of students with a specific shoe size.

Shoe size(x)	Number of students, f
39	3
40	17
41	29
42	34
43	12

The number of anything is called its frequency, where f stands for frequency.

A frequency table is a quick way of writing a long list of numbers. For instance, this table tells us that 3 students have a shoe size of 39, and 17 students have a shoe size of 40, etc.

Data can also be presented as a **grouped frequency** table. The specific data values are not included in the table, instead they are grouped. You will need to know:

- **the groups are commonly known as classes**
- **how to find the class boundaries**
- **how to find the midpoint of a class**
- **how to find the class width.**

Example 2 SKILLS INTERPRETATION

The time, x seconds, taken by a random sample of females to run 400 m is measured and is shown in two different tables.

a Write down the class boundaries for the first row of each table.

b Find the midpoint and class width for the first row for each table.

Table 1

Time to run 400 m (s)	Number of females f
55–65	2
65–70	25
70–75	30
75–90	13

Table 2

Time to run 400 m (s)	Number of females f
55–65	2
66–70	25
71–75	30
76–90	13

It may seem that the classes overlap. However, this is not the case, as 55–65 is the shorthand form of writing $55 \leqslant x < 65$

The data has gaps and therefore the class boundaries are halfway between 55 and 65.

a The class boundaries for Table 1 are 55 s, 65 s as the data has no gaps and therefore the class boundaries are the numbers of the class. The class boundaries for Table 2 are 54.5 s, 65.5 s because the data has gaps.

b The midpoint for Table 1 is $\frac{1}{2}(55 + 65) = 60$
The midpoint for Table 2 is $\frac{1}{2}(54.5 + 65.5) = 60$
The class width for Table 1 is $65 - 55 = 10$
The class width for Table 2 is $65.5 - 54.5 = 11$

Exercise 2A SKILLS INTERPRETATION

1 State whether each of the following variables is qualitative or quantitative:
   a The height of a building
   b The colour of a jumper
   c Time spent waiting in a queue
   d Shoe size
   e Names of students in a school

2 State which of the following statements are true:
   a The weight of apples is discrete data.
   b The number of apples on the trees in an orchard is discrete data.
   c The amount of time it takes a train to make a journey is continuous data.
   d Simhal collected data on car colours by standing at the end of her road and writing down the car colours. The data she collected is quantitative.

3 The distribution of the lifetimes of torch batteries are shown in the grouped frequency table below.
   a Write down the class boundaries for the second group.
   b Work out the midpoint of the fifth group.

Lifetime (Nearest 0.1 of an hour)	Frequency
5.0–5.9	5
6.0–6.9	8
7.0–7.9	10
8.0–8.9	22
9.0–9.9	10
10.0–10.9	2

4 The grouped frequency table below shows the distributions of the weights of 16-week-old kittens.
   a Write down the class boundaries for the third group.
   b Work out the midpoint of the second group.

Weight (kg)	Frequency
1.2–1.3	8
1.3–1.4	28
1.4–1.5	32
1.5–1.6	22

Hint Sometimes it is not possible or practical to count the number of all the objects in a set, but that number is still discrete. For example, counting the number of apples on all the trees in an orchard or the number of bricks in a multi-storey building might not be possible (or desirable!) but nonetheless these are still discrete numbers.

2.2 Measures of central tendency

A **measure of location** is a single value which describes a position in a data set. If the single value describes the centre of the data, it is called a **measure of central tendency**. You should already know how to work out the **mean**, **median** and **mode** of a set of ungrouped data and from ungrouped frequency tables.

- **The mode or modal class is the value or class that occurs most often.**
- **The median is the middle value when the data values are put in order.**
- **The mean can be calculated using the formula $\bar{x} = \frac{\Sigma x}{n}$**

Notation
- $\bar{x}$ represents the **mean** of the data. You say 'x bar'.
- Σx represents the sum of the data values.
- n is the number of data values.

Combining means

If set A, of size n_1, has mean $\bar{x}_1$ and set B, of size n_2, has a mean $\bar{x}_2$, then the mean of the combined set of A and B is:

$$\bar{x} = \frac{n_1\bar{x}_1 + n_2\bar{x}_2}{n_1 + n_2}$$

Example 3 SKILLS INTERPRETATION

The mean of a sample of 25 observations is 6.4. The mean of a second sample of 30 observations is 7.2. Calculate the mean of all 55 observations.

For the first set of observations:

$\bar{x} = \frac{\Sigma x}{n}$, so $6.4 = \frac{\Sigma x}{25}$

$\Sigma x = 6.4 \times 25 = 160$ — Sum of data values = mean × number of data values

For the second set of observations:

$\bar{y} = \frac{\Sigma y}{m}$, so $7.2 = \frac{\Sigma y}{30}$

$\Sigma y = 7.2 \times 30 = 216$

Mean $= \frac{160 + 216}{25 + 30} = 6.84$ (3 s.f.)

Notation You can use x and y to represent two different data sets. You need to use different letters for the number of observations in each data set.

You need to decide on the best measure to use in particular situations.

- **Mode** This is used when data are qualitative, or when quantitative with either a single mode or two modes (bimodal). There is no mode if each value occurs just once.
- **Median** This is used for quantitative data. It is usually used when there are extreme values, as they do not affect it as much as they affect the mean.
- **Mean** This is used for quantitative data and uses all the pieces of data. It therefore gives a true measure of the data. However, it is affected by extreme values.

You can calculate the mean and median for discrete data presented in a frequency table.

- **For data given in a frequency table, the mean can be calculated using the formula**

$$\bar{x} = \frac{\sum xf}{\sum f}$$

Notation
- $\sum xf$ is the sum of the products of the data values and their frequencies.
- $\sum f$ is the sum of the frequencies.

Example 4 SKILLS REASONING/ARGUMENTATION

Li Wei records the shirt collar size, x, of the male students in his year. The results are shown in the table.

Shirt collar size	15	15.5	16	16.5	17
Frequency	3	17	29	34	12

For these data, find:

a the mode **b** the median **c** the mean.

d Explain why a shirt manufacturer might use the mode when planning production numbers.

a Mode = 16.5

16.5 is the collar size with the highest frequency.

b There are 95 observations so the median is the $\frac{95+1}{2} = 48$th.

There are 20 observations up to 15.5 and 49 observations up to 16.

The 48th observation is therefore 16.

Median = 16

c $\bar{x} = \frac{15 \times 3 + 15.5 \times 17 + 16 \times 29 + 16.5 \times 34 + 17 \times 12}{95}$

$= \frac{45 + 263.5 + 464 + 561 + 204}{95} = \frac{1537.5}{95} = 16.2$

d The mode is an actual data value and gives the manufacturer information on the most common size worn/purchased.

The mean is not one of the data values and the median is not necessarily indicative of the most popular collar size.

Exercise 2B SKILLS REASONING/ARGUMENTATION

1 Priyanka collected wild mushrooms every day for a week. When she got home each day she weighed them to the nearest 100 g. The weights are shown below:

500 700 400 300 900 700 700

a Write down the mode for these data.

b Calculate the mean for these data.

c Find the median for these data.

On the next day, Priyanka collected 650 g of wild mushrooms.

d Write down the effect this will have on the mean, the mode and the median.

Hint Try to answer part **d** without recalculating the averages. You could recalculate to check your answer.

2 Taha collects six pieces of data, x_1, x_2, x_3, x_4, x_5 and x_6. He works out that Σx is 256.2

a Calculate the mean for these data.

Taha collects another piece of data. It is 52.

b Write down the effect this piece of data will have on the mean.

3 The daily mean visibility, v metres, for Kuala Lumpur in May and June was recorded each day. The data are summarised as follows:

May: $n = 31$, $\Sigma v = 724\,000$

June: $n = 30$, $\Sigma v = 632\,000$

a Calculate the mean visibility in each month.

b Calculate the mean visibility for the total recording period.

4 A small workshop records how long it takes, in minutes, for each of their workers to make a certain item. The times are shown in the table.

Worker	A	B	C	D	E	F	G	H	I	J
Time in minutes	7	12	10	8	6	8	5	26	11	9

a Write down the mode for these data.

b Calculate the mean for these data.

c Find the median for these data.

d The manager wants to give the workers an idea of the average time they took. Write down, with a reason, which of the answers to **a**, **b** and **c** she should use.

5 The frequency table shows the number of breakdowns, b, per month recorded by a lorry firm over a certain period of time.

Breakdowns	0	1	2	3	4	5
Frequency	8	11	12	3	1	1

a Write down the modal number of breakdowns.

b Find the median number of breakdowns.

c Calculate the mean number of breakdowns.

d In a brochure about how many loads reach their destination on time, the firm quotes one of the answers to **a**, **b** or **c** as the number of breakdowns per month for its vehicles. Write down which of the three answers the firm should quote in the brochure.

6 The table shows the frequency distribution for the number of petals in the flowers of a group of celandines.

Number of petals	5	6	7	8	9
Frequency	8	57	29	3	1

Calculate the mean number of petals.

(P) 7 A scientist is investigating how many eggs the endangered kakapo bird lays in each brood cycle. The results are given in this frequency table.

Number of eggs	1	2	3
Frequency	7	p	2

If the mean number of eggs is 1.5, find the value of p.

Problem-solving

Use the formula for the mean of an ungrouped frequency table to write an equation involving p.

You can calculate the mean, the class containing the median, and the modal class for continuous data presented in a grouped frequency table by finding the midpoint of each class interval.

Example 5 SKILLS INTERPRETATION

The length, x mm, to the nearest mm, of a random sample of pine cones is measured. The data are shown in the table.

Length of pine cone (mm)	30–31	32–33	34–36	37–39
Frequency	2	25	30	13

a Write down the modal class. **b** **Estimate** the mean. **c** Find the median class.

a Modal class = 34–36

b Mean = $\frac{30.5 \times 2 + 32.5 \times 25 + 35 \times 30 + 38 \times 13}{70}$

= 34.54

c There are 70 observations so the median is the 35.5th.
The 35.5th observation will lie in the class 34–36.

The modal class is the class with the highest frequency.

Use $\bar{x} = \frac{\Sigma xf}{\Sigma f}$, taking the midpoint of each class interval as the value of x. The answer is an estimate because you don't know the exact data values.

Exercise 2C SKILLS INTERPRETATION

1 The weekly wages (to the nearest €) of the production line workers in a small factory are shown in the table.

a Write down the modal class.

b Calculate an estimate of the mean wage.

c Write down the interval containing the median.

Weekly wage (€)	Frequency
175–225	4
226–300	8
301–350	18
351–400	28
401–500	7

(E) **2** The noise levels at 30 locations near an outdoor concert venue were measured to the nearest decibel. The data collected are shown in the grouped frequency table.

Noise (decibels)	65–69	70–74	75–79	80–84	85–89	90–94	95–99
Frequency	1	4	6	6	8	4	1

a Calculate an estimate of the mean noise level. **(1 mark)**

b Explain why your answer to part **a** is an estimate. **(1 mark)**

(E) **3** The table shows the daily mean temperatures in Addis Ababa for the 30 days of June one year.

Temperature (°C)	$8 \leqslant t < 10$	$10 \leqslant t < 12$	$12 \leqslant t < 14$	$14 \leqslant t < 16$	$16 \leqslant t < 18$	$18 \leqslant t < 20$	$20 \leqslant t < 22$
Frequency	1	2	4	4	10	4	5

a Write down the modal class. **(1 mark)**

b Calculate an estimate for the mean daily mean temperature. **(1 mark)**

(P) **4** Two shops (A and B) recorded the ages of their workers.

Age of worker	16–25	26–35	36–45	46–55	56–65	66–75
Frequency A	5	16	14	22	26	14
Frequency B	4	12	10	28	25	13

By comparing estimated means for each shop, determine which shop is better at employing older workers.

Problem-solving

Since age is always rounded **down**, the class boundaries for the 16–25 group are 16 and 26. This means that the midpoint of the class is 21.

2.3 Other measures of location

The median describes the middle of the data set. It splits the data set into two equal (50%) halves.

You can calculate other **measures of location** such as **quartiles** and **percentiles**.

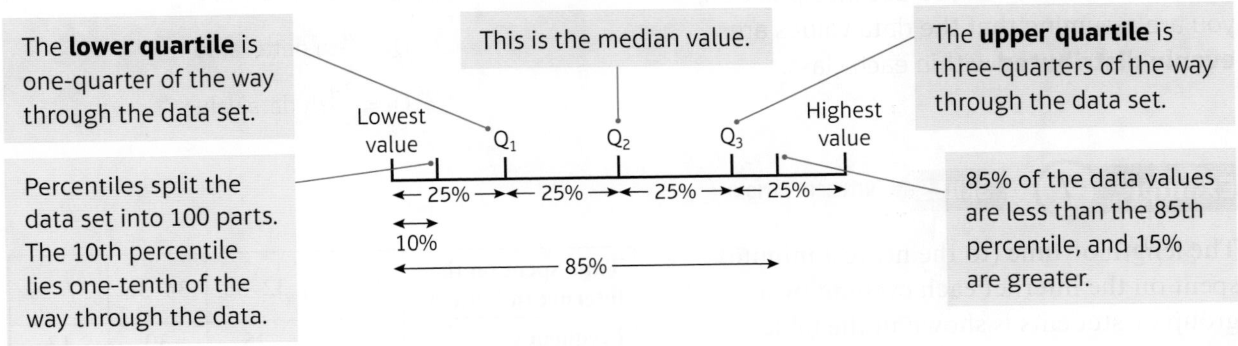

The **lower quartile** is one-quarter of the way through the data set.

This is the median value.

The **upper quartile** is three-quarters of the way through the data set.

Lowest value Q_1 Q_2 Q_3 Highest value

← 25% →← 25% →← 25% →← 25% →

10%

85%

Percentiles split the data set into 100 parts. The 10th percentile lies one-tenth of the way through the data.

85% of the data values are less than the 85th percentile, and 15% are greater.

Use these rules to find the upper and lower quartiles for **discrete data**.

- **To find the lower quartile for discrete data, divide n by 4. If this is a whole number, the lower quartile is halfway between this data point and the one above. If it is not a whole number, round *up* and pick this data point.**

Notation Q_1 is the lower quartile, Q_2 is the median and Q_3 is the upper quartile.

- **To find the upper quartile for discrete data, find $\frac{3}{4}$ of n. If this is a whole number, the upper quartile is halfway between this data point and the one above. If it is not a whole number, round *up* and pick this data point.**

Example 6

The data below shows how far (in kilometres) 20 employees live from their place of work.

1	3	3	3	4	4	6	7	7	7
9	10	11	11	12	13	14	16	18	23

Find the median and quartiles for these data.

$Q_2 = \frac{20+1}{2}$th value = 10.5th value

$Q_2 = \frac{7+9}{2} = 8$ km

Q_1 = 5.5th value

Q_1 = 4 km

Q_3 = 15.5th value

Q_3 = 12.5 km

Q_2 is the median. It lies halfway between the 10th and 11th data values (7 km and 9 km respectively).

$\frac{20}{4} = 5$ so the lower quartile is halfway between the 5th and 6th data values.

$\frac{3 \times 20}{4} = 15$ so the upper quartile is halfway between the 15th and 16th data values.

When data are presented in a grouped frequency table you can use a technique called **interpolation** to estimate the median, quartiles and percentiles. When you use interpolation, you are assuming that the data values are **evenly distributed** within each class.

Watch out For **grouped continuous** data, or data presented in a cumulative frequency table:

$Q_1 = \frac{n}{4}$th data value

$Q_2 = \frac{n}{2}$th data value

$Q_3 = \frac{3n}{4}$th data value

Example 7

SKILLS INTERPRETATION

The length of time (to the nearest minute) spent on the internet each evening by a group of students is shown in the table.

Time spent on the internet (minutes)	30–31	32–33	34–36	37–39
Frequency	2	25	30	13

a Find an estimate for the upper quartile.

b Find an estimate for the 10th percentile.

a Upper quartile: $\frac{3 \times 70}{4} = 52.5$th value

Using interpolation:

33.5	Q_3	36.5
27	52.5	57

$$\frac{Q_3 - 33.5}{36.5 - 33.5} = \frac{52.5 - 27}{57 - 27}$$

$$\frac{Q_3 - 33.5}{3} = \frac{25.5}{30}$$

$$Q_3 = 36.05$$

b The 10th percentile is the 7th data value.

$$\frac{P_{10} - 31.5}{33.5 - 31.5} = \frac{7 - 2}{27 - 2}$$

$$\frac{P_{10} - 31.5}{2} = \frac{5}{25}$$

$$P_{10} = 31.9$$

The endpoints on the line represent the class boundaries.

The values on the bottom are the cumulative frequencies for the previous classes and this class.

Problem-solving

Use proportion to estimate Q_3. The 52.5th value lies $\frac{52.5 - 27}{57 - 27}$ of the way into the class, so Q_3 lies $\frac{Q_3 - 33.5}{36.5 - 33.5}$ of the way between the class boundaries. Equate these two fractions to form an equation and solve to find Q_3.

Notation You can write the 10th percentile as P_{10}.

Exercise 2D SKILLS INTERPRETATION

1 The daily mean pressure (hPa) during the last 16 days of July in Perth is recorded. The data are given below:

1024 1022 1021 1013 1009 1018 1017 1024
1027 1029 1031 1025 1017 1019 1017 1014

Notation hPa (hectopascal) is the SI unit used to measure atmospheric pressure in weather and meteorology.

a Find the median pressure for that period.

b Find the lower and upper quartiles.

2 Zaynep records the number of books in the collections of students in her year. The results are in the table below.

Number of books	35	36	37	38	39
Frequency	3	17	29	34	12

Find Q_1, Q_2 and Q_3.

Hint This is an ungrouped frequency table so you do not need to use interpolation. Use the rules for finding the median and quartiles of **discrete** data.

(E) 3 A hotel is worried about the reliability of its lift. It keeps a weekly record of the number of times it breaks down over a period of 26 weeks. The data collected are summarised in the table opposite.

Use interpolation to estimate the median number of breakdowns.

Number of breakdowns	**Frequency**
0–1	18
2–3	7
4–5	1

(2 marks)

4 The weights of 31 cows were recorded to the nearest kilogram. The weights are shown in the table.

Weight of cow (kg)	300–349	350–399	400–449	450–499	500–549
Frequency	3	6	10	7	5

a Find an estimate for the median weight.

b Find the lower quartile, Q_1.

c Find the upper quartile, Q_3.

d Interpret the meaning of the value you have found for the upper quartile in part **c**.

(E) 5 A roadside assistance company kept a record over a week of the amount of time, in minutes, people were kept waiting for assistance. The times are shown below.

Time waiting, t (minutes)	$20 \leqslant t < 30$	$30 \leqslant t < 40$	$40 \leqslant t < 50$	$50 \leqslant t < 60$	$60 \leqslant t < 70$
Frequency	6	10	18	13	2

a Find an estimate for the mean time spent waiting. **(1 mark)**

b Calculate the 65th percentile. **(2 marks)**

The firm writes the following statement for an advertisement:

Only 10% of our customers have to wait longer than 56 minutes.

c By calculating a suitable percentile, comment on the validity of this claim. **(3 marks)**

(E) **6** The table shows the recorded wingspans, in metres, of 100 endangered California condor birds.

Wingspan, *w* (m)	$1.0 \leqslant w < 1.5$	$1.5 \leqslant w < 2.0$	$2.0 \leqslant w < 2.5$	$2.5 \leqslant w < 3.0$	$3.0 \leqslant w$
Frequency	4	20	37	28	11

a Estimate the 80th percentile and interpret the value. **(3 marks)**

b State why it is not possible to estimate the 90th percentile. **(1 mark)**

2.4 Measures of spread

A measure of spread is a measure of how spread out the data are. Here are two simple **measures of spread**.

- **The range is the difference between the largest and smallest values in the data set.**
- **The interquartile range (IQR) is the difference between the upper quartile and the lower quartile, $Q_3 - Q_1$.**

Notation Measures of spread are sometimes called **measures of dispersion** or **measures of variation**.

The range takes into account all of the data but can be affected by extreme values. The interquartile range is not affected by extreme values but only considers the spread of the middle 50% of the data.

- **The interpercentile range is the difference between the values for two given percentiles.**

The 10th to 90th interpercentile range is often used since it is not affected by extreme values but still considers 80% of the data in its calculation.

Example 8 SKILLS INTERPRETATION

The table shows the masses, in tonnes, of 120 African bush elephants.

Mass, *m* (tonnes)	$4.0 \leqslant m < 4.5$	$4.5 \leqslant m < 5.0$	$5.0 \leqslant m < 5.5$	$5.5 \leqslant m < 6.0$	$6.0 \leqslant m < 6.5$
Frequency	13	23	31	34	19

Find estimates for:

a the range **b** the interquartile range **c** the 10th to 90th interpercentile range.

a Range is $6.5 - 4.0 = 2.5$ tonnes

The largest possible value is 6.5 and the smallest possible value is 4.0.

b Q_1 = 30th data value: 4.87 tonnes

Use interpolation: $\frac{Q_1 - 4.5}{5.0 - 4.5} = \frac{30 - 13}{23}$

Q_3 = 90th data value: 5.84 tonnes

Use interpolation: $\frac{Q_3 - 5.5}{6.0 - 5.5} = \frac{90 - 67}{34}$

The interquartile range is therefore $5.84 - 4.87 = 0.97$ tonnes

c 10th percentile = 12th data value: 4.46 tonnes

90th percentile = 108th data value: 6.18 tonnes

The 10th to 90th interpercentile range is therefore $6.18 - 4.46 = 1.72$ tonnes

Use interpolation to find the 10th and 90th percentiles, then work out the difference between them.

Exercise 2E

SKILLS INTERPRETATION

(P) 1 The lengths of a number of slow worms were measured, to the nearest mm. The results are shown in the table.

Length of slow worms (mm)	Frequency
125–139	4
140–154	4
155–169	2
170–184	7
185–199	20
200–214	24
215–229	10

a Work out how many slow worms were measured.

b Estimate the interquartile range for the lengths of the slow worms.

c Calculate an estimate for the mean length of the slow worms.

d Estimate the number of slow worms whose length is more than one interquartile range above the mean.

Problem-solving

For part **d**, work out $\bar{x}$ + IQR, and determine which class interval it falls in. Then use proportion to work out how many slow worms from that class interval you need to include in your estimate.

(E) 2 The table shows the monthly income for workers in a factory.

Monthly income, x ($)	$900 \leqslant x < 1000$	$1000 \leqslant x < 1100$	$1100 \leqslant x < 1200$	$1200 \leqslant x < 1300$
Frequency	3	24	28	15

a Calculate the 34% to 66% interpercentile range. **(3 marks)**

b Estimate the number of data values that fall within this range. **(2 marks)**

(E) 3 A train travelled from Manchester to Liverpool. The times, to the nearest minute, it took for the journey were recorded over a certain period. The times are shown in the table.

Journey time (minutes)	15–16	17–18	19–20	21–22
Frequency	5	10	35	10

a Calculate the 5% to 95% interpercentile range. **(3 marks)**

b Estimate the number of data values that fall within this range. **(1 mark)**

(E/P) 4 The daily mean temperature (°C) in Santiago for each of the first ten days of June is given below:

14.3 12.7 12.4 10.9 9.4 13.2 12.1 10.3 10.3 10.6

a Calculate the median and interquartile range. **(2 marks)**

The median daily mean temperature in Santiago during the first 10 days of May was 9.9 °C and the interquartile range was 3.9 °C.

b Compare the data for May with the data for June. **(2 marks)**

The 10% to 90% interpercentile range for the daily mean temperature in Santiago during July was 5.4 °C.

c Estimate the number of days in July on which the daily mean temperature fell within this range. **(1 mark)**

2.5 Variance and standard deviation

Another measure that can be used to work out the spread of a data set is the **variance**.
This makes use of the fact that each data point deviates from the mean by the amount $x - \bar{x}$.

- Variance $= \dfrac{\Sigma(x-\bar{x})^2}{n} = \dfrac{\Sigma x^2}{n} - \left(\dfrac{\Sigma x}{n}\right)^2 = \dfrac{S_{xx}}{n}$

  where $S_{xx} = \Sigma(x-\bar{x})^2 = \Sigma x^2 - \dfrac{(\Sigma x)^2}{n}$

Notation S_{xx} is a **summary statistic**, which is used to make formulae easier to use and learn.

The second version of the formula, $\dfrac{\Sigma x^2}{n} - \left(\dfrac{\Sigma x}{n}\right)^2$, is easier to work with when given raw data.
It can be thought of as 'the mean of the squares minus the square of the mean'.

The third version, $\dfrac{S_{xx}}{n}$, is easier to use if you can use your calculator to find S_{xx} quickly.

The units of the variance are the units of the data squared. You can find a related measure of spread that has the same units as the data.

- **The standard deviation is the square root of the variance:**

$$\sigma = \sqrt{\frac{\Sigma(x-\bar{x})^2}{n}} = \sqrt{\frac{\Sigma x^2}{n} - \left(\frac{\Sigma x}{n}\right)^2} = \sqrt{\frac{S_{xx}}{n}}$$

Notation σ is the symbol we use for the standard deviation of a data set. Hence σ^2 is used for the variance.

Example 9 SKILLS EXECUTIVE FUNCTION

The marks gained in a test by seven randomly selected students are:

3 4 6 2 8 8 5

Find the variance and standard deviation of the marks of the seven students.

$\Sigma x = 3 + 4 + 6 + 2 + 8 + 8 + 5 = 36$

$\Sigma x^2 = 9 + 16 + 36 + 4 + 64 + 64 + 25 = 218$

variance, $\sigma^2 = \dfrac{218}{7} - \left(\dfrac{36}{7}\right)^2 = 4.69$

standard deviation, $\sigma = \sqrt{4.69} = 2.17$

Use the 'mean of the squares minus the square of the mean':

$$\sigma^2 = \frac{\Sigma x^2}{n} - \left(\frac{\Sigma x}{n}\right)^2$$

- **You can use these versions of the formulae for variance and standard deviation for grouped data that is presented in a frequency table:**
  - $\sigma^2 = \dfrac{\Sigma f(x-\bar{x})^2}{\Sigma f} = \dfrac{\Sigma fx^2}{\Sigma f} - \left(\dfrac{\Sigma fx}{\Sigma f}\right)^2$
  - $\sigma = \sqrt{\dfrac{\Sigma f(x-\bar{x})^2}{\Sigma f}} = \sqrt{\dfrac{\Sigma fx^2}{\Sigma f} - \left(\dfrac{\Sigma fx}{\Sigma f}\right)^2}$

  where f is the frequency for each group and Σf is the total frequency.

Example 10

Shamsa records the time spent out of school during the lunch hour to the nearest minute, x, of the students in her year.
The results are shown in the table.

Time spent out of school, x (min)	35	36	37	38
Frequency	3	17	29	34

Calculate the standard deviation of the time spent out of school.

$\Sigma fx^2 = 3 \times 35^2 + 17 \times 36^2 + 29 \times 37^2 + 34 \times 38^2 = 114\,504$

$\Sigma fx = 3 \times 35 + 17 \times 36 + 29 \times 37 + 34 \times 38 = 3082$

$\Sigma f = 3 + 17 + 29 + 34 = 83$

$\sigma^2 = \frac{114\,504}{83} - \left(\frac{3082}{83}\right)^2 = 0.741\,47\ldots$

$\sigma = \sqrt{0.741\,47\ldots} = 0.861$ (3 s.f.)

Hint The values of Σfx^2, Σfx and Σf are sometimes given with the question.

σ^2 is the variance, and σ is the standard deviation.
Use $\sigma^2 = \frac{\Sigma fx^2}{\Sigma f} - \left(\frac{\Sigma fx}{\Sigma f}\right)^2$

If the data are given in a grouped frequency table, you can calculate **estimates** for the variance and standard deviation of the data using the **midpoint** of each class interval.

Example 11

SKILLS EXECUTIVE FUNCTION

Akira recorded the length, in minutes, of each phone call she made for a month.
The data are summarised in the table below.

Length of phone call, l (min)	$0 < l \leqslant 5$	$5 < l \leqslant 10$	$10 < l \leqslant 15$	$15 < l \leqslant 20$	$20 < l \leqslant 60$	$60 < l \leqslant 70$
Frequency	4	15	5	2	0	1

Calculate an estimate of the standard deviation of the length of Akira's phone calls.

Length of phone call, l (min)	Frequency	Midpoint x	fx	fx^2
$0 < l \leqslant 5$	4	2.5	$4 \times 2.5 = 10$	$4 \times 6.25 = 25$
$5 < l \leqslant 10$	15	7.5	112.5	843.75
$10 < l \leqslant 15$	5	12.5	62.5	781.25
$15 < l \leqslant 20$	2	17.5	35	612.5
$20 < l \leqslant 60$	0	40	0	0
$60 < l \leqslant 70$	1	65	65	4225
total	27		285	6487.5

You can use a table like this to keep track of your working.

$\Sigma fx^2 = 6487.5$ $\quad \Sigma fx = 285$ $\quad \Sigma f = 27$

$\sigma^2 = \frac{6487.5}{27} - \left(\frac{285}{27}\right)^2 = 128.858\,02$

$\sigma = \sqrt{128.858\,02} = 11.4$ (3 s.f.)

Exercise 2F SKILLS EXECUTIVE FUNCTION

1 The summary data for a variable x are: $\Sigma x = 24$ $\Sigma x^2 = 78$ $n = 8$

Find:

a the mean

b the variance σ^2

c the standard deviation σ.

(E) 2 Ten collie dogs are weighed (w kg). The summary data for the weights are:

$\Sigma w = 241$ $\Sigma w^2 = 5905$

Use this summary data to find the standard deviation of the collies' weights. **(2 marks)**

3 Eight students' heights (h cm) are measured. They are as follows:

165 170 190 180 175 185 176 184

a Work out the mean height of the students.

b Given $\Sigma h^2 = 254\,307$, work out the variance. Show all your working.

c Work out the standard deviation.

(P) 4 For a set of 10 numbers: $\Sigma x = 50$ $\Sigma x^2 = 310$

For a different set of 15 numbers: $\Sigma x = 86$ $\Sigma x^2 = 568$

Find the mean and the standard deviation of the combined set of 25 numbers.

(E) 5 Nahab asks the students in his year group how much allowance they get per week. The results, rounded to the nearest Omani Riyals, are shown in the table.

Number of OMR	8	9	10	11	12
Frequency	14	8	28	15	20

a Work out the mean and standard deviation of the allowance. Give units with your answer. **(3 marks)**

b How many students received an allowance amount more than one standard deviation above the mean? **(2 marks)**

(E) 6 In a student group, a record was kept of the number of days of absence each student had over one particular term. The results are shown in the table.

Number of days absent	0	1	2	3	4
Frequency	12	20	10	7	5

Work out the standard deviation of the number of days absent. **(2 marks)**

(E/P) **7** A certain type of machine contained a part that tended to wear out after different amounts of time. The time it took for 50 of the parts to wear out was recorded. The results are shown in the table.

Lifetime, h (hours)	$5 < h \leqslant 10$	$10 < h \leqslant 15$	$15 < h \leqslant 20$	$20 < h \leqslant 25$	$25 < h \leqslant 30$
Frequency	5	14	23	6	2

The manufacturer makes the following claim:

> 90% of the parts tested lasted longer than one standard deviation below the mean.

Problem-solving

You need to calculate estimates for the mean and the standard deviation, then estimate the number of parts that lasted longer than one standard deviation below the mean.

Comment on the accuracy of the manufacturer's claim, giving relevant numerical evidence. **(5 marks)**

(E) **8** The daily mean wind speed, x (knots) in Chicago is recorded. The summary data are:

$\Sigma x = 243 \qquad \Sigma x^2 = 2317$

a Work out the mean and the standard deviation of the daily mean wind speed. **(2 marks)**

The highest recorded wind speed was 17 knots and the lowest recorded wind speed was 4 knots.

b Estimate the number of days in which the wind speed was greater than one standard deviation above the mean. **(2 marks)**

c State one assumption you have made in making this estimate. **(1 mark)**

Challenge

The manager at a local bakery calculates the mean and standard deviation of the number of loaves of bread bought per person in a random sample of her customers as 0.787 and 0.99 respectively. If each loaf costs \$1.04, calculate the mean and standard deviation of the amount spent on loaves per person.

2.6 Coding

Coding is a way of simplifying statistical calculations. Each data value is coded to make a new set of data values which are easier to work with.

In your exam, you will usually have to code values using a formula like this: $y = \frac{x - a}{b}$

where a and b are constants that you have to choose, or are given with the question.

When data are coded, different statistics change in different ways.

- **If data are coded using the formula $y = \frac{x - a}{b}$**
  - **the mean of the coded data is given by $\bar{y} = \frac{\bar{x} - a}{b}$**
  - **the standard deviation of the coded data is given by $\sigma_y = \frac{\sigma_x}{b}$, where σ_x is the standard deviation of the original data.**

Hint You usually need to find the mean and standard deviation of the **original data** given the statistics for the **coded data**. You can rearrange the formulae as:

- $\bar{x} = b\bar{y} + a$
- $\sigma_x = b\sigma_y$

Example 12 SKILLS INTERPRETATION

A scientist measures the temperature, x °C, at five different points in a nuclear reactor. Her results are given below:

332 °C 355 °C 306 °C 317 °C 340 °C

a Use the coding $y = \frac{x - 300}{10}$ to code these data.

b Calculate the mean and standard deviation of the coded data.

c Use your answer to part **b** to calculate the mean and standard deviation of the original data.

a

Original data, x	332	355	306	317	340
Coded data, y	3.2	5.5	0.6	1.7	4.0

When $x = 332$, $y = \frac{332 - 300}{10} = 3.2$

b $\Sigma y = 15$, $\Sigma y^2 = 59.74$

$\bar{y} = \frac{15}{5} = 3$

$\sigma_y^2 = \frac{59.74}{5} - \left(\frac{15}{5}\right)^2 = 2.948$

$\sigma_y = \sqrt{2.948} = 1.72$ (3 s.f.)

c $3 = \frac{\bar{x} - 300}{10}$ so $\bar{x} = 30 + 300 = 330$ °C

Substitute into $\bar{y} = \frac{\bar{x} - a}{b}$ and solve to find $\bar{x}$.
You could also use $\bar{x} = b\bar{y} + a$ with $a = 300$, $b = 10$ and $\bar{y} = 3$.

$1.72 = \frac{\sigma_x}{10}$ so $\sigma_x = 17.2$ °C (3 s.f.)

Substitute into $\sigma_y = \frac{\sigma_x}{b}$ and solve to find σ_x.
You could also use $\sigma_x = b\sigma_y$ with $\sigma_y = 1.72$ and $b = 10$.

Example 13 SKILLS INTERPRETATION

Data on the maximum gust, g knots, are recorded in Chicago during May and June.

The data were coded using $h = \frac{g - 5}{10}$ and the following statistics found:

$S_{hh} = 43.58$ $\bar{h} = 2$ $n = 61$

Calculate the mean and standard deviation of the maximum gust in knots.

$2 = \frac{\bar{g} - 5}{10}$

Use the formula for the mean of a coded variable: $\bar{h} = \frac{\bar{g} - a}{b}$ with $a = 5$ and $b = 10$.

$\bar{g} = 2 \times 10 + 5 = 25$ knots

$\sigma_h = \sqrt{\frac{43.58}{61}} = 0.845...$

$\sigma_h = \frac{\sigma_g}{10}$

Calculate the standard deviation of the coded data using $\sigma_h = \sqrt{\frac{S_{hh}}{n}}$, then use the formula for the standard deviation of a coded variable: $\sigma_h = \frac{\sigma_g}{b}$ with $b = 10$.

$\sigma_g = \sigma_h \times 10 = 8.45$ knots (3 s.f.)

Example 14

As seen in Example 11, Akira recorded the length, in minutes, of each phone call she made for a month, as summarised in the table below. This example will now show you how to solve this type of question with a different method.

Use $y = \frac{x - 7.5}{5}$ to calculate an estimate for:

a the mean

b the **standard deviation**.

Length of phone call	Number of occasions
$0 < l \leqslant 5$	4
$5 < l \leqslant 10$	15
$10 < l \leqslant 15$	5
$15 < l \leqslant 20$	2
$20 < l \leqslant 60$	0
$60 < l \leqslant 70$	1

a

Length of phone call	Number of occasions	Midpoint x	$y = \frac{x - 7.5}{5}$
$0 < l \leqslant 5$	4	2.5	−1
$5 < l \leqslant 10$	15	7.5	0
$10 < l \leqslant 15$	5	12.5	1
$15 < l \leqslant 20$	2	17.5	2
$20 < l \leqslant 60$	0	40	6.5
$60 < l \leqslant 70$	1	65	11.5
Total	27		

Mean of coded data:

$= \frac{16.5}{27} = 0.6111$

Mean of original data

$= 0.6111 = \frac{x - 7.5}{5}$

$0.6111 \times 5 = x - 7.5$

$x = 10.56$

b

Length of phone call	Number of occasions	Midpoint x	$y = \frac{x - 7.5}{5}$	fy	fy^2
$0 < l \leqslant 5$	4	2.5	−1	−4	4
$5 < l \leqslant 10$	15	7.5	0	0	0
$10 < l \leqslant 15$	5	12.5	1	5	5
$15 < l \leqslant 20$	2	17.5	2	4	8
$20 < l \leqslant 60$	0	40	6.5	0	0
$60 < l \leqslant 70$	1	65	11.5	11.5	132.25
Total	27			16.5	149.25

Standard deviation of coded data $= \sqrt{\frac{149.25}{27} - \left(\frac{16.5}{27}\right)^2} = 2.27$

Standard deviation of original data $= 2.27 \times 5 = 11.35$

Exercise 2G SKILLS INTERPRETATION

1 A set of data values, x, is shown below:

110 90 50 80 30 70 60

a Code the data using the coding $y = \frac{x}{10}$

b Calculate the mean of the coded data values.

c Use your answer to part **b** to calculate the mean of the original data.

2 A set of data values, x, is shown below:

52 73 31 73 38 80 17 24

a Code the data using the coding $y = \frac{x-3}{7}$

b Calculate the mean of the coded data values.

c Use your answer to part **b** to calculate the mean of the original data.

(E) **3** The coded mean price of televisions in a shop was worked out. Using the coding $y = \frac{x-65}{200}$ the mean price was 1.5. Find the true mean price of the televisions. **(2 marks)**

4 The coding $y = x - 40$ gives a standard deviation for y of 2.34

Write down the standard deviation of x.

Watch out Adding or subtracting constants does not affect how spread out the data are, so you can ignore the '−40' when finding the standard deviation for x.

(P) **5** A study was performed to investigate how long a mobile phone battery lasts if the phone is not used. The grouped frequency table shows the battery life (b hours) of a random sample of 100 different mobile phones.

Battery life (b hours)	Frequency (f)	Midpoint (x)	$y = \frac{x-14}{2}$
11–21	11		
21–27	24		
27–31	27		
31–37	26		
37–43	12		

a Copy and complete the table.

b Use the coding $y = \frac{x-14}{2}$ to calculate an estimate of the mean battery life.

(P) **6** The lifetime, x, in hours, of 70 light bulbs is shown in the table below.

Lifetime, x (hours)	$20 < x \leqslant 22$	$22 < x \leqslant 24$	$24 < x \leqslant 26$	$26 < x \leqslant 28$	$28 < x \leqslant 30$
Frequency	3	12	40	10	5

The data are coded using $y = \frac{x-1}{20}$

a Estimate the mean of the coded values $\bar{y}$.

b Hence find an estimate for the mean lifetime of the light bulbs, $\bar{x}$.

c Estimate the standard deviation of the lifetimes of the light bulbs.

Problem-solving

Code the midpoints of each class interval. The midpoint of the $22 < x \leqslant 24$ class interval is 23, so the coded midpoint will be $\frac{23-1}{20} = 1.1$

(E) **7** The weekly income, i, of 100 workers was recorded.

The data were coded using $y = \frac{i - 90}{100}$ and the following summations were obtained:

$\Sigma y = 131$, $\Sigma y^2 = 176.84$

Estimate the standard deviation of the actual workers' weekly income. **(2 marks)**

(E) **8** A meteorologist collected data on the annual rainfall, x mm, at six randomly selected places.

The data were coded using $s = 0.01x - 10$ and the following summations were obtained:

$\Sigma s = 16.1$, $\Sigma s^2 = 147.03$

Work out an estimate for the standard deviation of the actual annual rainfall. **(2 marks)**

(E/P) **9** The daily mean pressure, p hPa, in Accra during August is recorded.

The data are coded using $c = \frac{p}{2} - 500$ and the following summary statistics were obtained:

$n = 30 \qquad \bar{c} = 10.15 \qquad S_{cc} = 296.4$

Find the mean and standard deviation of the daily mean pressure. **(4 marks)**

Chapter review 2

SKILLS PROBLEM-SOLVING

1 On a science test, the mean mark for a group of eight students is 65. The mean mark for a second group of 12 students is 72. Calculate the mean mark for the combined group of 20 students.

2 The data set below shows the prices (x) of six shares on a particular day in the year 2007:

807 967 727 167 207 767

a Code the data using the coding $y = \frac{x - 7}{80}$

b Calculate the mean of the coded data values.

c Use your answer to part **b** to calculate the mean of the original data.

3 Different teachers using different methods taught two groups of students. Both groups of students took the same examination at the end of the course. The students' marks are shown in the grouped frequency table.

Exam mark	20–29	30–39	40–49	50–59	60–69	70–79	80–89
Frequency group *A*	1	3	6	6	11	10	8
Frequency group *B*	1	2	4	13	15	6	3

a Work out an estimate of the mean mark for group A and an estimate of the mean mark for group B.

b Write down whether or not the answer to **a** suggests that one method of teaching is better than the other. Give a reason for your answer.

4 The lifetimes of 80 batteries, to the nearest hour, are shown in the table below.

Lifetime (hours)	6–10	11–15	16–20	21–25	26–30
Frequency	2	10	18	45	5

a Write down the modal class for the lifetime of the batteries.

b Use interpolation to find the median lifetime of the batteries.

The midpoint of each class is represented by x and its corresponding frequency by f, giving $\Sigma fx = 1645$.

c Calculate an estimate of the mean lifetime of the batteries.

Another batch of 12 batteries is found to have an estimated mean lifetime of 22.3 hours.

d Estimate the mean lifetime for all 92 batteries.

5 A frequency distribution is shown below.

Class interval	1–20	21–40	41–60	61–80	81–100
Frequency	5	10	15	12	8

Use interpolation to find an estimate for the interquartile range.

6 A frequency distribution is shown below.

Class interval	1–10	11–20	21–30	31–40	41–50
Frequency	10	20	30	24	16

a Use interpolation to estimate the value of the 30th percentile.

b Use interpolation to estimate the value of the 70th percentile.

c Hence estimate the 30% to 70% interpercentile range.

(E) **7** The times it took a random sample of runners to complete a race are summarised in the table.

Time taken, t (minutes)	20–29	30–39	40–49	50–59	60–69
Frequency	5	10	36	20	9

a Use interpolation to estimate the interquartile range. **(3 marks)**

The midpoint of each class was represented by x and its corresponding frequency by f giving:

$\Sigma fx = 3740 \qquad \Sigma fx^2 = 183\,040$

b Estimate the variance and standard deviation for these data. **(3 marks)**

8 The heights of 50 clover flowers are summarised in the table.

Height, x (mm)	$90 \leqslant x < 95$	$95 \leqslant x < 100$	$100 \leqslant x < 105$	$105 \leqslant x < 110$	$110 \leqslant x < 115$
Frequency	5	10	26	8	1

a Find Q_1.

b Find Q_2.

c Find the interquartile range.

d Use $\Sigma fx = 5075$ and $\Sigma fx^2 = 516\,112.5$ to find the standard deviation.

E/P **9** The daily mean temperatures recorded in Dakar, Senegal, during September are shown in the table below.

Temp (°C)	$25 \leqslant t < 27$	$27 \leqslant t < 29$	$29 \leqslant t < 31$
Frequency	12	14	4

a Estimate the mean and standard deviation of the temperatures. **(3 marks)**

b Use linear interpolation to find an estimate for the 10% to 90% interpercentile range. **(3 marks)**

c Estimate the number of days in September when the daily mean temperature in Dakar is more than one standard deviation greater than the mean. **(2 marks)**

E **10** The daily mean wind speed, w knots, was recorded at Toronto Pearson International Airport, during May. The data were coded using $z = \frac{w - 3}{2}$

Summary statistics were calculated for the coded data:

$n = 31$ $\Sigma z = 106$ $S_{zz} = 80.55$

a Find the mean and standard deviation of the coded data. **(2 marks)**

b Work out the mean and standard deviation of the daily mean wind speed at Toronto Pearson International Airport during May. **(2 marks)**

E **11** 20 endangered owls were caught for ringing (wrapping a label around their legs to help identify them). Their wingspans (x cm) were measured to the nearest centimetre.

The following summary statistics were worked out:

$\Sigma x = 316$ $\Sigma x^2 = 5078$

a Work out the mean and the standard deviation of the wingspans of the 20 birds. **(3 marks)**

One more bird was caught. It had a wingspan of 13 centimetres.

b Without doing any further calculation, say how you think this extra wingspan will affect the mean wingspan. **(1 mark)**

20 eagles were also caught for ringing. Their wingspans (y cm) were also measured to the nearest centimetre and the data coded using $z = \frac{y - 5}{10}$

The following summary statistics were obtained from the coded data:

$\Sigma z = 104$ $S_{zz} = 1.8$

c Work out the mean and standard deviation of the wingspans of the eagles. **(5 marks)**

Challenge

A biologist recorded the heights, x cm, of 20 plant seedlings.
She calculated the mean and standard deviation of her results:

$\bar{x} = 3.1$ cm $\sigma = 1.4$ cm

The biologist subsequently discovered she had written down one value incorrectly. She replaced a value of 2.3 cm with a value of 3.2 cm.

Calculate the new mean and standard deviation of her data.

Summary of key points

1 The **mode** or **modal class** is the value or class that occurs most often.

2 The **median** is the middle value when the data values are put in order.

3 The **mean** can be calculated using the formula $\bar{x} = \frac{\Sigma x}{n}$

4 For data given in a frequency table, the mean can be calculated using the formula $\bar{x} = \frac{\Sigma xf}{\Sigma f}$

5 To find the **lower quartile** for discrete data, divide n by 4. If this is a whole number, the lower quartile is halfway between this data point and the one above. If it is not a whole number, round *up* and pick this data point.

6 To find the **upper quartile** for discrete data, find $\frac{3}{4}$ of n. If this is a whole number, the upper quartile is halfway between this data point and the one above. If it is not a whole number, round *up* and pick this data point.

7 The **range** is the difference between the largest and smallest values in a data set.

8 The **interquartile range** (IQR) is the difference between the upper quartile and the lower quartile, $Q_3 - Q_1$.

9 The **interpercentile range** is the difference between the values for two given percentiles.

10 **Variance** $= \frac{\Sigma(x-\bar{x})^2}{n} = \frac{\Sigma x^2}{n} - \left(\frac{\Sigma x}{n}\right)^2 = \frac{S_{xx}}{n}$, where $S_{xx} = \Sigma(x-\bar{x})^2 = \Sigma x^2 - \frac{(\Sigma x)^2}{n}$

11 The **standard deviation** is the square root of the variance:

$$\sigma = \sqrt{\frac{\Sigma(x-\bar{x})^2}{n}} = \sqrt{\frac{\Sigma x^2}{n} - \left(\frac{\Sigma x}{n}\right)^2} = \sqrt{\frac{S_{xx}}{n}}$$

12 You can use these versions of the formulae for variance and standard deviation for grouped data that is presented in a frequency table:

$$\sigma^2 = \frac{\Sigma f(x-\bar{x})^2}{\Sigma f} = \frac{\Sigma fx^2}{\Sigma f} - \left(\frac{\Sigma fx}{\Sigma f}\right)^2 \qquad \sigma = \sqrt{\frac{\Sigma f(x-\bar{x})^2}{\Sigma f}} = \sqrt{\frac{\Sigma fx^2}{\Sigma f} - \left(\frac{\Sigma fx}{\Sigma f}\right)^2}$$

where f is the frequency for each group and Σf is the total frequency.

13 If data are coded using the formula $y = \frac{x-a}{b}$

- the mean of the coded data is given by $\bar{y} = \frac{\bar{x}-a}{b}$
- the standard deviation of the coded data is given by $\sigma_y = \frac{\sigma_x}{b}$ where σ_x is the standard deviation of the original data.

14 If set A, of size n_1, has mean $\bar{x}_1$, and set B, of size n_2, has a mean $\bar{x}_2$, then the mean of the combined set of A and B is:

$$\bar{x} = \frac{n_1\bar{x}_1 + n_2\bar{x}_2}{n_1 + n_2}$$

3 REPRESENTATIONS OF DATA

2.1
2.4

Learning objectives

After completing this chapter you should be able to:

- Draw and interpret histograms → pages 30–34
- Identify outliers in data sets → pages 35–37
- Draw and interpret box plots → pages 38–40
- Draw and interpret stem and leaf diagrams → pages 40–44
- Work out whether or not data are skewed → pages 44–47
- Compare two data sets → pages 48–49

Prior knowledge check

1 The table shows the number of siblings for 60 students:

Number of siblings	Frequency
0	5
1	8
2	29
3	15
4	3

Draw a pie chart to show the data.

← International GCSE Mathematics

2 Work out the interquartile range for this set of data:

3, 5, 8, 8, 9, 11, 14, 15, 18, 20, 21, 24

← Statistics 1 Section 2.4

3 Work out the mean and standard deviation for this set of data:

17, 19, 20, 25, 28, 31, 32, 32, 35, 37, 38

← Statistics 1 Sections 2.2, 2.5

Visual representations can help to illustrate the key features of a data set without the need for complicated calculations. Graphs and charts are vital in many industries, from the financial sector to journalism. Graphs and charts help you to visualise complicated data, here for example showing the different food groups.

3.1 Histograms

Grouped continuous data can be represented in a **histogram**.

Generally, a histogram gives a good picture of how the data are distributed. It enables you to see a rough location, the general shape and how spread out the data are.

In a histogram, the **area** of the bar is proportional (related in size) to the frequency in each **class**. This allows you to use a histogram to represent grouped data with unequal class intervals.

- **In a histogram, to calculate the height of each bar (the frequency density) use the formula:**
  area of bar = k × frequency.
  k = 1 is the easiest value to use when drawing a histogram.
  If k = 1, then
  frequency density = $\frac{\text{frequency}}{\text{class width}}$

- **Joining the middle of the top of each bar in a histogram forms a frequency polygon.**

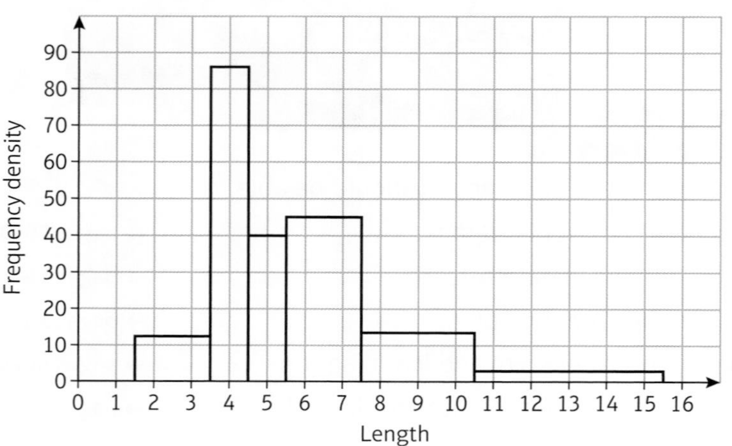

Example 1 SKILLS INTERPRETATION

In a random sample, 200 students were asked how long it took them to complete their homework the previous night. The times were recorded and summarised in the table below.

Time, t (minutes)	$25 \leqslant t < 30$	$30 \leqslant t < 35$	$35 \leqslant t < 40$	$40 \leqslant t < 50$	$50 \leqslant t < 80$
Frequency	55	39	68	32	6

a Draw a histogram and a frequency polygon to represent the data.

b Estimate how many students took between 36 and 45 minutes to complete their homework.

a

Time, t (minutes)	Frequency	Class width	Frequency density
$25 \leqslant t < 30$	55	5	11
$30 \leqslant t < 35$	39	5	7.8
$35 \leqslant t < 40$	68	5	13.6
$40 \leqslant t < 50$	32	10	3.2
$50 \leqslant t < 80$	6	30	0.2

Frequency density = $\frac{55}{5}$ = 11

Class width = 30 − 25 = 5

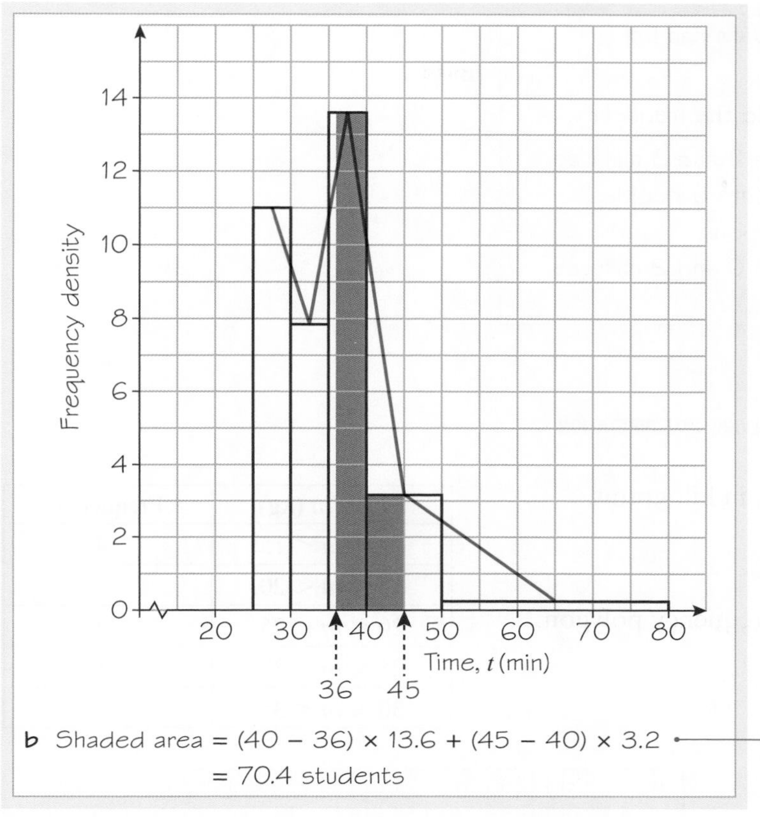

To draw the frequency polygon, join the middle of the top of each bar of the histogram.

To estimate the number of students who spent between 36 and 45 minutes, you need to find the area between 36 and 45.

Example 2 SKILLS INTERPRETATION

The histogram below displays the information gathered from 100 people, regarding how long, in minutes, they took to complete a word puzzle.

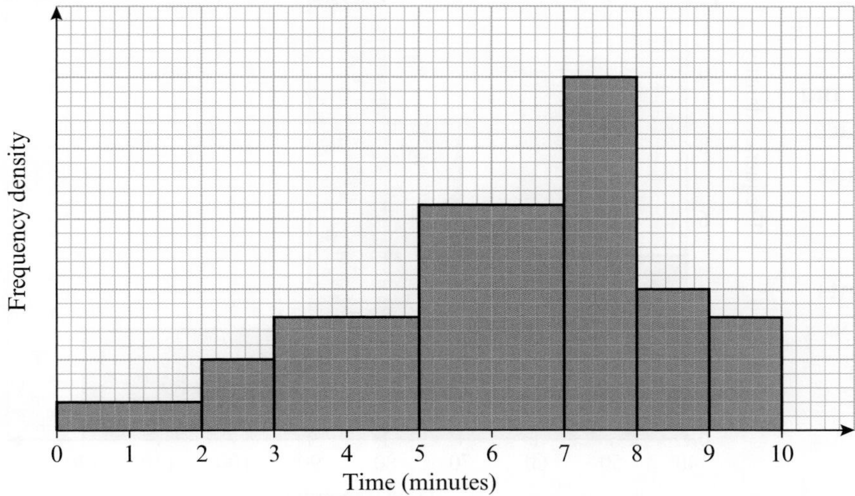

a Why should a histogram be used to represent these data?

b Write down the underlying feature associated with each of the bars in a histogram.

c Given that 5 people completed the puzzle between 2 and 3 minutes, find the number of people who completed the puzzle between 0 and 2 minutes.

a Time is continuous, and continuous data can be represented in a histogram.

b The area of the bar is proportional to the frequency.

c There are 25 small squares between 2 and 3 minutes.
Therefore, 25 small squares represents 5 people.
1 small square represents $\frac{1}{5}$ of a person.
There are 20 small squares between 0 and 2 minutes.
Thus, $20 \times \frac{1}{5} = 4$ people.

Exercise 3A

SKILLS PROBLEM-SOLVING; INTERPRETATION

1 The data in the table show the mass, in kilograms, of 50 adult puffer fish.

a Draw a histogram for these data.

b On the same set of axes, draw a frequency polygon.

Mass, m (kg)	Frequency
$10 \leqslant m < 15$	4
$15 \leqslant m < 20$	12
$20 \leqslant m < 25$	23
$25 \leqslant m < 30$	8
$30 \leqslant m < 35$	3

(P) 2 Some students took part in an obstacle race. The time for each student to complete the race was noted. The results are shown in the histogram.

a Give a reason to justify the use of a histogram to represent these data.

90 students took between 60 and 70 seconds to complete the race.

b Find the number of students who took between 40 and 60 seconds.

c Find the number of students who took 80 seconds or less.

d Calculate the total number of students who took part in the race.

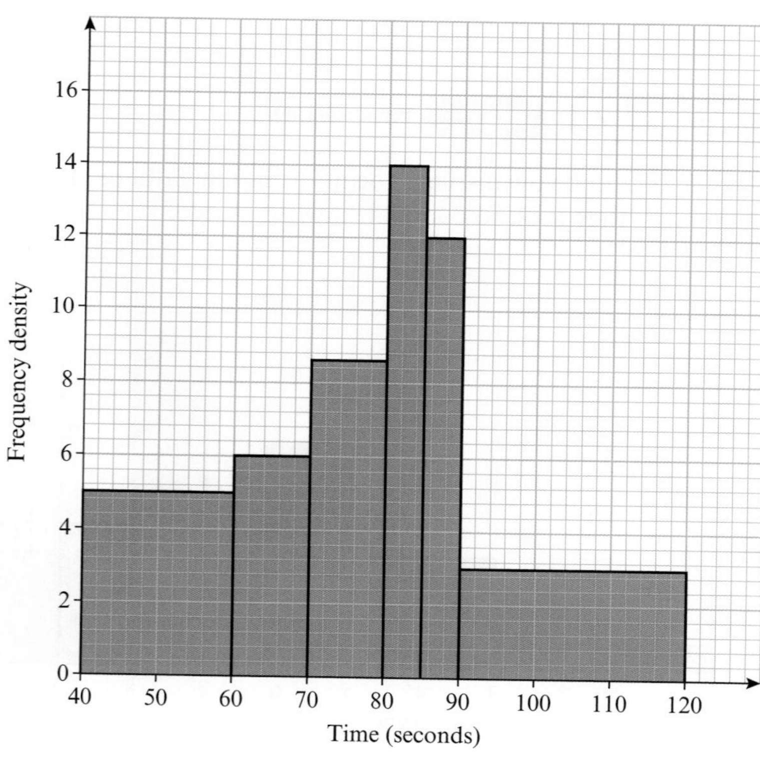

Watch out Frequency density × class width is always **proportional** to frequency in a histogram, but not necessarily **equal** to frequency.

(P) **3** A Fun Day committee at a local sports centre organised a tennis ball throwing competition. The distance thrown by every competitor was recorded and the data is shown in the histogram. Forty people threw the ball less than 20 m.

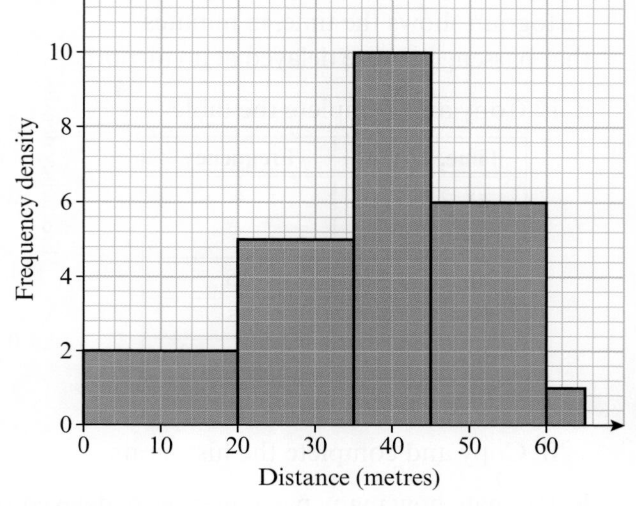

a Why is a histogram a suitable diagram to represent these data?

b How many people entered the competition?

c Estimate how many people threw between 30 and 40 metres.

d How many people threw between 45 and 65 metres?

e Estimate how many people threw less than 25 metres.

(P) **4** A farmer found the masses of a random sample of lambs. The masses were summarised in a grouped frequency table and represented by a histogram. The frequency for the class $28 \leqslant m < 32$ was 32.

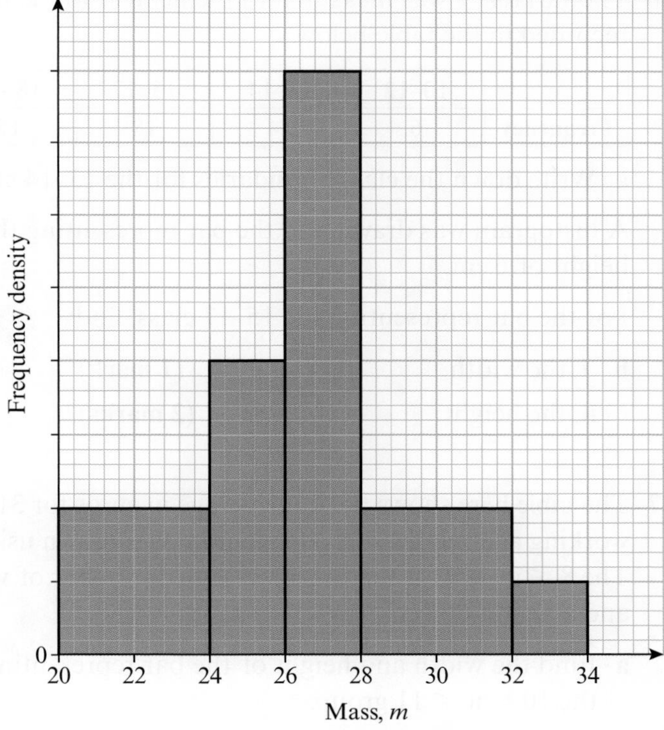

a Show that 25 small squares on the histogram represents 8 lambs.

b Find the frequency of the $24 \leqslant m < 26$ class.

c How many lambs did the farmer weigh in total?

d Estimate the number of lambs that had masses between 25 and 29 kg.

Problem-solving

You can use area to solve histogram problems where no vertical scale is given. You could also use the information given in the question to work out a suitable scale for the vertical axis.

E/P **5** The partially (not entirely) completed histogram shows the time, in minutes, that passengers were delayed at an airport.

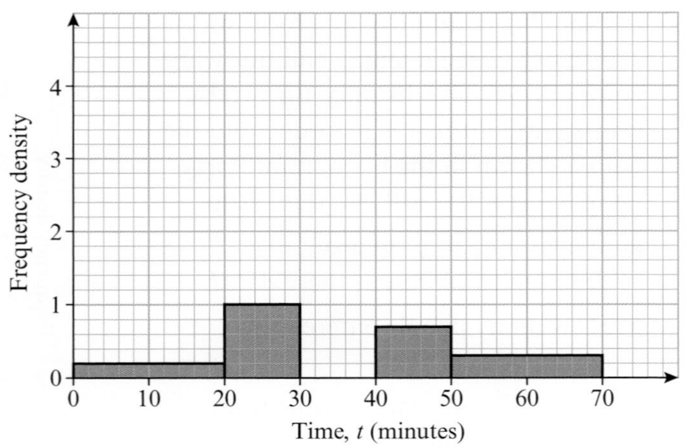

a **i** Copy and complete the table.

Time, t (min)	Frequency
$0 \leqslant t < 20$	4
$20 \leqslant t < 30$	
$30 \leqslant t < 35$	15
$35 \leqslant t < 40$	25
$40 \leqslant t < 50$	
$50 \leqslant t < 70$	

ii Copy and complete the histogram. **(4 marks)**

b Estimate how many passengers were delayed between 25 and 38 minutes. **(2 marks)**

E/P **6** The **variable** y was measured to the nearest whole number. 60 observations were taken and are recorded in the table below.

y	10–12	13–14	15–17	18–25
Frequency	6	24	18	12

a Write down the class boundaries for the 13–14 class. **(1 mark)**

A histogram was drawn and the bar representing the 13–14 class had a width of 4 cm and a height of 6 cm.

For the bar representing the 15–17 class, find:

b **i** the width **(1 mark)**

ii the height. **(2 marks)**

Problem-solving

Remember that area is proportional to frequency.

E/P **7** The table here shows the hourly wage in euros for 31 employees working at a retail store. A histogram was drawn using this data. The $8 \leqslant w < 10$ group was represented by a bar of width 1 cm and a height of 8 cm.

Hourly wage, w (€)	Frequency
$4 \leqslant w < 8$	4
$8 \leqslant w < 10$	8
$10 \leqslant w < 11$	6
$11 \leqslant w < 12$	7
$12 \leqslant w < 15$	5
$15 \leqslant w < 16$	1

a Find the width and height of the bar representing the $10 \leqslant w < 11$ group. **(2 marks)**

b Estimate the mean and standard deviation of the hourly wage of the employees working at the store. **(3 marks)**

c Use linear **interpolation** to find an estimate for the lower quartile of wages. **(2 marks)**

d Estimate how many employees had an hourly wage higher than the mean plus one standard deviation. **(2 marks)**

Challenge

The table below shows the lengths of 108 fish in an aquarium.

Length (cm)	5–10	10–20	20–25	25–30	30–40	40–60	60–90
Frequency	8	16	20	18	20	14	12

If the data were represented by a histogram, what would be the ratio of the heights of the shortest and highest bars?

3.2 Outliers

An **outlier** is an extreme value that lies outside the overall pattern of the data.

There are a number of different ways of calculating outliers, depending on the nature of the data and the calculations that you are asked to carry out.

- **A common definition of an outlier is any value that is:**
  - **either greater than $Q_3 + k(Q_3 - Q_1)$**
  - **or less than $Q_1 - k(Q_3 - Q_1)$**

Notation Q_1 and Q_3 are the first and third **quartiles**.

In the exam, you will be told which method to use to identify outliers in data sets, including the value of k.

Example 3 SKILLS ANALYSIS

The blood glucose levels of 30 females are recorded. The results, in mmol/litre, are shown below:

1.7, 2.2, 2.3, 2.3, 2.5, 2.7, 3.1, 3.2, 3.6, 3.7, 3.7, 3.7, 3.8, 3.8, 3.8,
3.8, 3.9, 3.9, 3.9, 4.0, 4.0, 4.0, 4.0, 4.4, 4.5, 4.6, 4.7, 4.8, 5.0, 5.1

An **outlier** is an observation that falls either 1.5 × the **interquartile range** above the upper quartile, or 1.5 × the interquartile range below the lower quartile.

a Find the quartiles. **b** Find any outliers.

a Q_1: $\frac{30}{4} = 7.5$; pick the 8th term = 3.2 — Work out $n \div 4$ and round up.

Q_3: $\frac{3(30)}{4} = 22.5$; pick the 23rd term = 4.0 — Work out $3n \div 4$ and round up.

Q_2: $\frac{30}{2} = 15$; pick the 15.5th term = 3.8 — Work out $n \div 2$ and go halfway to the next term.

b Interquartile range = 4.0 − 3.2 = 0.8

Outliers are values less than
3.2 − 1.5 × 0.8 = 2 — Use the definition of an outlier given in the question.
or greater than 4.0 + 1.5 × 0.8 = 5.2

Therefore 1.7 is the only outlier. — $1.7 < 2$, so it is an outlier.

Example 4 SKILLS ANALYSIS

The lengths, in cm, of 12 giant African land snails are given below:

17, 18, 18, 19, 20, 20, 20, 20, 21, 23, 24, 32

a Calculate the mean and standard deviation, given that $\Sigma x = 252$ and $\Sigma x^2 = 5468$.

b An outlier is an observation which lies ±2 standard deviations from the mean. Identify any outliers for these data.

Notation Σx is the sum of the data and Σx^2 is the sum of the square of each value.

a Mean $= \frac{\Sigma x}{n} = \frac{252}{12} = 21$ cm

Variance $= \frac{\Sigma x^2}{n} - \bar{x}^2 = \frac{5468}{12} - 21^2$

$= 14.666...$

Standard deviation $= \sqrt{14.666...}$

$= 3.83$ (3 s.f.)

b Mean − 2 × standard deviation

= 21 − 2 × 3.83 = 13.34

Mean + 2 × standard deviation

= 21 + 2 × 3.83 = 28.66

32 cm is an outlier.

Use the summary statistics given to work out the mean and standard deviation quickly.

Use the definition of an outlier given in the question.

Watch out Different questions might use different definitions of outliers. Read the question carefully before finding any outliers.

Sometimes outliers are legitimate values (values that are acceptable according to the rules) which could be correct. For example, there really could be a giant African land snail 32 cm long.

However, there are occasions when an outlier should be removed from the data since it is clearly an error and it would be misleading to keep it in. These data values are known as **anomalies** (values that are different from what is normal or expected).

- **The process of removing anomalies from a data set is known as cleaning the data.**

Anomalies can be the result of experimental or recording error, or could be data values which are not relevant to the investigation.

Watch out Be careful not to remove data values just because they do not fit the pattern of the data. You must justify why a value is being removed.

Here is an example where there is a clear **anomaly**:

Ages of people at a birthday party: 12, 17, 21, 33, 34, 37, 42, 62, 165

$\bar{x} = 47$ $\quad\sigma = 44.02\quad$ $\bar{x} + 2\sigma = 135.04$

The data value recorded as 165 is significantly higher than $\bar{x} + 2\sigma$, so it can be considered an outlier. An age of 165 is impossible, so this value must be an error. You can clean the data by removing this value before carrying out any analysis.

Notation You can write $165 \gg 135.04$ where $\gg$ is used to denote 'much greater than'. Similarly you can use $\ll$ to denote 'much less than'.

Exercise 3B SKILLS EXECUTIVE FUNCTION; ANALYSIS

1 Some data are collected. $Q_1 = 46$ and $Q_3 = 68$.

A value greater than $Q_3 + 1.5 \times (Q_3 - Q_1)$ or less than $Q_1 - 1.5 \times (Q_3 - Q_1)$ is defined as an outlier.

Using this rule, work out whether or not the following are outliers:

a 7 **b** 88 **c** 105

2 The masses of male and female turtles are given in grams. For males, the lower quartile was 400 g and the upper quartile was 580 g. For females, the lower quartile was 260 g and the upper quartile was 340 g.

An outlier is an observation that falls either 1 × the interquartile range above the upper quartile or 1 × the interquartile range below the lower quartile.

a Which of these male turtle masses would be outliers?

400 g 260 g 550 g 640 g

b Which of these female turtle masses would be outliers?

170 g 300 g 340 g 440 g

c What is the largest mass a male turtle can be without being an outlier?

Hint The definition of an outlier here is different from that in question 1. You will be told which rule to use in the exam.

3 The masses of arctic foxes are found and the mean mass was 6.1 kg. The variance was 4.2.

An outlier is an observation which lies ±2 standard deviations from the mean.

a Which of these arctic fox masses are outliers?

2.4 kg 10.1 kg 3.7 kg 11.5 kg

b What are the smallest and largest masses that an arctic fox can be without being an outlier?

(E) 4 The ages of nine people at a children's birthday party are recorded. $\Sigma x = 92$ and $\Sigma x^2 = 1428$.

a Calculate the mean and standard deviation of the ages. **(3 marks)**

An outlier is an observation which lies ±2 standard deviations from the mean.

One of the ages is recorded as 30.

b State, with a reason, whether or not this is an outlier. **(2 marks)**

c Suggest a reason why this age could be a legitimate data value. **(1 mark)**

d Given that all nine people were children, clean the data and recalculate the mean and standard deviation. **(3 marks)**

Problem-solving

After you clean the data you will need to find the new values for n, Σx and Σx^2.

3.3 Box plots

A **box plot** can be drawn to represent important features of the data. It shows the quartiles, maximum and minimum values and any outliers.

A box plot looks like this:

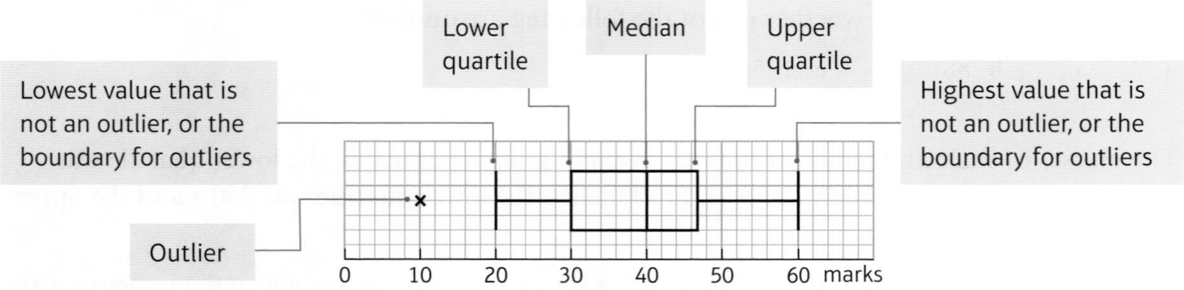

Two sets of data can be compared using box plots.

Example 5 SKILLS INTERPRETATION

a Draw a box plot for the data on blood glucose levels of females from Example 3. The data are summarised below.

Lower quartile = 3.2
Upper quartile = 4.0
Median = 3.8
Outlier = 1.7
Lowest non-outlier value = 2.2
Highest value = 5.1

The blood glucose levels of 30 males are recorded. The results are summarised below:

Lower quartile = 3.2
Upper quartile = 4.2
Median = 4.0
Lowest value = 1.2
Highest value = 6.0

An outlier is an observation that falls either 1.5 × the interquartile range above the upper quartile or 1.5 × the interquartile range below the lower quartile.

b Given that there are exactly two outliers for the males, draw a box plot for these data on the same diagram as the one for females.

c Compare the blood glucose levels for males and females.

a

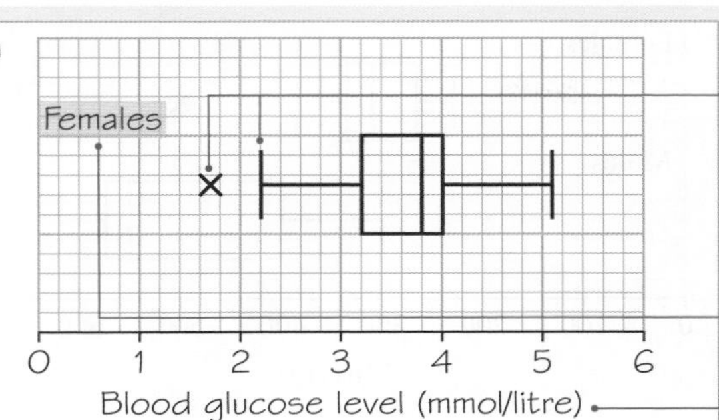

Use the summary data given in the question. The outlier is marked with a cross. The lowest value which is not an outlier is 2.2.

Always use a scale and label it. Remember to give your box plot a title.

b Outliers are values less than

$3.2 - 1.5 \times 1.0 = 1.7$

or values greater than

$4.2 + 1.5 \times 1.0 = 5.7$

There are two outliers: 1.2 and 6.0

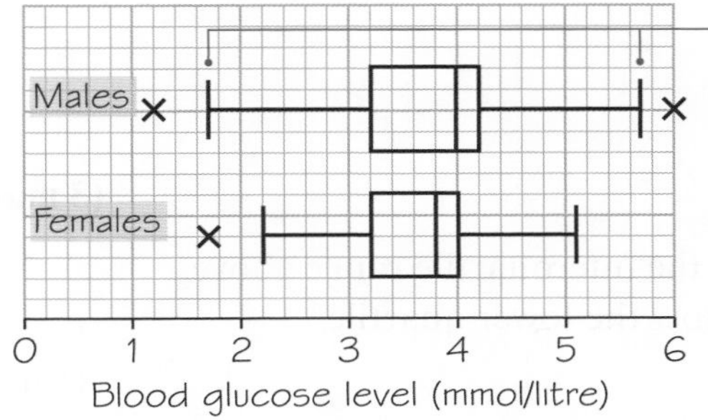

The ends of the whiskers are plotted at the outlier boundaries, as you do not know the greatest or least non-outlier values.

Problem-solving

When drawing two box plots, use the same scale so they can be compared. Remember to give each a title and label the axis.

c The median blood glucose level for females is lower than the median blood glucose level for males.
The interquartile range (the width of the box) and range for blood glucose levels are smaller for the females.

When comparing data you should compare a measure of location and a measure of spread. You should also write your interpretation in the context of the question.

Exercise 3C

SKILLS INTERPRETATION

1 A group of students took a test. The summary data are shown in the table.

Lowest mark	Lower quartile	Median	Upper quartile	Highest mark
5	21	28	36	58

Given that there were no outliers, draw a box plot to illustrate these data.

2 Here is a box plot of marks in an examination.

a Write down the upper and lower quartiles.

b Write down the median.

c Work out the interquartile range.

d Work out the range.

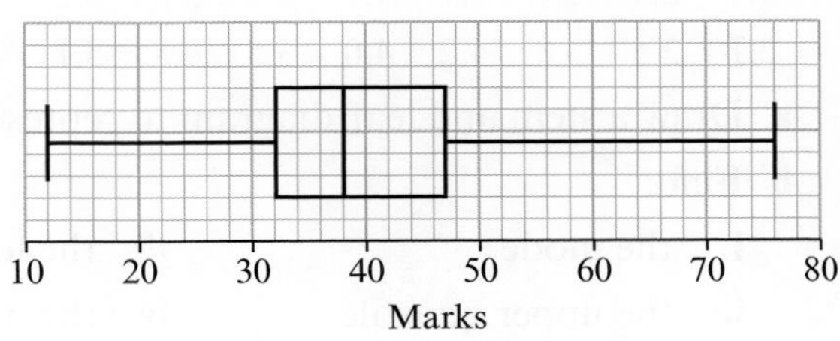

(P) **3** The masses of male and female turtles are given in grams. The data are summarised in the box plots.

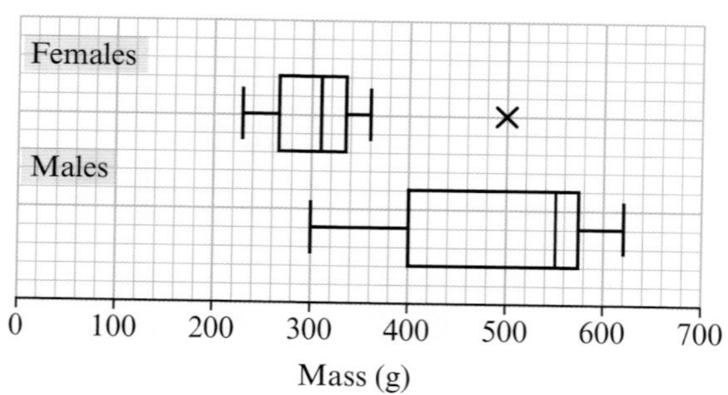

a Compare and contrast the masses of the male and female turtles.

b A turtle was found to have a mass of 330 grams. State whether it is likely to be a male or a female. Give a reason for your answer.

c Write down the size of the largest female turtle.

(E) **4** The average weight (in kg) for 30 different breeds of dog are shown below.

13	15	16	19	20
21	22	22	24	24
25	25	26	26	26
27	29	29	30	30
33	33	38	46	48

a Calculate Q_1, Q_2 and Q_3. **(3 marks)**

An outlier is defined as a value which lies either 1.5 × the interquartile range above the upper quartile, or 1.5 × the interquartile range below the lower quartile.

b Show that 46 kg and 48 kg are outliers. **(1 mark)**

c Draw a box plot for this data. **(3 marks)**

3.4 Stem and leaf diagrams

- A **stem and leaf diagram** is used to order and present data given to 2 or 3 significant figures. Each number is first split into its stem and leaf. For example, take the number 42:

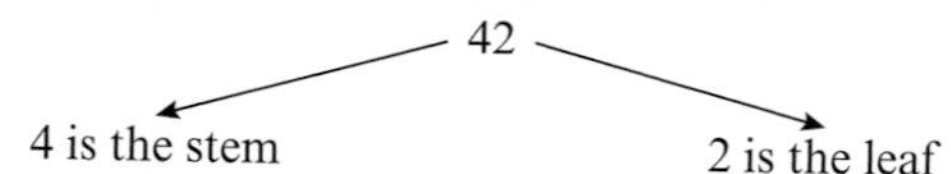

- It enables the shape of the distribution of the data to be revealed, and quartiles can easily be found from the diagram.
- Two sets of data can be compared using back to back stem and leaf diagrams.

Example 6 SKILLS INTERPRETATION; EXECUTIVE FUNCTION

The blood glucose levels of 30 males are recorded. The results, in mmol/litre, are given below.

4.4 2.4 5.1 3.7 4.7 2.2 3.8 4.2 5.0 4.7 4.1 4.6 4.7 3.7 3.6
2.1 2.5 3.8 4.2 4.0 3.5 4.8 5.1 4.5 3.6 1.4 3.2 4.7 3.6 5.2

a Draw a stem and leaf diagram to represent the data.

b Find:

i the mode **ii** the lower quartile
iii the upper quartile **iv** the median.

a Step 1: Rearrange the numbers in ascending order.

1.4 2.1 2.2 2.4 2.5 3.2 3.5 3.6 3.6 3.6 3.7 3.7 3.8 3.8 4.0
4.1 4.2 4.2 4.4 4.5 4.6 4.7 4.7 4.7 4.7 4.8 5.0 5.1 5.1 5.2

Step 2: Choose an appropriate stem and leaf for the data. For these data, the whole number part is chosen as the stem and the decimal part is chosen as the leaf.

Step 3: Draw the stem and leaf diagram.

Stem	Leaf
1	4
2	1 2 4 5
3	2 5 6 6 6 7 7 8 8
4	0 1 2 2 4 5 6 7 7 7 7 8
5	0 1 1 2

Step 4: Include a key.

Key: 1 | 4 = 1.4

Stem	Leaf
1	4
2	1 2 4 5
3	2 5 6 6 6 7 7 8 8
4	0 1 2 2 4 5 6 7 7 7 7 8
5	0 1 1 2

This row contains all the numbers between 5.0 and 5.2

b Key: 1 | 4 = 1.4

Stem	Leaf	
1	4	(1)
2	1 2 4 5	(4)
3	2 5 6 6 6 7 7 8 8	(9)
4	0 1 2 2 4 5 6 7 7 7 7 8	(12)
5	0 1 1 2	(4)

This row contains all the numbers between 2.0 and 2.5

This is the number of pieces of data in the row.

i From the diagram, you can see the mode is 4.7 as it occurs the most frequently.

ii Lower quartile: $\frac{30}{4} = 7.5$, so pick the 8th term which is 3.6

iii Upper quartile $\frac{3(30)}{4} = 22.5$, so pick the 23rd term which is 4.7

iv Median $\frac{30}{2} = 15$, so pick the 15.5th term which is 40.5 (halfway between 4.0 and 4.1)

Example 7 SKILLS INTERPRETATION; EXECUTIVE FUNCTION

Achara recorded the resting pulse rate for the 16 boys and 23 girls in her year at school. The results were as follows:

Girls

55	80	84	91	80	92
98	40	60	64	66	72
96	85	88	90	76	54
58	92	78	80	79	

Boys

80	60	91	65
67	59	75	46
72	71	74	57
64	60	50	68

a Construct a back to back stem and leaf diagram to represent these data.

b Comment on your results.

a Use the steps outlined in Example 6 to complete the stem and leaf diagram. The lowest value always goes next to the stem when ordering.

Girls		Boys
0	4	6
8 5 4	5	0 7 9
6 4 0	6	0 0 4 5 7 8
9 8 6 2	7	1 2 4 5
8 5 4 0 0 0	8	0
8 6 2 2 1 0	9	1

Key: 0 | 4 | 6 means 40 for the girls and 46 for the boys

b The back to back stem and leaf diagram shows that the resting pulse rate for the boys tends to be lower than that for the girls.

Example 8 SKILLS ANALYSIS

The blood glucose levels of 30 females are recorded. The results, in mmol/litre, are shown in the stem and leaf diagram below:

Stem	Leaf	
2	2 2 3 3 5 7	(6)
3	1 2 6 7 7 7 8 8 8 8 9 9 9	(13)
4	0 0 0 0 4 5 6 7 8	(9)
5	1 5	(2)

Key: 2 | 1 = 2.1

An outlier is an observation that falls either 1.5 × the interquartile range above the upper quartile or 1.5 × the interquartile range below the lower quartile.

a Find the quartiles. **b** Find any outliers.

a Lower quartile: $\frac{30}{4}$ = 7.5, so pick the 8th term = 3.2

Upper quartile: $\frac{3(30)}{4}$ = 22.5, so pick the 23rd term = 4.0

Median: $\frac{30}{2}$ = 15, so pick the 15.5th term = 3.8

> **b** Interquartile range = 4.0 − 3.2 = 0.8
> Outliers are values less than 3.2 − (1.5 × 0.8) = 2
> or values greater than 4.0 + (1.5 × 0.8) = 5.2
> Therefore 5.5 is an outlier.

Exercise 3D

SKILLS INTERPRETATION; EXECUTIVE FUNCTION

1 Thirty college students were asked how many movies they had in their collection. The results are as follows:

12	25	34	17	12	18	29	34	45	6	15	9	25	3	29
22	20	32	15	15	19	12	26	27	27	32	35	42	26	25

Draw a stem and leaf diagram to represent these data.

a Find the median.

b Find the lower quartile.

c Find the upper quartile.

2 The following stem and leaf diagram shows some information about the marks gained by a group of students in a statistics test.

Key: 2|3 means 23 marks

Stem	Leaf	
0	8 9	(2)
1	2 5 5 9	(4)
2	3 6 6 6 7	(5)
3	4 4 5 7 7 7 7 7 9	(9)
4	5 8 8 9	(4)

a Write down the highest mark.

b Write down the lowest mark.

c How many students scored 26 marks?

d What is the modal mark?

e Find the median.

f Find the lower quartile.

g Find the upper quartile.

3 A class of 16 boys and 13 girls completed a Physics test. The test was marked out of 60. Their marks are shown below:

Boys				Girls			
45	54	32	60	26	54	47	32
28	34	54	56	34	34	45	46
32	29	47	48	39	52	24	28
44	45	56	57	33			

a Draw back to back stem and leaf diagrams to represent these data.

b Comment on your results.

4 The stem and leaf diagram below shows the median age, in years, of a selection of African elephants in Tanzania.

Stem	Leaf
1	5 6 6 6 7 7 7 7 7 7 8 8 8 8 8 8 8 8 8 9 9 9 9 9 9 9 9 9 9 9
2	0 0 0 0 0 0 0 1 1 1 1 1 3 3 3 4 5 7
3	4 4
4	1

Key: 1 | 8 = 18 years

Find:

a the median

b the interquartile range and any outliers.

3.5 Skewness

The shape (**skewness**) of a data set can be described using diagrams, measures of location and measures of spread.

- **A distribution can be symmetrical, have a positive skew or have a negative skew.**

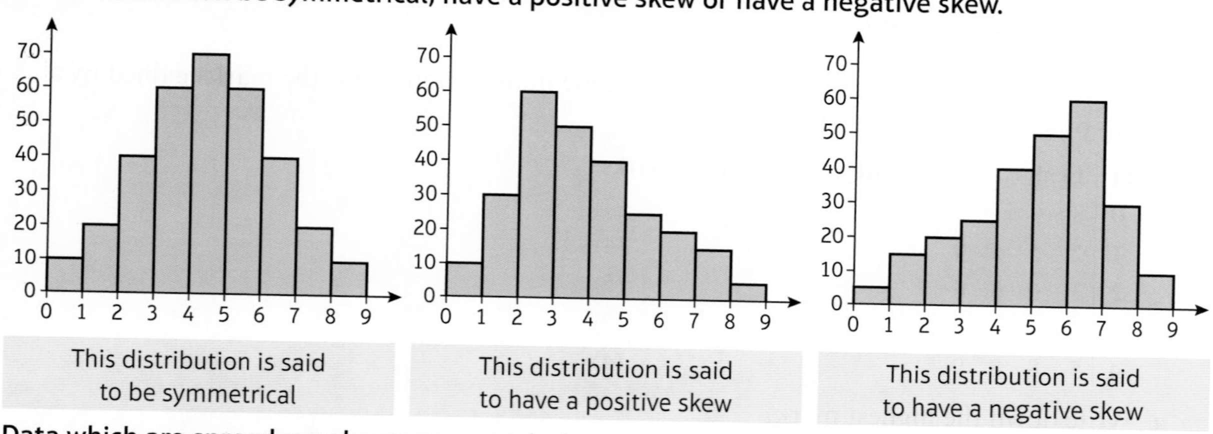

This distribution is said to be symmetrical

This distribution is said to have a positive skew

This distribution is said to have a negative skew

- **Data which are spread evenly are symmetrical.**
- **Data which are mostly at lower values have a positive skew.**
- **Data which are mostly at higher values have a negative skew.**

There are several ways of comparing skewness. Sometimes you will be told which to use, and sometimes you will have to choose one depending on what data you have available.

You can see the shape of the data from a box plot.

You can also look at the quartiles.

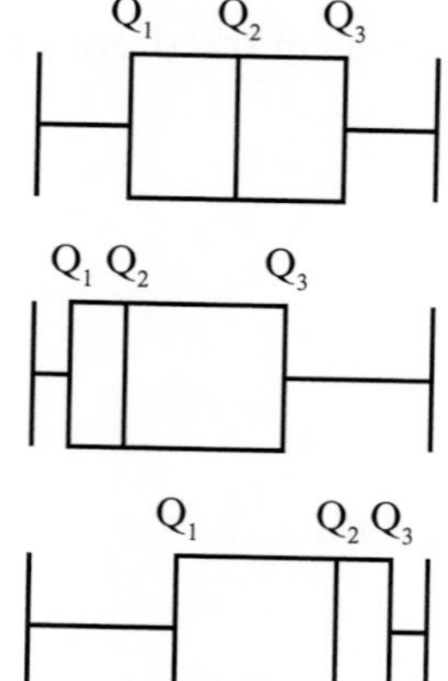

Symmetrical $Q_2 - Q_1 = Q_3 - Q_2$

Positive Skew $Q_2 - Q_1 < Q_3 - Q_2$

Negative Skew $Q_2 - Q_1 > Q_3 - Q_2$

Another test uses the measures of location:

- Mode = median = mean describes a distribution which is **symmetrical**
- Mode < median < mean describes a distribution with a **positive skew**
- Mode > median > mean describes a distribution with a **negative skew**

You can also calculate $\frac{3(\text{mean} - \text{median})}{\text{standard deviation}}$ which tells you how **skewed** the data are.

Negative skew ← Symmetrical 0 → Positive skew

- A value of 0 implies that the mean = median and the distribution is **symmetrical**
- A positive value implies that the median < mean and the distribution is **positively skewed**
- A negative value implies that median > mean and the distribution is **negatively skewed**

The further from 0 the value is, the more likely the data will be skewed.

SKILLS ANALYSIS

The following stem and leaf diagram shows the scores obtained by a group of students in a test.

Key: 6|1 means 61

Score		
2	1 2 8	(3)
3	3 4 7 8 9	(5)
4	1 2 3 5 6 7 9	(7)
5	0 2 3 3 5 5 6 8 9 9	(10)
6	1 2 2 3 4 4 5 6 6 8 8 8 9 9	(14)
7	0 2 3 4 5 7 8 9	(8)
8	0 1 4	(3)

The modal value is 68, the mean is 57.46 and the standard deviation is 15.7 for these data.

a Find the three quartiles for this data set.

b Calculate the value of $\frac{3(\text{mean} - \text{median})}{\text{standard deviation}}$ and comment on the skewness.

c Use two further methods to show that the data are negatively skewed.

a Q_1: $\frac{50}{4} = 12.5$, therefore we use the 13th term = 46

Q_2: $\frac{50}{2} = 25$, therefore we use the mean of the 25th and 26th terms = 60

Q_3: $\frac{3(50)}{4} = 37.5$, therefore we use the 38th term = 69

b $\frac{3(\text{mean} - \text{median})}{\text{standard deviation}} = \frac{3(57.46 - 60)}{15.7} = -0.486$

Therefore the data are negatively skewed.

c $(Q_3 - Q_2) < (Q_2 - Q_1)$

$9 < 14$

Therefore negatively skewed

Mean < median < mode

$57.46 < 60 < 68$

Therefore negatively skewed

Exercise 3E

SKILLS ANALYSIS

1 In a survey of the earnings of some college students who worked weekend jobs, the median wage was \$36.50. The 75th percentile was \$45.75 and the interquartile range was \$30.50. Use the quartiles to describe the skewness of the distributions.

2 A group of estate agents recorded the time spent on the first meeting with a random sample of 120 of their clients. The mean time spent with their clients is 31.1 minutes and the variance is 78.05. The median time is 29.7 minutes and Q_1 and Q_3 values are 25.8 minutes and 34.8 minutes.

One measure of skewness is found using $\frac{3(\text{mean} - \text{median})}{\text{standard deviation}}$

a Evaluate this measure and describe the skewness of the data

The estate agents are undecided whether to use the median and quartiles, or the mean and standard deviation to summarise the data.

b State, giving a reason, which you would recommend for them to use.

3 The following stem and leaf diagram summarises the wing length, to the nearest mm, of a random sample of 67 birds.

	Wing length	Key: 5 | 0 means 50 mm
5	0 0 0 1 1 2 2 3 3 3 4 4	(12)
5	5 5 6 6 6 7 8 8 9 9	(10)
6	0 1 1 1 3 3 4 4 4 4	(10)
6	5 5 6 7 8 9 9	(7)
7	1 1 2 2 3 3	(6)
7	5 7 9 9	(4)
8	1 1 1 2 2 3 3 4	(8)
8	7 8 9	(3)
9	0 1 1 2	(4)
9	5 7 9	(3)

a Write down the mode.

b Find the median and quartiles of the data.

c Construct a box plot to represent the data.

d Comment on the skewness of the distribution.

e Calculate the mean and standard deviation for the data.

f Use another method to shows that the data is skewed.

g State, giving a reason, which of **b** or **e** would you recommend using to summarise the data in the diagram.

Challenge

An orange farmer randomly selects 120 oranges from her farm.
The histogram below shows the diameters (in mm) of the oranges.

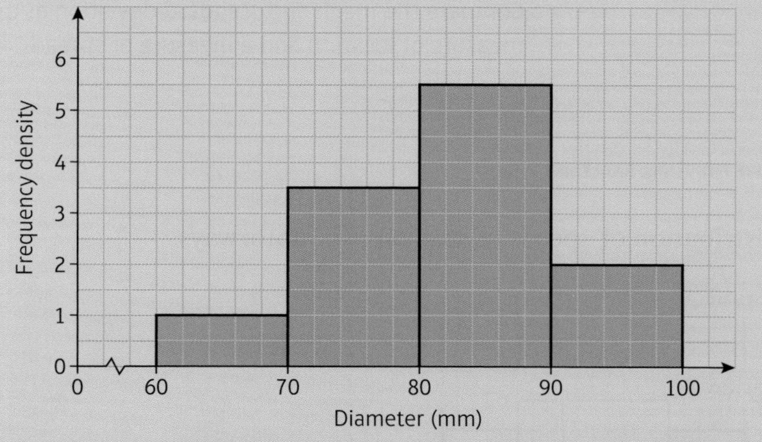

Calculate an estimate of the mean and standard deviation. Comment on why the mean is only an estimate, whether there any outliers, and the type of skewness displayed by the histogram.

3.6 Comparing data

- **When comparing data sets you can comment on:**
  - **a measure of location**
  - **a measure of spread**

You can compare data by using the mean and standard deviation or by using the median and interquartile range. If the data set contains extreme values, then the median and interquartile range are more appropriate statistics to use.

Watch out Do not use the median with the standard deviation or the mean with the interquartile range.

Example 10 SKILLS ANALYSIS

The daily mean temperature (°C) during August is recorded at London Heathrow Airport and Dubai International Airport.

For London Heathrow, $\Sigma x = 562.0$ and $\Sigma x^2 = 10\,301.2$

a Calculate the mean and standard deviation for London Heathrow.

For Dubai International, the mean temperature was 31 °C with a standard deviation of 1.35 °C.

b Compare the data for the two airports using the information given.

a $\bar{x} = 562.0 \div 31 = 18.12\ldots = 18.1\,°\text{C}$ (3 s.f.)

$$\sigma = \sqrt{\frac{10\,301.2}{31} - \left(\frac{562.0}{31}\right)^2} = 1.906\ldots$$

$$= 1.91\,°\text{C (3 s.f.)}$$

b The mean daily temperature at Dubai International is significantly higher and the spread of temperatures is lower than at London Heathrow.

Use $\bar{x} = \frac{\Sigma x}{n}$. There are 31 days in August, so $n = 31$.

Use your calculator to do this calculation in one step. Round your final answer to 3 significant figures.

Compare the mean and standard deviation as a measure of location and a measure of spread.

Exercise 3F SKILLS EXECUTIVE FUNCTION; ANALYSIS

(P) **1** The box plots below show the distribution of speeds of cars on two motorways.

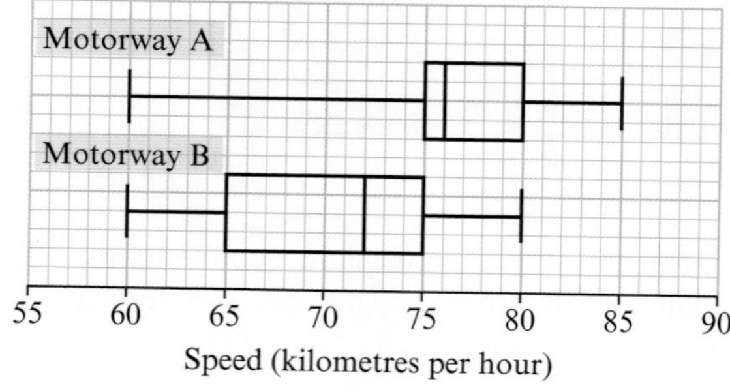

Compare the distributions of the speeds on the two motorways.

(P) **2** Two classes of primary school children complete a puzzle. Summary statistics for the times the children took, in minutes, are shown in the table.

	n	Σx	Σx^2
Class 2B	20	650	22 000
Class 2F	22	598	19 100

Calculate the mean and standard deviation of the times and compare the distributions.

3 The stem and leaf diagram below shows the age, in years, of the members of a sports club.

Male		Female
8 8 7 6	**1**	6 6 6 7 7 8 8 9
7 6 5 5 3 3 2 1	**2**	1 3 3 4 5 7 8 8 9 9
9 8 4 4 3	**3**	2 3 3 4 7
5 2 1	**4**	0 1 8
9 0	**5**	0

Key: 1 | 4 | 0 represents a male aged 41 and a female aged 40

a Find the median and interquartile range for the males.

b The median and interquartile ranges for the females are 27 and 15 respectively.

Make two comparisons between the ages of the males and females.

(E/P) **4** In the box plots here, the marks for a group of students taking their Mathematics exam for the first time are shown on the top.

The marks for a group of students who are retaking their Mathematics exam are shown on the bottom.

Compare and contrast the marks between the two groups taking the exam. **(3 marks)**

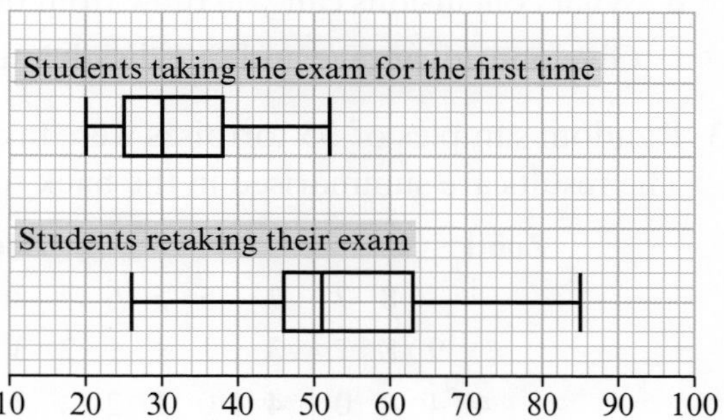

Chapter review 3

SKILLS PROBLEM-SOLVING; ANALYSIS

1 Aroon and Bassam decided to go on a touring holiday in Europe for the whole of July. They recorded the distance they drove, in kilometres, each day:

155, 164, 168, 169, 173, 175, 177, 178, 178, 178, 179, 179, 179, 184, 184, 185, 185, 188, 192, 193, 194, 195, 195, 196, 204, 207, 208, 209, 211, 212, 226

a Draw a stem and leaf diagram and find Q_1, Q_2 and Q_3.

Outliers are values that lie below $Q_1 - 1.5(Q_3 - Q_1)$ or above $Q_3 + 1.5(Q_3 - Q_1)$.

b Find any outliers.

c Draw a box plot of these data.

d Comment on the skewness of the distribution.

(P) **2** Cross-country runners from the Marathon Club and the Runners Club were keen to see which club had the faster runners overall. They decided that all the members from both clubs would take part in a cross-country run. The time each runner took to complete the run was recorded.

The results are summarised in the box plots.

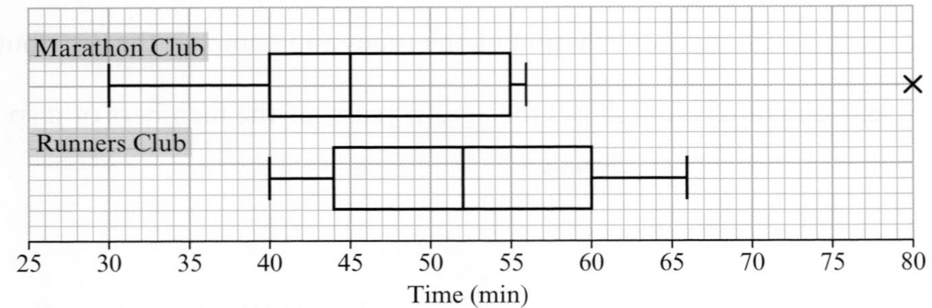

a Write down the time by which 50% of the Marathon Club runners had completed the run.

b Write down the time by which 75% of the Runners Club runners had completed the run.

c Explain what is meant by the cross (×) on the Marathon Club box plot.

d Compare and contrast these two box plots.

e What conclusions can you draw from this information about which club has the faster runners?

f Give one advantage and one disadvantage of comparing distributions using box plots.

3 Random samples of 35 tortoises were taken from two different zoos and their ages were recorded. The results are summarised in the back to back stem and leaf diagram below.

Zoo 1		Zoo 2
8 7	**2**	5 5 6 7 8 8 9
9 8 7	**3**	1 1 1 2 3 4 4 5 6 7 9
4 4 4 0	**4**	0 1 2 4 7
6 6 5 2 2	**5**	0 0 5 5 5
8 6 5 4 2 1 1	**6**	2 5 6 6
8 6 6 6 4 3 1 1	**7**	0 5
9 8 4 3 2	**8**	
4	**9**	9

Key: 7|3|1 means 37-year-olds for Zoo 1 and 31-year-olds for Zoo 2

a The lower quartile, median and upper quartile for Zoo 1 are 44, 64 and 76 years respectively. Find the median and the quartiles for Zoo 2.

b An outlier is a value that falls either:
more than $1.5 \times (Q_3 - Q_1)$ above Q_3 or
more than $1.5 \times (Q_3 - Q_1)$ below Q_1

State any outliers in the above data for Zoo 2.

c State the skewness of each distribution. Justify your answer.

(P) **4** The histogram shows the time taken by a group of 58 girls to run a measured distance.

a Work out the number of girls who took longer than 56 seconds.

b Estimate the number of girls who took between 52 and 55 seconds.

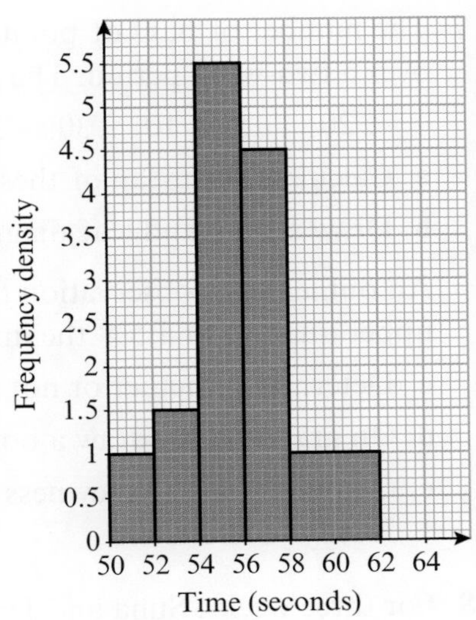

(E/P) **5** The table gives the distances travelled to school, in km, of the population of children in a particular region of the United Kingdom.

Distance, *d* (km)	$0 \leqslant d < 1$	$1 \leqslant d < 2$	$2 \leqslant d < 3$	$3 \leqslant d < 5$	$5 \leqslant d < 10$	$10 \leqslant d$
Number	2565	1784	1170	756	630	135

A histogram of these data was drawn with distance along the horizontal axis.
A bar of horizontal width 1.5 cm and height 5.7 cm represented the 0–1 km group.

Find the widths and heights, in cm, to 1 decimal place, of the bars representing the following groups:

a $2 \leqslant d < 3$ **b** $5 \leqslant d < 10$ **(5 marks)**

6 The labelling on bags of garden compost indicates that the bags have a mass of 20 kg.
The actual masses of a random sample of 50 bags are summarised in the table opposite.

Mass, *m* (kg)	**Frequency**
$14.6 \leqslant m < 14.8$	1
$14.8 \leqslant m < 18.0$	0
$18.0 \leqslant m < 18.5$	5
$18.5 \leqslant m < 20.0$	6
$20.0 \leqslant m < 20.2$	22
$20.2 \leqslant m < 20.4$	15
$20.4 \leqslant m < 21.0$	1

a On graph paper, draw a histogram of these data.

b Estimate the mean and standard deviation of the mass of a bag of compost.
(You may use $\Sigma fy = 988.85$, $\Sigma fy^2 = 19\,602.84$)

c Using linear interpolation, estimate the median.

d One measure of skewness is given by $\dfrac{3(\text{mean} - \text{median})}{\text{standard deviation}}$. Evaluate this coefficient for the data.

e Comment on the skewness of the distribution of the weights of bags of compost.

7 The number of bags of potato crisps sold per day in a coffee shop was recorded over a two-week period. The results are shown below.

20 15 10 30 33 40 5 11 13 20 25 42 31 17

a Calculate the mean of these data.

b Draw a stem and leaf diagram and find the median and quartiles for these data.

An outlier is an observation that falls either 1.5 × the interquartile range above the upper quartile or 1.5 × the interquartile range below the lower quartile.

c Determine whether or not any items of data are outliers.

d On graph paper, draw a box plot to represent these data. Show your scale clearly.

e Comment on the skewness of the distribution of bags of crisps sold per day. Justify your answer.

8 For three weeks, Suha and Jameela each count the number of bicycles they see on their routes to school. The data they collected are summarised in this back to back stem and leaf diagram.

Suha		Jameela
9 9 7 5	**0**	6 6
7 6 5 3 3 2 2 2 1 1	**1**	1 1 5
5 3 3 2 2	**2**	1 2 2 2 3 7 7 8 9
2 1	**3**	2 3 4 7 7 8
	4	2

Key: 5|0|6 means Suha counts 5 bicycles and Jameela counts 6 bicycles

a Write down the modal number of bicycles Jameela counts on her route.

The quartiles are summarised in the table below:

	Suha	Jameela
Lower quartile	X	21
Median	13	Y
Upper quartile	Z	33

b Find the values of X, Y, and Z.

(E) **9** The table shows summary statistics of the mean daily temperature in Toronto in April 1987 and April 2015.

	Min	Max	Median	Σx	Σx^2
1987	7.0	17.0	11.85	356.1	4408.9
2015	10.1	14.1	12.0	364.1	4450.2

a Calculate the mean of the mean daily temperatures in each of the two years. **(2 marks)**

b In 2015, the standard deviation was 1.02. Compare the mean daily temperatures in the two years. **(2 marks)**

c A recorded temperature is considered 'normal' for the time of year if it is within one standard deviation of the mean. Estimate for how many days in April 2015 a 'normal' mean daily temperature was recorded. State one assumption you have made in making the estimate. **(3 marks)**

Challenge

The table shows the lengths of the films in a film festival, to the nearest minute.

Length (min)	Frequency
70–89	4
90–99	17
100–109	20
110–139	9
140–179	2

A histogram is drawn to represent the data, and the bar representing the 90–99 class is 3 cm higher than the bar representing the 70–89 class.

Find the height of the bar chart representing the 110–139 class.

Summary of key points

1. A common definition of an outlier is any value that is:
   - greater than $Q_3 + k(Q_3 - Q_1)$
   - or less than $Q_1 - k(Q_3 - Q_1)$
2. The process of removing anomalies from a data set is known as cleaning the data.
3. On a histogram, to calculate the height of each bar (the **frequency density**) use the formula:
   area of bar $= k \times$ frequency
4. Joining the middle of the top of each bar in a histogram forms a frequency polygon.
5. When comparing data sets you can comment on:
   - a measure of location
   - a measure of spread
6. A stem and leaf diagram reveals the shape of the data and enables quartiles to be found.
7. Two sets of data can be compared using back to back stem and leaf diagrams.
8. A box plot represents important features of the data. It shows quartiles, maximum and minimum values, and any outliers.
9. Box plots can be used to compare two sets of data.
10. Diagrams, measures of location, and measures of spread can be used to describe the shape (skewness) of a data set.
11. You can describe whether a distribution is skewed using
    - quartiles
    - shape from box plots
    - measures of location
    - the formula $\frac{3(\text{mean} - \text{median})}{\text{standard deviation}}$, where a larger value means greater skew.

4 PROBABILITY

3.1
3.2
3.3
3.4

Learning objectives

After completing this chapter you should be able to:

- Understand the vocabulary used in probability → pages 55-57
- Draw and interpret Venn diagrams → pages 57-60
- Understand mutually exclusive and independent events and determine whether or not two events are independent → pages 60-63
- Understand and interpret set notation → pages 63-67
- Understand conditional probability → pages 68-74
- Use probability formulae → pages 74-77
- Use and understand tree diagrams → pages 77-82

Prior knowledge check

1 A bag contains three red balls, four yellow balls and two orange balls. A ball is chosen at random from the bag. Write down the probability that the ball is:

a orange **b** yellow **c** not red **d** green.

← International GCSE Mathematics

2 Three coins are flipped. Write down all the possible outcomes.

← International GCSE Mathematics

3 Layla rolls a dice. She keeps rolling until she rolls a 6. Work out the probability that Layla rolls the dice:

a exactly three times

b fewer than three times

c more than three times.

← International GCSE Mathematics

Sports teams use past performance to estimate probabilities and plan strategies. In softball and baseball, a player's batting average is an estimate of the probability that he or she will make a hit.

4.1 Understanding the vocabulary used in probability

If you want to predict the chance of something happening, you use **probability**.

An **experiment** is a repeatable process that gives rise to a number of **outcomes**.

An **event** is a collection of one or more outcomes.

A **sample space** is the set of all possible outcomes.

Where outcomes are **equally likely**, the probability of an event is the number of outcomes in the event divided by the total number of possible outcomes.

All events have probability between 0 (impossible) and 1 (certain). Probabilities are usually written as fractions or decimals.

Dice, cards, spinners, etc. are used as theoretical props throughout this chapter to explore the idea of chance and probability only.

Example 1

Two fair spinners each have four sectors numbered 1 to 4. The two spinners are spun together and the sum of the numbers indicated on each spinner is recorded.

Find the probability of the spinners indicating a sum of:

a exactly 5 **b** more than 5.

Draw a **sample space** diagram showing all possible outcomes.

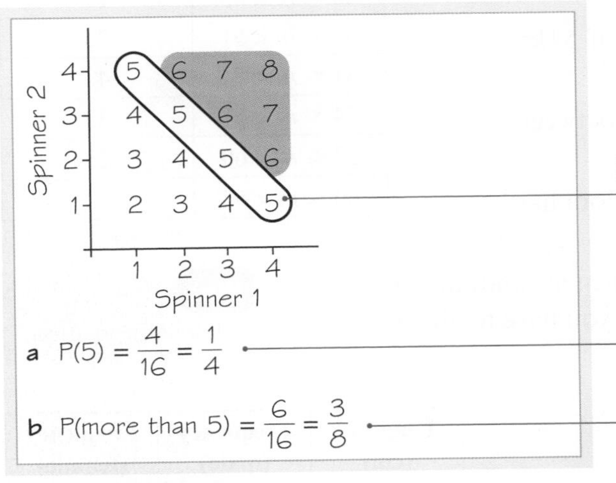

There are 4 × 4 = 16 points. Each of these points is equally likely because the spinners are fair.

There are 4 outcomes for part **a**.

There are four 5s and 16 outcomes altogether.

P( ) is short for 'probability of'. The answer P(5) can also be written as 0.25

There are six sums more than 5 for this part (shaded blue). They form the top right corner of the diagram.

The answer can also be written as 0.375

Example 2 SKILLS CRITICAL THINKING

The table shows the times taken, in minutes, for a group of students to complete a number puzzle.

Time, t (min)	$5 \leqslant t < 7$	$7 \leqslant t < 9$	$9 \leqslant t < 11$	$11 \leqslant t < 13$	$13 \leqslant t < 15$
Frequency	6	13	12	5	4

Find the probability that a randomly selected student finished the number puzzle:

a in under 9 minutes **b** in over 10.5 minutes.

a P(finished in under 9 minutes) = $\frac{19}{40}$

b 3 + 5 + 4 = 12

P(finished in over 10.5 minutes) = $\frac{12}{40} = \frac{3}{10}$

There are 40 students overall.

6 + 13 = 19 finished in under 9 minutes.

Problem-solving

Use interpolation: 10.5 minutes lies $\frac{3}{4}$ of the way through the $9 \leqslant t < 11$ class, so $\frac{1}{4}$ of 12 is 3.

Your answer is an estimate because you don't know the exact number of students who took longer than 10.5 seconds.

Exercise 4A SKILLS CRITICAL THINKING

1 Two coins are tossed. Find the probability of both coins showing the same outcome.

2 Two six-sided dice are rolled and their product, X, is recorded.

a Draw a sample space diagram showing all the possible outcomes of this experiment.

b Find the probability of each event:

i $X = 24$ **ii** $X < 5$ **iii** X is even.

P **3** The masses of 140 adult Bullmastiff dogs are recorded in a table. One dog is chosen at random.

Mass, m (kg)	Frequency
$45 \leqslant m < 48$	17
$48 \leqslant m < 51$	25
$51 \leqslant m < 54$	42
$54 \leqslant m < 57$	33
$57 \leqslant m < 60$	21
$60 \leqslant m < 63$	2

a Find the probability that the dog has a mass of 54 kg or more.

b Find the probability that the dog has a mass between 48 kg and 57 kg.

The probability that a Rottweiler chosen at random has a mass under 53 kg is 0.54.

c Is it more or less likely that a Bullmastiff chosen at random has a mass under 53 kg? State one assumption that you have made in making your decision.

Hint

Use interpolation.

P **4** The lengths, in cm, of 240 koalas are recorded in a table. One koala is chosen at random.

Length, l (cm)	Frequency (male)	Frequency (female)
$65 \leqslant l < 70$	4	14
$70 \leqslant l < 75$	20	15
$75 \leqslant l < 80$	24	32
$80 \leqslant l < 85$	47	27
$85 \leqslant l < 90$	31	26

a Find the probability that the koala is female.

b Find the probability that the koala is less than 80 cm long.

c Find the probability that the koala is a male between 75 cm and 85 cm long.

Koalas under 72 cm long are called juvenile.

d Estimate the probability that a koala chosen at random is juvenile. State one assumption you have made in making your estimate.

5 The histogram shows the distribution of masses, in kg, of 70 adult cats.

a Find the probability that a cat chosen at random has a mass more than 5 kg. **(2 marks)**

b Estimate the probability that a cat chosen at random has a mass less than 6.5 kg. **(3 marks)**

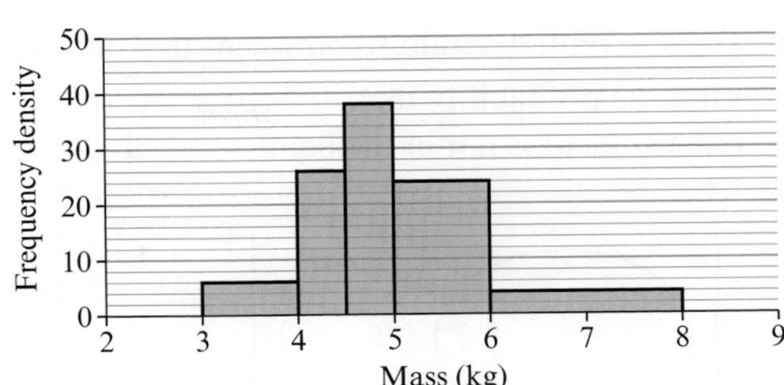

Challenge

SKILLS CRITICAL THINKING

Samira picks one card at random from group A and one card at random from group B.

She records the product, Y, of the two cards as the result of her experiment. Given that x is an integer and that P(Y is even) = P($Y \geqslant 20$), find the possible values of x.

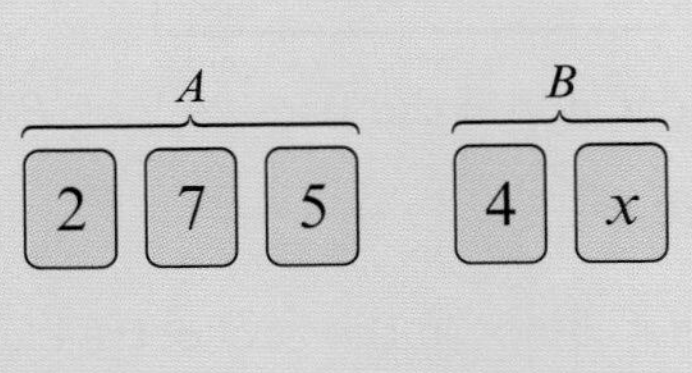

4.2 Venn diagrams

- **A Venn diagram can be used to represent events graphically. Frequencies or probabilities can be placed in the regions of the Venn diagram.**

A rectangle represents the sample space, $\mathscr{E}$, and it contains closed curves that represent events.

For events A and B in a sample space $\mathscr{E}$:

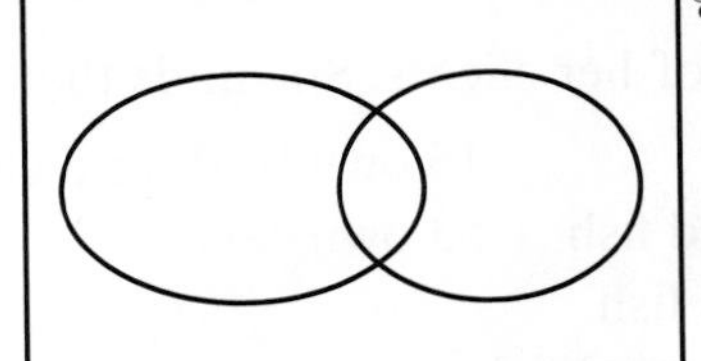

The symbol $\mathscr{E}$ is used to represent the **whole sample space**.

1 The event A **and** B

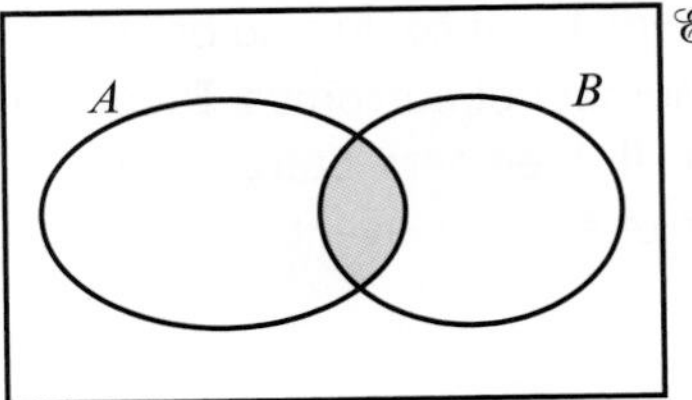

This event is also called the **intersection** of A and B. It represents the event that both A and B occur.

2 The event A **or** B

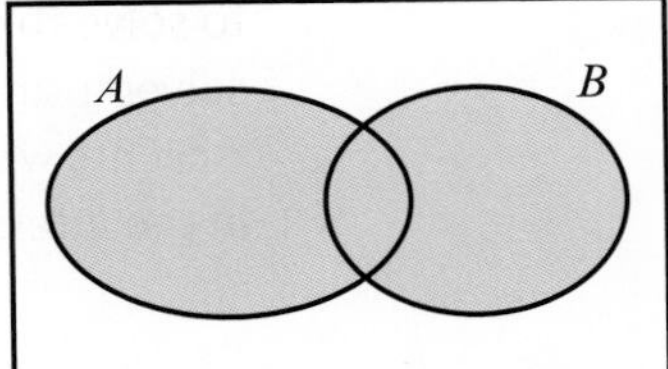

This event is also called the **union** of A and B. It represents the event that either A or B, or both, occur.

3 The event **not** A

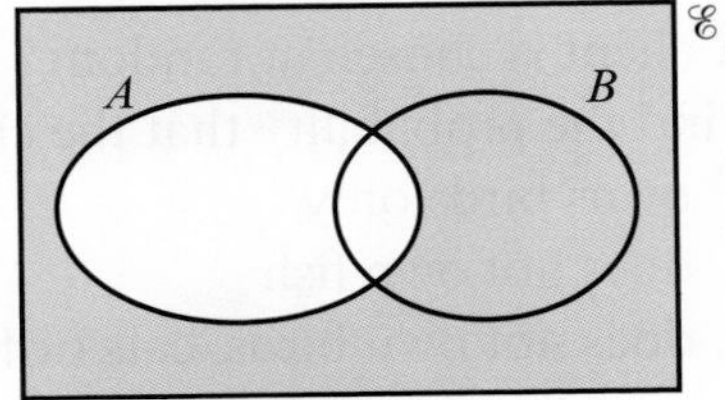

This event is also called the **complement** of A. It represents the event that A does not occur. P(not A) = 1 – P(A)

You can write numbers of outcomes (frequencies) or the probability of the events in a Venn diagram to help solve problems.

SKILLS INTERPRETATION

In a class of 30 students, 7 are in the orchestra club, 5 are in the band, and 2 are in both the orchestra club and the band. A student is chosen at random from the class.

a Draw a Venn diagram to represent this information.

b Find the probability that:

i the student is not in the band **ii** the student is not in the orchestra club or the band.

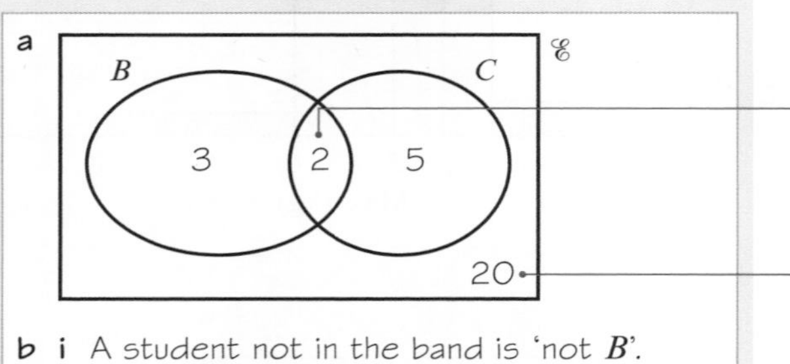

Put the number in both the orchestra club and the band in the intersection of B and C.

This region represents the events in the sample space that are not in C or B:

$30 - (3 + 2 + 5) = 20$

b i A student not in the band is 'not B'.

$\text{P(not } B) = \frac{25}{30} = \frac{5}{6}$

There are $5 + 20 = 25$ outcomes not in B, out of 30 equally likely outcomes.

ii P(student is not in the orchestra club or the band)

$= \frac{20}{30} = \frac{2}{3}$

20 outcomes are in neither event.

Example 4 SKILLS DECISION-MAKING

A vet surveys 100 of her clients. She finds that:

25 own birds
15 own birds and cats
11 own birds and fish
53 own cats
10 own cats and fish
7 own birds, cats and fish
40 own fish

A client is chosen at random.
Find the probability that the client:

a owns birds only

b does not own fish

c does not own birds, cats or fish.

Problem-solving

A Venn diagram showing probabilities is used to solve this problem, but it could also be solved using the number of outcomes. There are 7 clients who own all three pets. Start with 0.07 in the intersection of all three events.

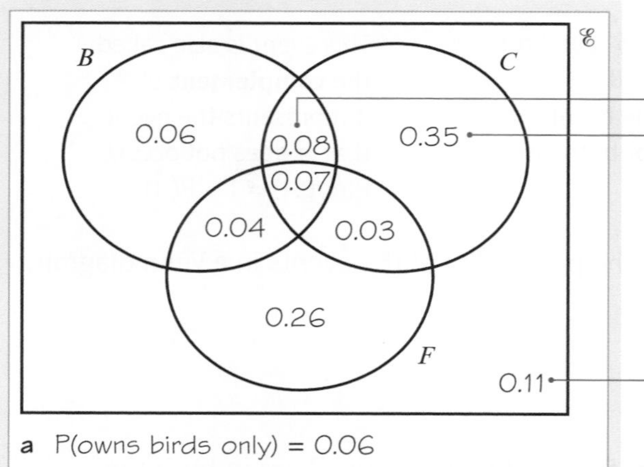

Work outward to the intersections.
$0.15 - 0.07 = 0.08$

Each of 'birds only', 'cats only' and 'fish only' can be worked out by further subtractions:
$0.53 - (0.08 + 0.07 + 0.03) = 0.35$ for 'cats only'

As the probability of the whole sample space is 1, the final area is $1 - (0.26 + 0.04 + 0.07 + 0.03 + 0.06 + 0.08 + 0.35) = 0.11$

a P(owns birds only) = 0.06

b P(does not own fish) = 1 − 0.4 = 0.6

c P(does not own birds, cats or fish) = 0.11

This is the value on the Venn diagram outside B, C and F.

1 There are 25 students in a tutor group at International College. There are 16 students in the tutor group studying Arabic, 14 studying English, and 6 students studying both English and Arabic.

a Draw a Venn diagram to represent this information.

b Find the probability that a randomly chosen student in the tutor group:

i studies English
ii studies English and Arabic
iii studies English but not Arabic
iv does not study English or Arabic.

2 There are 125 diners in a restaurant who were surveyed to find out if they had ordered garlic bread, pasta or cheesecake:

15 had ordered all three items
43 had ordered garlic bread
40 had ordered pasta
44 had ordered cheesecake
20 had ordered pasta and cheesecake
26 had ordered garlic bread and cheesecake
25 had ordered garlic bread and pasta

a Draw a Venn diagram to represent this information.

b A diner is chosen at random. Find the probability that the diner ordered:

i all three items
ii pasta but not cheesecake and not garlic bread
iii garlic bread and pasta but not cheesecake
iv none of these items.

3 A group of 275 people at a music festival were asked if they play guitar, piano or drums:

1 person plays all three instruments
65 people play guitar and piano
10 people play piano and drums
30 people play guitar and drums
15 people play piano only
20 people play guitar only
35 people play drums only

a Draw a Venn diagram to represent this information.

b A festival goer is chosen at random from the group.
Find the probability that the person chosen:

i plays the piano
ii plays at least two of the instruments
iii plays exactly one of the instruments
iv plays none of the instruments.

(P) 4 The probability that a child in a school has blue eyes is 0.27 and the probability that the child has black hair is 0.35. The probability that the child will have black hair or blue eyes or both is 0.45. A child is chosen at random from the school. Find the probability that the child has:

a black hair and blue eyes

b black hair but not blue eyes

c neither feature.

Hint Draw a Venn diagram to help you.

(E/P) 5 A patient going into a doctor's waiting room reads *Hiya* magazine with probability 0.6 and *Dakor* magazine with probability 0.4. The probability that the patient reads either one or both of the magazines is 0.7. Find the probability that the patient reads:

a both magazines **(2 marks)**

b *Hiya* magazine only. **(2 marks)**

E/P **6** The Venn diagram shows the probabilities of members of a sports club taking part in various activities.

A represents the event that the member takes part in archery.

B represents the event that the member takes part in badminton.

C represents the event that the member takes part in croquet.

Given that $P(B) = 0.45$:

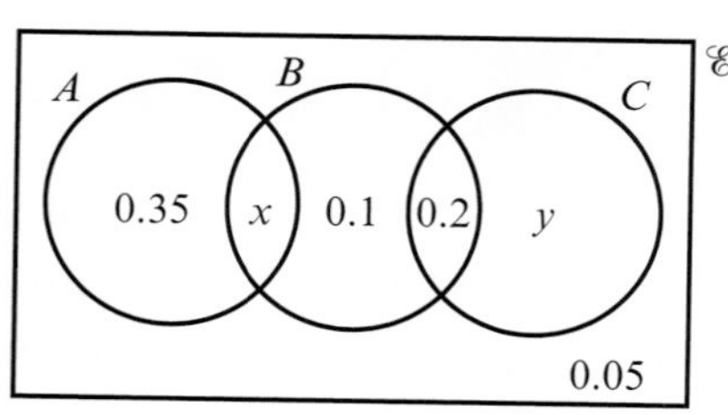

a find x **(1 mark)**

b find y. **(2 marks)**

E/P **7** The Venn diagram shows the probabilities that students at a junior college study certain subjects.

M represents the event that the student studies Mathematics.

P represents the event that the student studies Physics.

H represents the event that the student studies History.

Given that $P(M) = P(P)$, find the values of p and q.

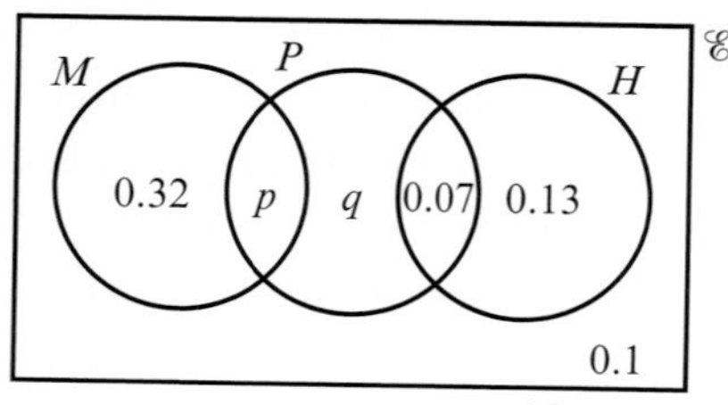

(4 marks)

Challenge

SKILLS PROBLEM-SOLVING

The Venn diagram shows the probabilities of a group of children liking three types of music.

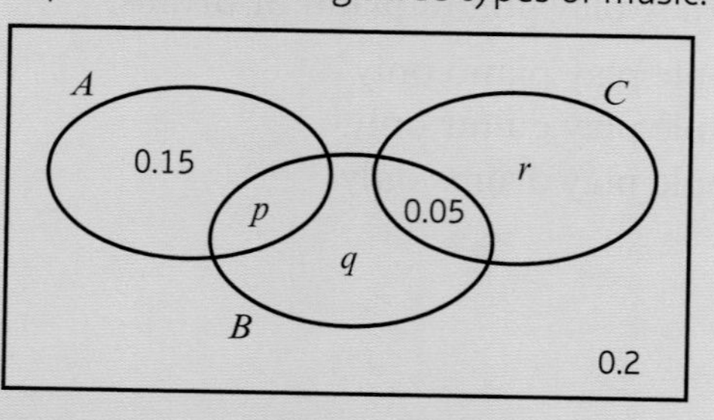

Given that $P(B) = 2P(A)$ and that $P(\text{not } C) = 0.83$, find the values of p, q and r.

4.3 Mutually exclusive and independent events

When events have no outcomes in common they are called **mutually exclusive**.

In a Venn diagram, the closed curves do not overlap and you can use a simple addition rule to work out combined probabilities:

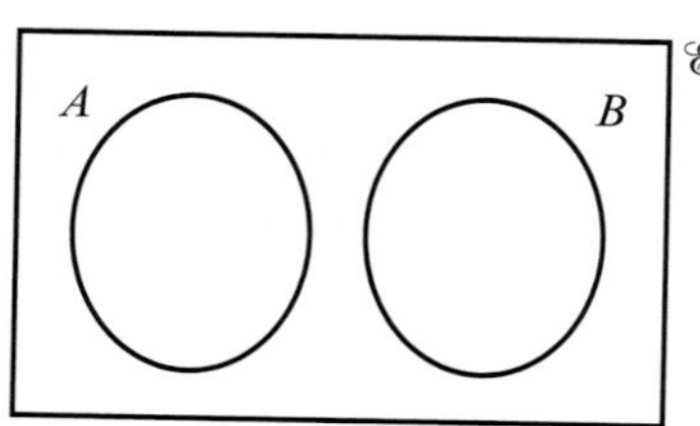

- For mutually exclusive events, $P(A \text{ or } B) = P(A) + P(B)$

When one event has no effect on another, they are **independent**. Therefore if A and B are independent, the probability of A happening is the same whether or not B happens.

- For **independent events**, $P(A \text{ and } B) = P(A) \times P(B)$

You can use this **multiplication rule** to determine whether or not events are independent.

Example 5 SKILLS PROBLEM-SOLVING

Events A and B are mutually exclusive events, where $P(A) = 0.2$ and $P(B) = 0.4$

Find: **a** $P(A \text{ or } B)$ **b** $P(A \text{ but not } B)$ **c** $P(\text{neither } A \text{ nor } B)$

a

$P(A \text{ or } B) = P(A) + P(B)$
$= 0.2 + 0.4 = 0.6$

b $P(A \text{ but not } B) = P(A) = 0.2$

c $P(\text{neither } A \text{ nor } B) = 0.4$

A and *B* are mutually exclusive so the closed curves do not intersect.

Use the simple addition rule.

Everything in *A* is not in *B*, because the events are mutually exclusive.

This is everything outside of both circles: $1 - P(A \text{ or } B)$

Example 6

Events A and B are independent events, where $P(A) = \frac{1}{3}$ and $P(B) = \frac{1}{5}$

Find $P(A \text{ and } B)$.

$P(A \text{ and } B) = P(A) \times P(B) = \frac{1}{3} \times \frac{1}{5} = \frac{1}{15}$

A and *B* are independent so you can use the multiplication rule for independent events.

Example 7 SKILLS PROBLEM-SOLVING

The Venn diagram shows the number of students in a class who watch any of three popular TV programmes, A, B and C.

a Find the probability that a student chosen at random watches B or C or both.

b Determine whether watching A and watching B are independent events.

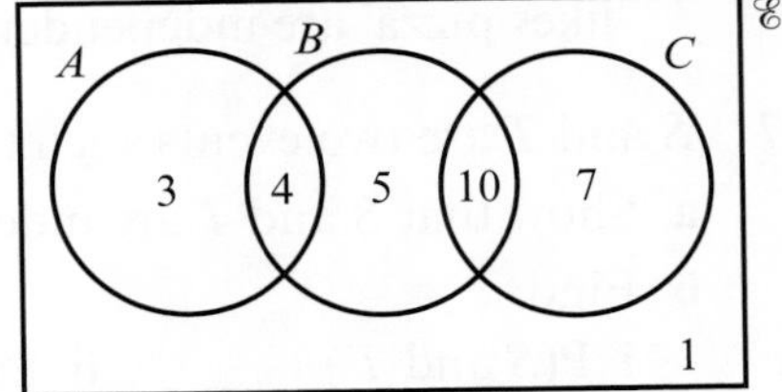

a $4 + 5 + 10 + 7 = 26$

$P(\text{watches } B \text{ or } C \text{ or both}) = \frac{26}{30} = \frac{13}{15}$

b $P(A) = \frac{3 + 4}{30} = \frac{7}{30}$

$P(B) = \frac{4 + 5 + 10}{30} = \frac{19}{30}$

$P(A \text{ and } B) = \frac{4}{30} = \frac{2}{15}$

$P(A) \times P(B) = \frac{7}{30} \times \frac{19}{30} = \frac{133}{900}$

So $P(A \text{ and } B) \neq P(A) \times P(B)$

Therefore watching A and watching B are *not* independent events.

Take the probabilities from the Venn diagram.

Multiply the two probabilities and check whether or not they give the same answer as $P(A \text{ and } B)$.

Problem-solving

Show your calculations and then write down a conclusion stating whether or not the events are independent.

Exercise 4C SKILLS PROBLEM-SOLVING

1 Events A and B are mutually exclusive. $P(A) = 0.2$ and $P(B) = 0.5$
  a Draw a Venn diagram to represent these two events.
  b Find P(A or B).
  c Find P(neither A nor B).

2 Two fair dice are rolled and the result on each one is recorded. Show that the events 'the sum of the scores on the dice is 4' and 'both dice land on the same number' are not mutually exclusive.

3 $P(A) = 0.5$ and $P(B) = 0.3$. Given that events A and B are independent, find P(A and B).

4 $P(A) = 0.15$ and P(A and B) $= 0.045$. Given that events A and B are independent, find $P(B)$.

5 The Venn diagram shows the number of children in a play group that like playing with bricks (B), action figures (F) or trains (T).

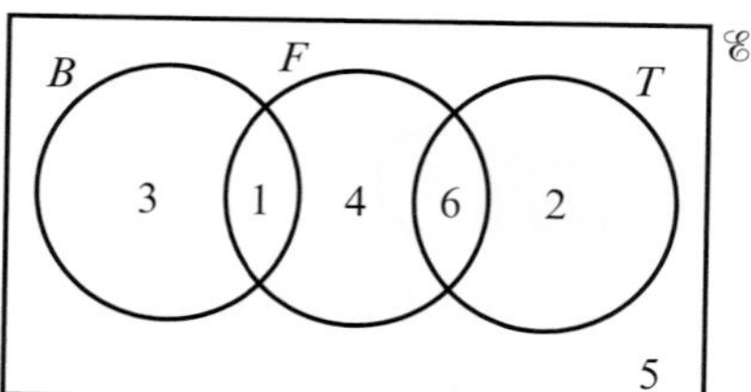

  a State, with a reason, which two types of toy are mutually exclusive.
  b Determine whether or not the events 'plays with bricks' and 'plays with action figures' are independent.

(E) 6 The Venn diagram shows the probabilities that a group of students like pasta (A) or pizza (B).

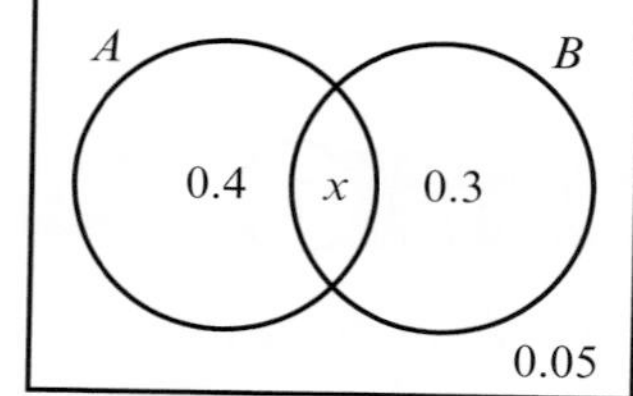

  a Write down the value of x. **(1 mark)**
  b Determine whether the events 'likes pasta' and 'likes pizza' are independent. **(3 marks)**

(P) 7 S and T are two events such that $P(S) = 0.3$, $P(T) = 0.4$ and P(S but not T) $= 0.18$
  a Show that S and T are independent.
  b Find:
    i P(S and T)   ii P(neither S nor T).

(E/P) 8 W and X are two events such that $P(W) = 0.5$, P(W and not X) $= 0.25$ and P(neither W nor X) $= 0.3$. State, with a reason, whether W and X are independent events. **(3 marks)**

(E/P) 9 The Venn diagram shows the probabilities of members of a social club taking part in charitable activities.

A represents taking part in an archery competition.

R represents taking part in a raffle.

F represents taking part in a fun run.

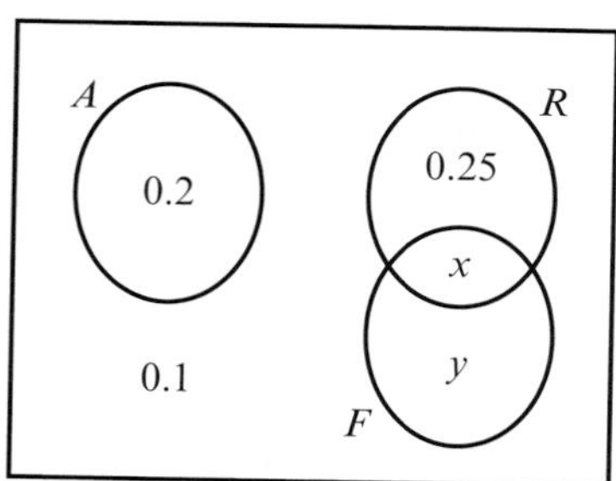

The probability that a member takes part in the archery competition or the raffle is 0.6.

  a Find the value of x and the value of y. **(2 marks)**
  b Show that events R and F are not independent. **(3 marks)**

P **10** In the Venn diagram shown here, given that events A and B are independent, find the two possible values for p and q.

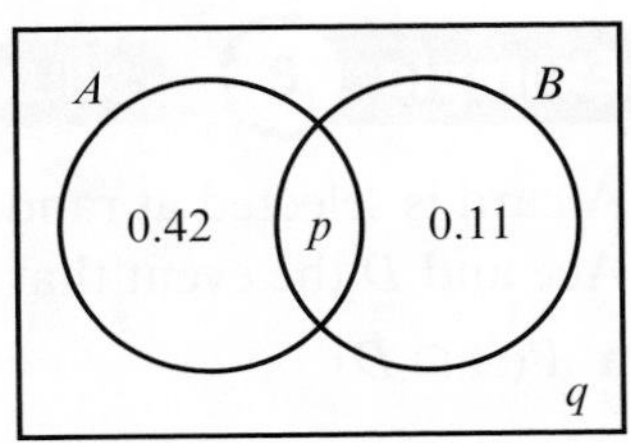

Challenge

SKILLS PROBLEM-SOLVING

A and B are independent events in a sample space $\mathscr{E}$.
Given that A and B are independent, prove that:

a A and 'not B' are independent

b 'not A' and 'not B' are independent.

4.4 Set notation

You can use **set notation** to describe events within a sample space. This can help you abbreviate probability statements.

For example:

- **The event (A and B) can be written as $A \cap B$. The '$\cap$' symbol is the symbol for intersection.**

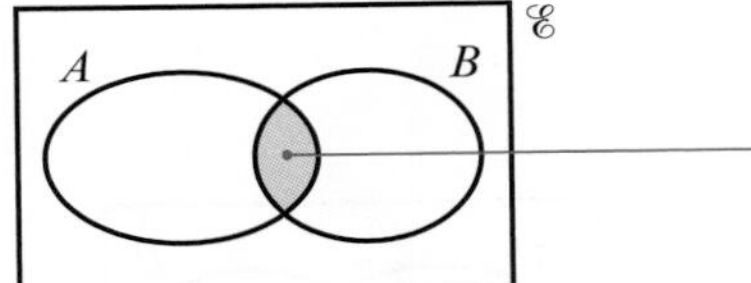

The **intersection** of A and B is written as $A \cap B$.
If A and B are independent, $P(A \cap B) = P(A) \times P(B)$

Notation If two events, A and B, are mutually exclusive, then their intersection is the **empty set**, $\varnothing$. You can write $A \cap B = \varnothing$.

- **The event (A or B) can be written as $A \cup B$. The '$\cup$' symbol is the symbol for union.**

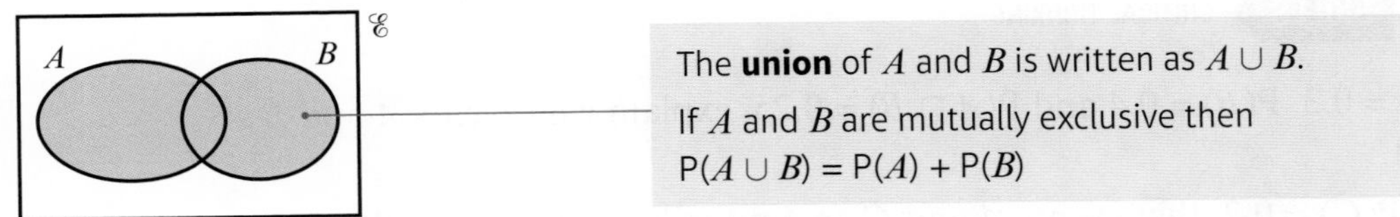

The **union** of A and B is written as $A \cup B$.
If A and B are mutually exclusive then
$P(A \cup B) = P(A) + P(B)$

- **The event (not A)can be written as A'. This is also called the complement of A.**

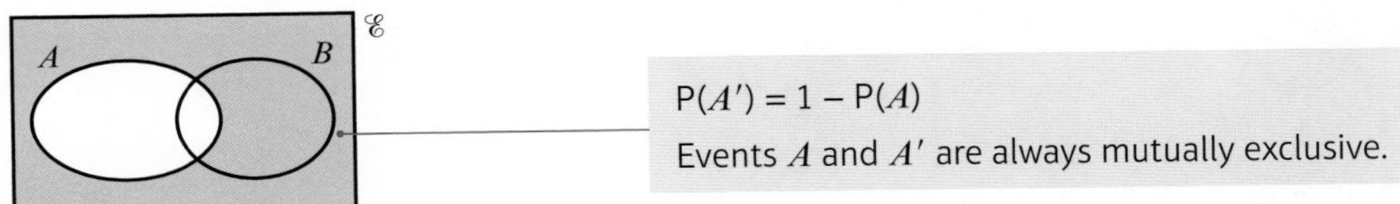

$P(A') = 1 - P(A)$
Events A and A' are always mutually exclusive.

Example 8 SKILLS PROBLEM-SOLVING

A card is selected at random from a pack of 52 playing cards. Let A be the event that the card is an Ace and D the event that the card is a diamond. Find:

a $P(A \cap D)$ **b** $P(A \cup D)$ **c** $P(A')$ **d** $P(A' \cap D)$

Draw a Venn diagram:

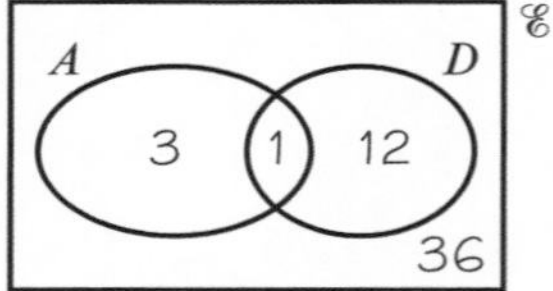

Notation Venn diagrams can show either probabilities or the number of outcomes in each event.
$n(A)$ is the notation used to indicate the number of outcomes. For example, there are four Aces so $n(A) = 4$ and there is one Ace of diamonds so $n(A \cap D) = 1$.

a $A \cap D$ is the event 'the card chosen is the Ace of diamonds'.

$P(A \cap D) = \frac{1}{52}$

There is one outcome in $A \cap D$ and 52 outcomes in ℰ so the probability is $\frac{1}{52}$

b $A \cup D$ is the event 'the card chosen is an Ace or a diamond or both'.

$P(A \cup D) = \frac{16}{52} = \frac{4}{13}$

$n(A \cup D) = 3 + 12 + 1 = 16$

c A' is the event 'the card chosen is not an Ace'.

$P(A') = \frac{48}{52} = \frac{12}{13}$

d $A' \cap D$ is the event 'the card chosen is not an Ace and is a diamond'.

$P(A' \cap D) = \frac{12}{52} = \frac{3}{13}$

This is the set of all outcomes that are not in A but **are** in D.

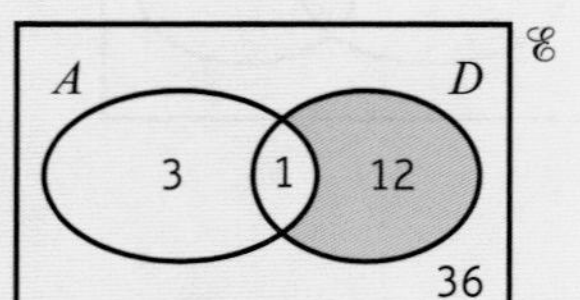

Example 9  SKILLS CRITICAL THINKING

a Given that $P(A) = 0.3$, $P(B) = 0.4$ and $P(A \cap B) = 0.25$, explain why events A and B are not independent.

b Given also that $P(C) = 0.2$, that events A and C are mutually exclusive and that events B and C are independent, draw a Venn diagram to illustrate the events A, B and C, showing the probabilities for each region.

c Find $P((A \cap B') \cup C)$

a $P(A) \times P(B) = 0.3 \times 0.4 = 0.12$

$P(A) \times P(B) \neq P(A \cap B)$ so A and B are not independent.

b

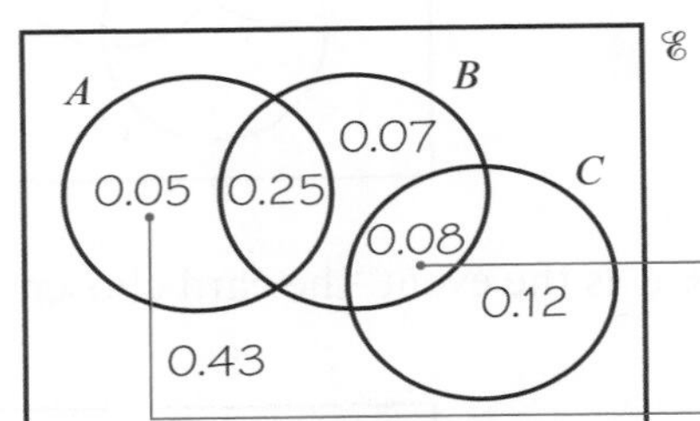

c $P(A \cap B') = 0.05$

$P((A \cap B') \cup C) = 0.05 + 0.2 = 0.25$

Problem-solving

When transferring information to a Venn diagram, work from the intersections outward if possible.

Since B and C are independent, $P(B \cap C) = 0.4 \times 0.2 = 0.08$

Since A and C are mutually exclusive, A overlaps only with B. This region representing just A is $0.3 - 0.25 = 0.05$

This is the region inside set A but outside set B.

Add the two probabilities, since it is a union relationship and there is no overlap.

Exercise 4D

SKILLS INTERPRETATION; CRITICAL THINKING

1 Use set notation to describe the area shaded blue in each of these Venn diagrams:

a
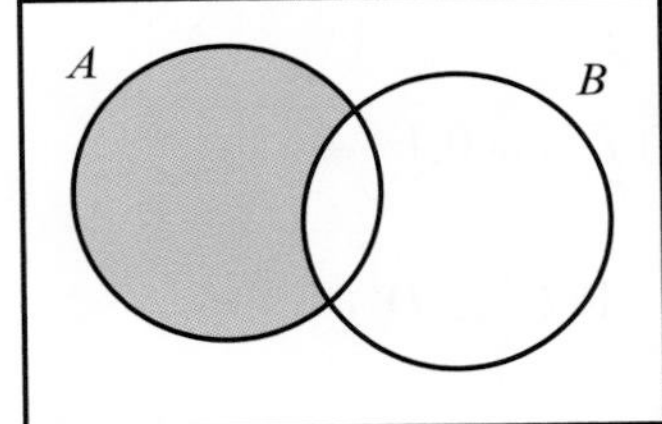

b
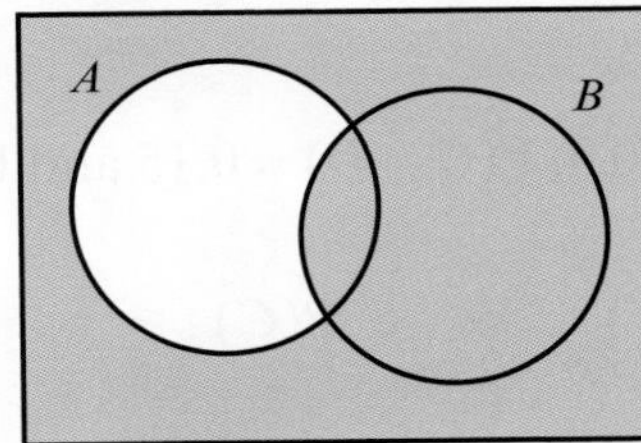

c
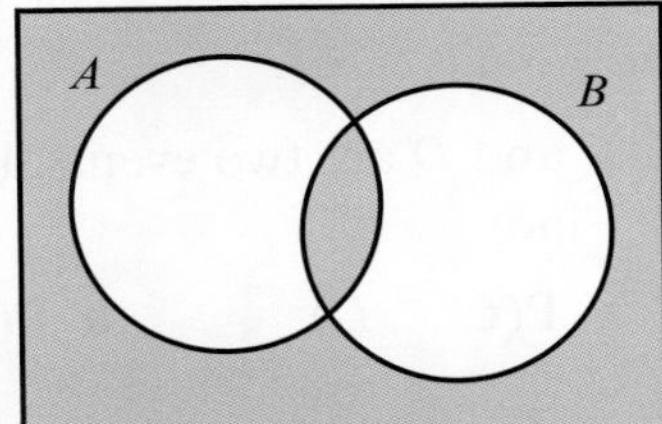

d
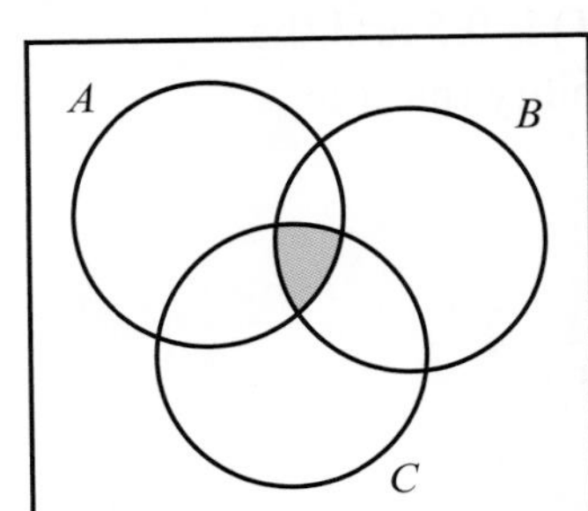

e
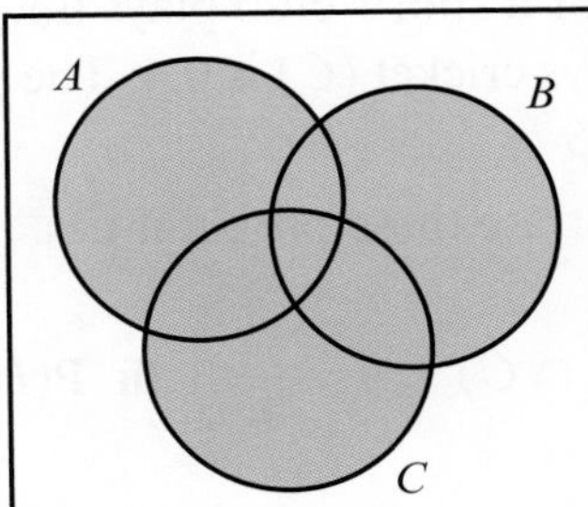

f
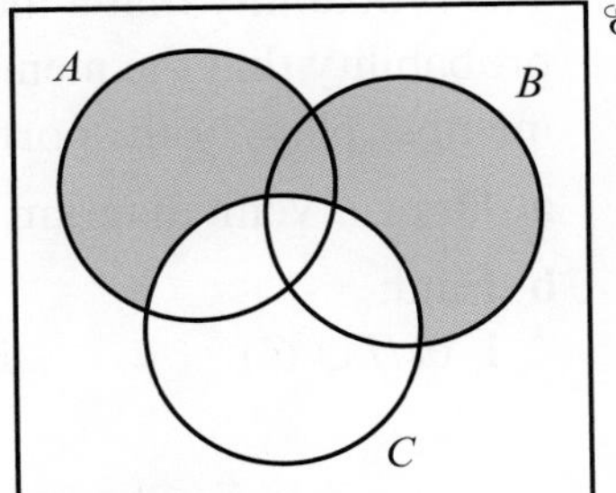

2 On copies of this Venn diagram, shade:

a $A \cup B'$

b $A' \cap B'$

c $(A \cap B)'$

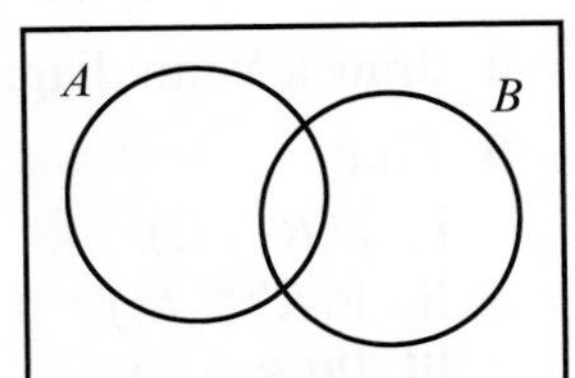

3 On copies of this Venn diagram, shade:

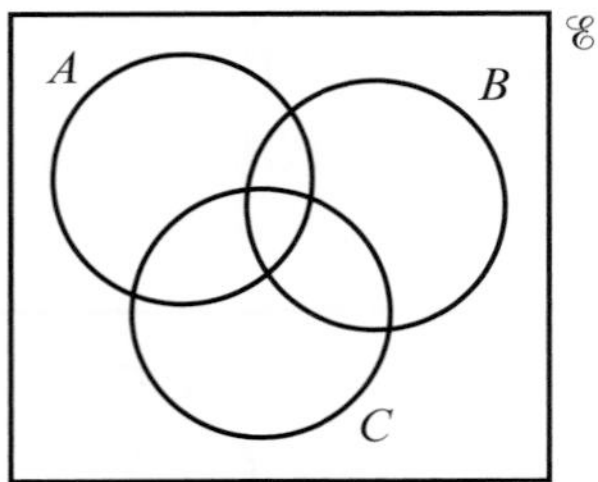

a $(A \cap B) \cup C$

b $(A' \cup B') \cap C$

c $(A \cap B \cap C')'$

4 A card is chosen at random from a pack of 52 playing cards. C is the event 'the card chosen is a club' and K is the event 'the card chosen is a King'.
The Venn diagram shows the number of outcomes for each event.

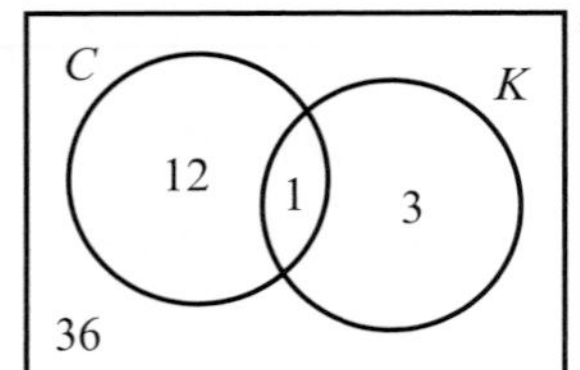

Find:

a $P(K)$ **b** $P(C)$ **c** $P(C \cap K)$

d $P(C \cup K)$ **e** $P(C')$ **f** $P(K' \cap C)$

5 A and B are two events. $P(A) = 0.5$, $P(B) = 0.2$ and $P(A \cap B) = 0.1$
Find:

a $P(A \cup B)$ **b** $P(B')$

c $P(A \cap B')$ **d** $P(A \cup B')$

Hint Draw a Venn diagram.

6 C and D are two events. $P(D) = 0.4$, $P(C \cap D) = 0.15$ and $P(C' \cap D') = 0.1$
Find:

a $P(C' \cap D)$ **b** $P(C \cap D')$ **c** $P(C)$ **d** $P(C' \cup D')$

7 The probability that a member of a sports club plays hockey (H) is 0.5 and the probability that the member plays cricket (C) is 0.4. The probability that the member plays both sports is 0.25

a Draw a Venn diagram to illustrate these probabilities.

b Find:

i $P(H \cup C)$ **ii** $P(H' \cap C)$ **iii** $P(H \cup C')$

(P) **8** A bag contains 50 counters numbered from 1 to 50. The counters are either red or blue. A counter is picked at random. The two events R and E are the events 'counter is red' and 'counter is even-numbered' respectively. Given that $n(R) = 17$, $n(E) = 30$ and $n(R \cup E) = 40$,

a draw a Venn diagram to illustrate the outcomes.

b Find:

i $n(R \cap E)$

ii $P(R' \cap E')$

iii $P((R \cap E)')$

Watch out $n(R)$ represents the **number** of outcomes in the event R, whereas $P(R)$ represents the **probability** that the event R occurs.

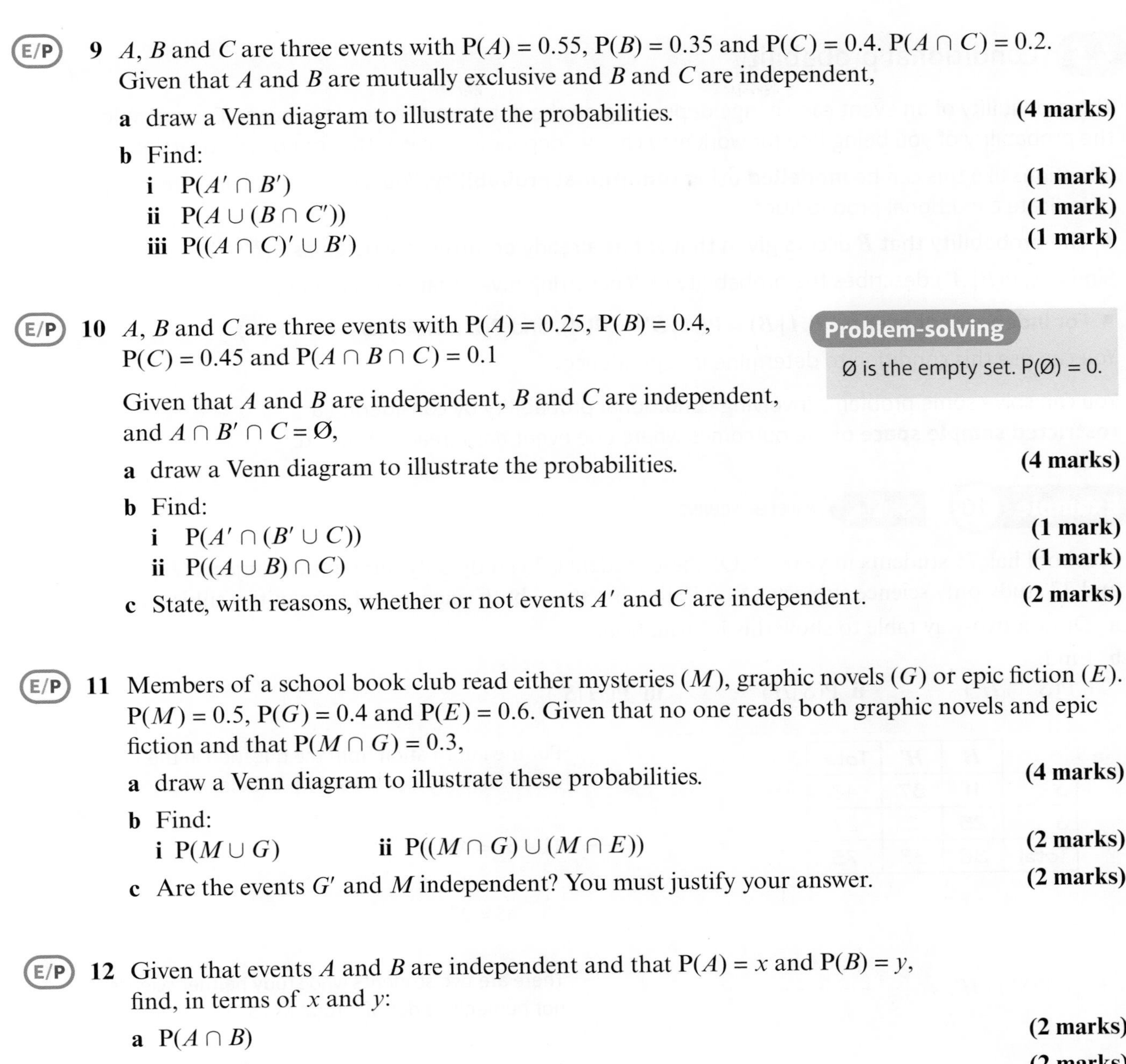

E/P **9** A, B and C are three events with $P(A) = 0.55$, $P(B) = 0.35$ and $P(C) = 0.4$. $P(A \cap C) = 0.2$. Given that A and B are mutually exclusive and B and C are independent,

a draw a Venn diagram to illustrate the probabilities. **(4 marks)**

b Find:

i $P(A' \cap B')$ **(1 mark)**

ii $P(A \cup (B \cap C'))$ **(1 mark)**

iii $P((A \cap C)' \cup B')$ **(1 mark)**

E/P **10** A, B and C are three events with $P(A) = 0.25$, $P(B) = 0.4$, $P(C) = 0.45$ and $P(A \cap B \cap C) = 0.1$

Given that A and B are independent, B and C are independent, and $A \cap B' \cap C = \varnothing$,

Problem-solving

$\varnothing$ is the empty set. $P(\varnothing) = 0$.

a draw a Venn diagram to illustrate the probabilities. **(4 marks)**

b Find:

i $P(A' \cap (B' \cup C))$ **(1 mark)**

ii $P((A \cup B) \cap C)$ **(1 mark)**

c State, with reasons, whether or not events A' and C are independent. **(2 marks)**

E/P **11** Members of a school book club read either mysteries (M), graphic novels (G) or epic fiction (E). $P(M) = 0.5$, $P(G) = 0.4$ and $P(E) = 0.6$. Given that no one reads both graphic novels and epic fiction and that $P(M \cap G) = 0.3$,

a draw a Venn diagram to illustrate these probabilities. **(4 marks)**

b Find:

i $P(M \cup G)$ **ii** $P((M \cap G) \cup (M \cap E))$ **(2 marks)**

c Are the events G' and M independent? You must justify your answer. **(2 marks)**

E/P **12** Given that events A and B are independent and that $P(A) = x$ and $P(B) = y$, find, in terms of x and y:

a $P(A \cap B)$ **(2 marks)**

b $P(A \cup B)$ **(2 marks)**

c $P(A \cup B')$ **(2 marks)**

Challenge

SKILLS
CRITICAL THINKING

Given that events A, B and C are all independent and that $P(A) = x$, $P(B) = y$ and $P(C) = z$, find, in terms of x, y and z:

a $P(A \cap B \cap C)$ **b** $P(A \cup B \cup C)$ **c** $P((A \cup B') \cap C)$

4.5 Conditional probability

The probability of an event can change depending on the outcome of a previous event. For example, the probability of you being late for work may change depending on whether or not you oversleep.

Situations like this can be **modelled** using **conditional probability**. You use a vertical line symbol '|' to indicate conditional probabilities.

- **The probability that B occurs given that A has already occurred is written as $P(B|A)$.**

Similarly, $P(B|A')$ describes the probability of B occurring given that A has not occurred.

- **For independent events, $P(A|B) = P(A|B') = P(A)$, and $P(B|A) = P(B|A') = P(B)$.**

You can use this condition to determine independence.

You can solve some problems involving conditional probability by considering a **restricted sample space** of the outcomes where one event has already occurred.

Example 10 SKILLS PROBLEM-SOLVING

A school has 75 students in year 12. Of these students, 25 study only humanities subjects (H) and 37 study only science subjects (S). 11 students study both science and humanities subjects.

a Draw a two-way table to show this information.

b Find:

i $P(S' \cap H')$ **ii** $P(S|H)$ **iii** $P(H|S')$

a

	H	H'	Total
S	**11**	**37**	48
S'	**25**	2	27
Total	36	39	**75**

Put the information from the question in the table. These values are shown in bold.

$11 + 37 = 48$

$75 - 48 = 27$

b i $P(S' \cap H') = \frac{2}{75}$

There are two students who study neither science nor humanities out of a total of 75.

ii $P(S|H) = \frac{11}{36}$

Given that H is already true, you need to **restrict the sample space** to those 36 students. 11 of them also study science.

iii $P(H|S') = \frac{25}{27}$

There are 25 humanities students out of the 27 students who do not study science.

Example 11 SKILLS PROBLEM-SOLVING; ANALYSIS

Two four-sided dice are thrown together, and the sum of the numbers shown is recorded.

a Draw a sample-space diagram showing the possible outcomes.

b Given that at least one dice lands on a 3, find the probability that the sum on the two dice is exactly 5.

c State one modelling assumption used in your calculations.

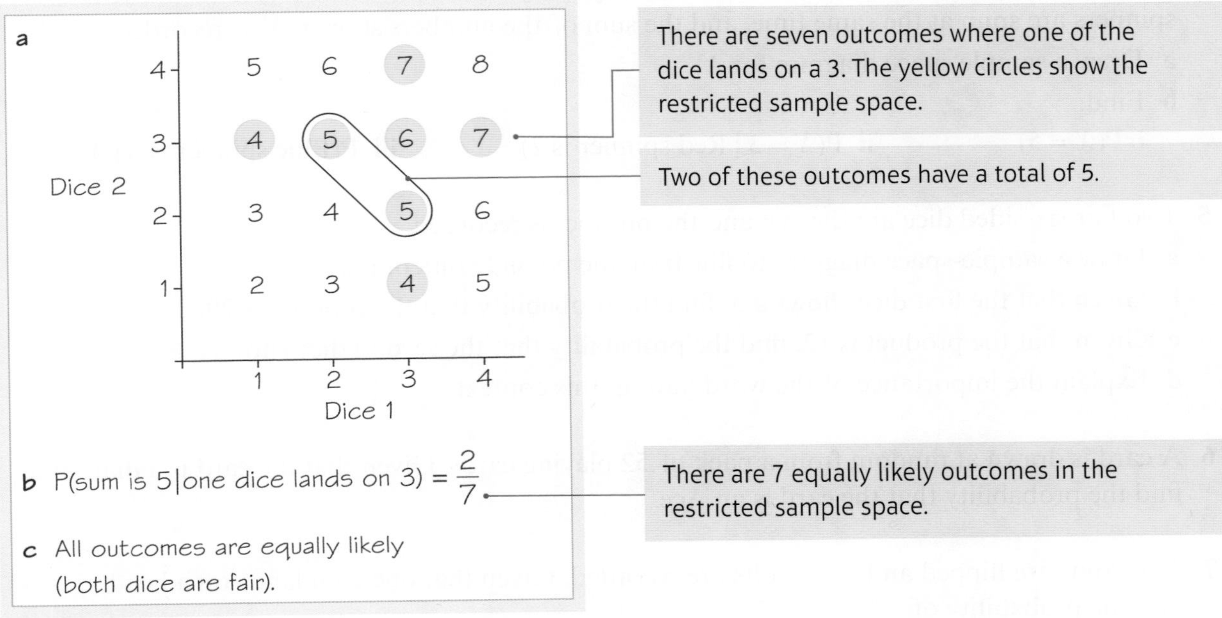

Exercise 4E SKILLS PROBLEM-SOLVING; ANALYSIS

1 The two-way table shows the fast-food preferences of 60 students in a school.

	Pizza	Curry	Total
Year 10	11	18	29
Year 11	14	17	31
Total	25	35	60

Find:

a P(Year 10) **b** P(Curry | Year 10) **c** P(Curry | Year 10) **d** P(Pizza | Year 11)

2 In a sports club, there are 75 members, of whom 32 are adults. Of the adult members, 15 play badminton and 17 play squash. There are 22 teenagers who play squash and the rest play badminton.

a Draw a two-way table to illustrate this situation.

b Find:

i P(Teenager | Squash) **ii** P(Adult | Badminton) **iii** P(Squash | Adult)

3 Eighty children are asked about their favourite ice-cream flavour. Of the 45 girls, 13 like vanilla, 12 like chocolate and the rest like strawberry. Of the boys, 2 like vanilla and 23 like strawberry. The rest like chocolate.

a Draw a two-way table to show this situation.

b Find:

i P(Boy | Strawberry) **ii** P(Girl | Vanilla) **iii** P(Chocolate | Boy)

4 A red and a blue spinner each have four equally likely outcomes, numbered 1 to 4. The two spinners are spun at the same time, and the sum of the numbers shown, X, is recorded.

a Draw a sample space diagram for X.

b Find:

i $P(X = 5)$ **ii** $P(X = 3 \mid \text{Red spinner is } 2)$ **iii** $P(\text{Blue spinner is } 3 \mid X = 5)$

5 Two fair six-sided dice are thrown and the product is recorded.

a Draw a sample-space diagram to illustrate the possible outcomes.

b Given that the first dice shows a 5, find the probability that the product is 20.

c Given that the product is 12, find the probability that the second dice shows a 6.

d Explain the importance of the word 'fair' in this context.

6 A card is drawn at random from a pack of 52 playing cards. Given that the card is a diamond, find the probability that the card is an Ace.

7 Two coins are flipped and the results are recorded. Given that one coin lands on a head, find the probability of:

a two heads **b** a head and a tail.

c State one modelling assumption used in your calculations.

(E) 8 120 students are asked about their viewing habits. 56 say they watch sports (S) and 77 say they watch dramas (D). Of those who watch dramas, 18 also watch sports.

a Draw a two-way table to show this information. **(2 marks)**

b One student is chosen at random. Find:

i $P(D')$ **(1 mark)**

ii $P(S' \cap D')$ **(1 mark)**

iii $P(S \mid D)$ **(1 mark)**

iv $P(D' \mid S)$ **(1 mark)**

(E) 9 A hiking group is made up of 63 women and 47 men. 26 of the women and 18 of the men use a walking stick.

a Draw a two-way table to show this information. **(2 marks)**

b One hiker is chosen at random. Find:

i P(Uses a stick) **(1 mark)**

ii P(Uses a stick | Female) **(1 mark)**

iii P(Male | Uses a stick) **(1 mark)**

(P) **10** A veterinary surgery has 750 registered pet owners. Of these, 450 are female. 320 of the pet owners own a cat and 250 own a budgie. Of the remaining pet owners, 25 are males who own another type of pet. No one owns more than one type of pet. 175 female owners have a cat. One owner is chosen at random.

F is the event that an owner is female.
B is the event that an owner has a budgie.
C is the event that an owner has a cat.

Find:

a $\text{P}(B' \cap C')$ **b** $\text{P}(B \mid F')$ **c** $\text{P}(F' \mid C)$ **d** $\text{P}((B' \cap C') \mid F)$

4.6 Conditional probabilities in Venn diagrams

You can find conditional probabilities from a Venn diagram by considering the section of the Venn diagram that corresponds to the restricted sample space.

Example 12 SKILLS PROBLEM-SOLVING; ANALYSIS

A and B are two events such that $\text{P}(A) = 0.55$, $\text{P}(B) = 0.4$ and $\text{P}(A \cap B) = 0.15$

a Draw a Venn diagram showing the probabilities for events A and B.

b Find:
i $\text{P}(A \mid B)$ **ii** $\text{P}(B \mid (A \cup B))$ **iii** $\text{P}(A' \mid B')$

a

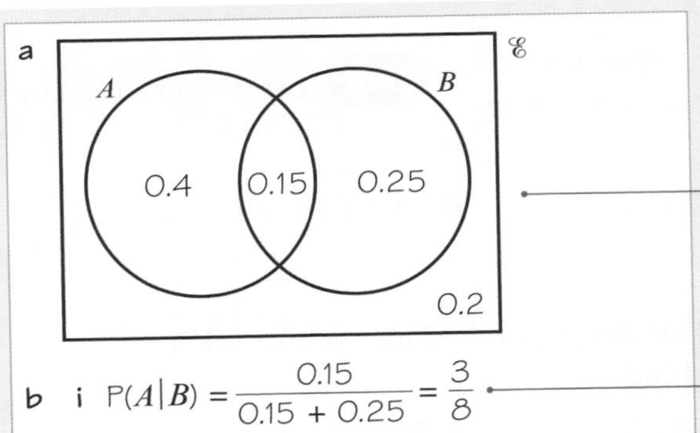

Use the information given to fill in the probabilities for each of the four regions in the Venn diagram.

b i $\text{P}(A|B) = \dfrac{0.15}{0.15 + 0.25} = \dfrac{3}{8}$

The sample space is restricted to just circle B. The part of circle A inside B has probability 0.15

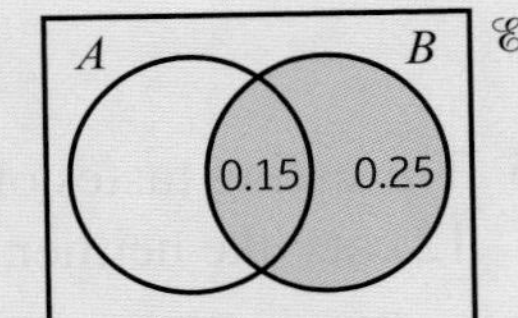

ii $\text{P}(B|A \cup B) = \dfrac{0.15 + 0.25}{0.4 + 0.15 + 0.25} = \dfrac{1}{2}$

The sample space is restricted to just the union of A and B.

iii $\text{P}(A'|B') = \dfrac{0.2}{0.4 + 0.2} = \dfrac{1}{3}$

Consider the restricted sample space first. This is everything **not** inside circle B.

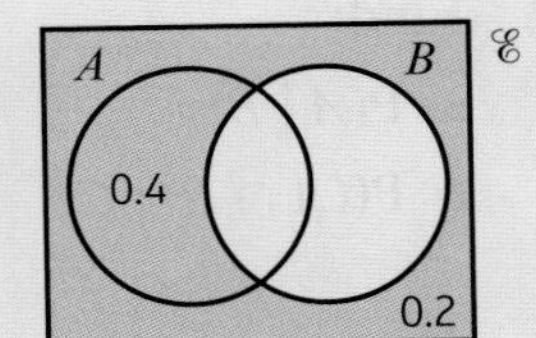

Exercise 4F SKILLS PROBLEM-SOLVING; ANALYSIS

1 The Venn diagram shows the probabilities for two events, A and B.

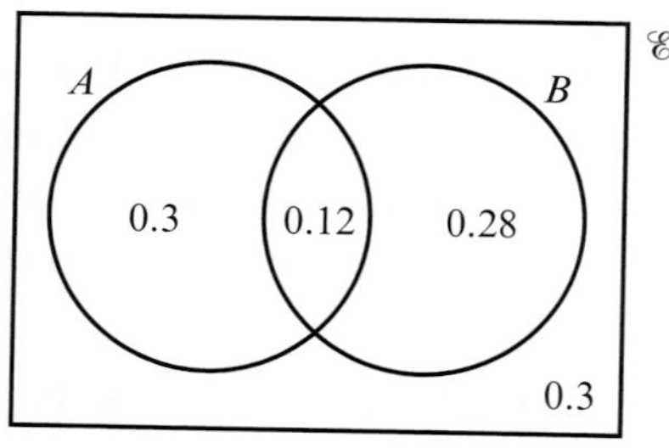

Find:

a $P(A \cup B)$ **b** $P(A \mid B)$

c $P(B \mid A')$ **d** $P(B \mid A \cup B)$

2 C and D are two events such that $P(C) = 0.8$, $P(D) = 0.4$ and $P(C \cap D) = 0.25$

a Draw a Venn diagram showing the probabilities for events C and D.

b Find:

i $P(C \cup D)$ **ii** $P(C \mid D)$ **iii** $P(D \mid C)$ **iv** $P(D' \mid C')$

3 S and T are two events such that $P(S) = 0.5$ and $P(T) = 0.7$

a Given that S and T are independent, draw a Venn diagram showing the probabilities for events S and T.

b Find:

i $P(S \cap T)$ **ii** $P(S \mid T)$ **iii** $P(T \mid S')$ **iv** $P(S \mid S' \cup T')$

4 120 members of a youth club play either snooker (A) or pool (B) or neither. Given that 65 play snooker, 50 play pool and 20 play both, find:

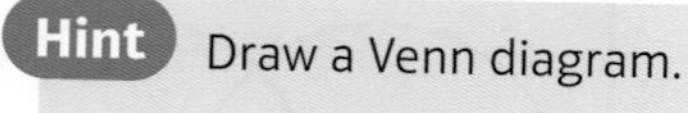

a $P(A \cap B')$ **b** $P(A \mid B)$ **c** $P(B \mid A')$ **d** $P(A \mid A \cup B)$

5 The eating tastes of 80 cats are recorded. 45 like Feskers (F) and 32 like Whilix (W). 12 cats like neither. One cat is chosen at random. Find:

a $P(F \cap W)$ **b** $P(F \mid W)$ **c** $P(W \mid F)$ **d** $P(W' \mid F')$

6 The Venn diagram shows the probabilities of three events, A, B and C.

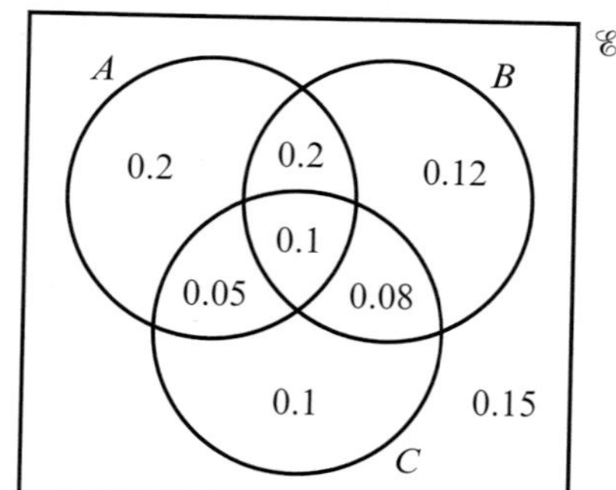

Find:

a $P(A \mid B)$ **b** $P(C \mid A')$

c $P((A \cap B) \mid C')$ **d** $P(C \mid (A' \cup B'))$

E/P **7** The Venn diagram shows the number of students in a class who watch any of 3 popular TV programmes A, B and C.

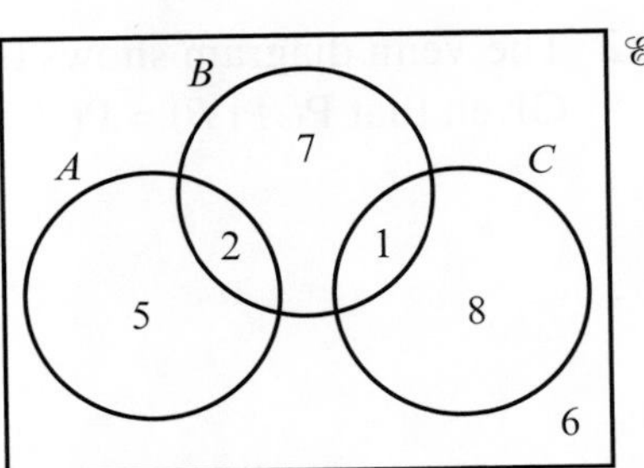

One of these students is selected at random. Given that the student watches at least one of the TV programmes, find the probability that the student watches:

a programme C **(2 marks)**

b exactly two of the programmes. **(2 marks)**

c Determine whether or not watching programme B and watching programme C are independent. **(3 marks)**

Problem-solving

If $P(A|B) = P(A)$ then events A and B are independent.

E/P **8** Three events, A, B and C are such that A and B are mutually exclusive, and B and C are independent. $P(A) = 0.2$, $P(B) = 0.6$ and $P(C) = 0.5$. Given that $P(A' \cap B' \cap C') = 0.1$,

a draw a Venn diagram to show the probabilities for events A, B and C. **(4 marks)**

b Find:

i $P(A \mid C)$ **(1 mark)**

ii $P(B \mid C')$ **(1 mark)**

iii $P(C \mid (A \cup B))$ **(1 mark)**

E/P **9** A doctor completes a medical study of 100 people, 5 of whom are known to have an illness and 95 of whom are known not to. A diagnostic test (a test to identify illness) is applied. All 5 of the people with the illness test positive, and 10 people without the illness also test positive. Given that event A = person has the disease and event B = person tests positive,

a draw a Venn diagram to represent this situation. **(3 marks)**

b Calculate $P(A \mid B)$ **(2 marks)**

c With reference to your answer to part **b**, comment on the usefulness of the diagnostic test. **(2 marks)**

P **10** Events A and B are such that $P(A) = 0.6$ and $P(B) = 0.7$. Given that $P(A' \cap B') = 0.12$, find:

a $P(B \mid A')$ **b** $P(B \mid A)$

c Explain what your answers to parts **a** and **b** tell you about events A and B.

E/P **11** The Venn diagram shows the probabilities for two events, A and B. Given that $P(A \mid B) = P(B')$, find the values of x and y.

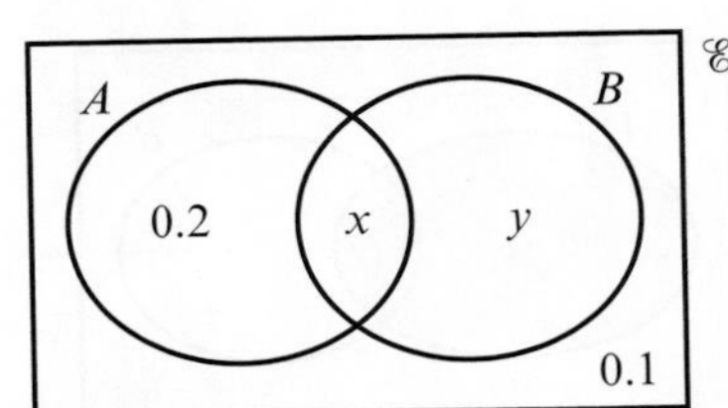

(3 marks)

E/P **12** The Venn diagram shows the probabilities for events A and B. Given that $P(A \mid B) = P(A')$, find the values of c and d.

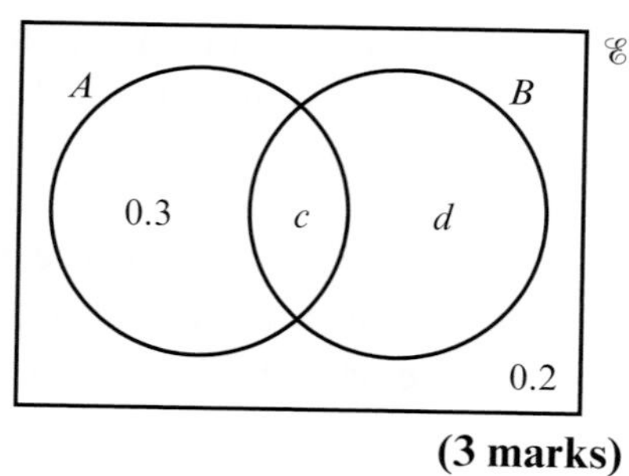

(3 marks)

4.7 Probability formulae

There is a formula you can use for two events that links the probability of the union and the probability of the intersection.

Let $P(A) = a$ and $P(B) = b$.

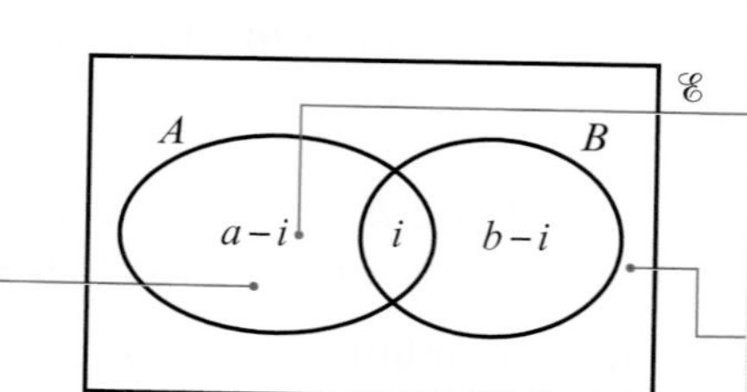

The probability of the intersection, $P(A \cap B)$, is i.

Subtract this probability from a and b and write the probabilities on the Venn diagram as shown.

The probability of $A \cup B$ is
$P(A \cup B) = (a - i) + (b - i) + i$
$= a + b - i$

Since $i = P(A \cap B)$ you can write the following **addition formula** for two events A and B:

- $\mathbf{P(A \cup B) = P(A) + P(B) - P(A \cap B)}$

Example 13 SKILLS CRITICAL THINKING

A and B are two events, with $P(A) = 0.6$, $P(B) = 0.7$ and $P(A \cup B) = 0.9$

Find $P(A \cap B)$.

Watch out You do not know whether A and B are independent so you can't use $P(A \cap B) = P(A) \times P(B)$. Use the addition formula.

$P(A \cup B) = P(A) + P(B) - P(A \cap B)$
So $P(A \cap B) = P(A) + P(B) - P(A \cup B)$
$= 0.6 + 0.7 - 0.9$
$= 0.4$

Rearrange the addition formula to make $P(A \cap B)$ the subject.

You can also use a Venn diagram in the explanation above to find a formula for $P(B \mid A)$:

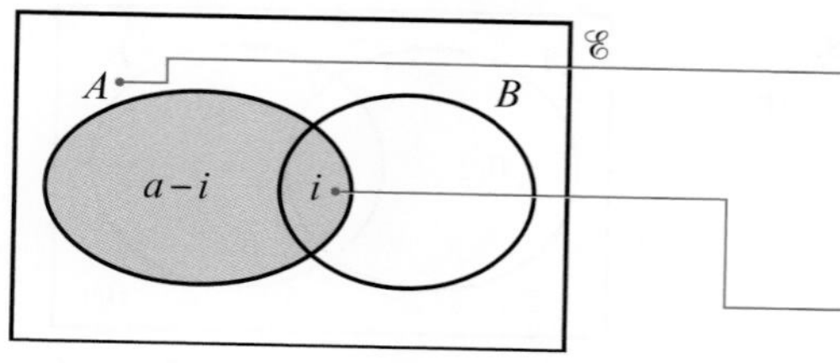

To find $P(B \mid A)$, restrict the sample space to the set of outcomes in which A has already occurred.

This is the subset of outcomes in the restricted sample space in which B occurs.

So $P(B \mid A) = \dfrac{i}{(a - i) + i} = \dfrac{i}{a}$

Since $P(B \cap A) = i$ and $P(A) = a$, you can write the following **multiplication formula** for conditional probability for two events A and B:

- $P(B \mid A) = \dfrac{P(B \cap A)}{P(A)}$, so $P(B \cap A) = P(B \mid A) \times P(A)$

Example 14 SKILLS CRITICAL THINKING

C and D are two events such that $P(C) = 0.2$, $P(D) = 0.6$ and $P(C \mid D) = 0.3$

Find:

a $P(C \cap D)$ **b** $P(D \mid C)$ **c** $P(C \cup D)$

a $P(C \cap D) = P(C \mid D) \times P(D)$
$= 0.3 \times 0.6 = 0.18$

b $P(D \mid C) = \dfrac{P(D \cap C)}{P(C)}$

$= \dfrac{0.18}{0.2} = 0.9$

c $P(C \cup D) = P(C) + P(D) - P(C \cap D)$
$= 0.2 + 0.6 - 0.18 = 0.62$

Use the multiplication formula.

Problem-solving

If you wanted to draw a Venn diagram to show these events it would help to find $P(C \cap D)$ first using the multiplication formula.

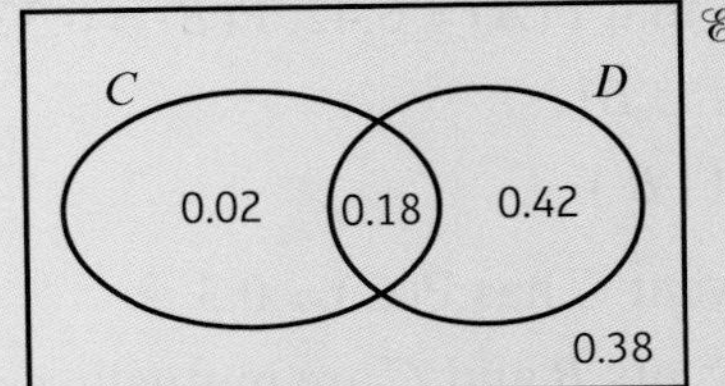

Exercise 4G SKILLS CRITICAL THINKING

1 A and B are two events where $P(A) = 0.4$, $P(B) = 0.5$ and $P(A \cup B) = 0.6$
Find:
a $P(A \cap B)$ **b** $P(A')$ **c** $P(A \cup B')$ **d** $P(A' \cup B)$

(P) 2 C and D are two events where $P(C) = 0.55$, $P(D) = 0.65$ and $P(C \cap D) = 0.4$
a Find $P(C \cup D)$.
b Draw a Venn diagram and use it to find:
i $P(C' \cap D')$ **ii** $P(C \mid D)$ **iii** $P(C \mid D')$
c Explain why events C and D are not independent.

3 E and F are two events where $P(E) = 0.7$, $P(F) = 0.8$ and $P(E \cap F) = 0.6$
a Find $P(E \cup F)$.
b Draw a Venn diagram and use it to find:
i $P(E \cup F')$ **ii** $P(E' \cap F)$ **iii** $P(E \mid F')$

(P) 4 There are two events T and Q where $P(T) = P(Q) = 3P(T \cap Q)$, and $P(T \cup Q) = 0.75$
Find:
a $P(T \cap Q)$ **b** $P(T)$ **c** $P(Q')$ **d** $P(T' \cap Q')$ **e** $P(T \cap Q')$

5 A survey of a large number of households in Istanbul was carried out. The survey showed that 70% have a freezer, 20% have a dishwasher and 80% have either a dishwasher or a freezer or both appliances. Find the probability that a randomly chosen household in Istanbul has both appliances.

6 A and B are two events such that $P(A) = 0.4$, $P(B) = 0.5$ and $P(A|B) = 0.4$. Find:

a $P(B \mid A)$ **b** $P(A' \cap B')$ **c** $P(A' \cap B)$

7 Let A and B be events such that $P(A) = \frac{1}{4}$, $P(B) = \frac{1}{2}$ and $P(A \cup B) = \frac{3}{5}$
Find:

a $P(A \mid B)$ **b** $P(A' \cap B)$ **c** $P(A' \cap B')$

8 C and D are two events where $P(C|D) = \frac{1}{3}$, $P(C|D') = \frac{1}{5}$ and $P(D) = \frac{1}{4}$. Find:

a $P(C \cap D)$ **b** $P(C \cap D')$ **c** $P(C)$
d $P(D \mid C)$ **e** $P(D' \mid C)$ **f** $P(D' \mid C')$

(E) **9** Given that $P(A) = 0.42$, $P(B) = 0.37$ and $P(A \cap B) = 0.12$, find:

a $P(A \cup B)$ **(2 marks)**
b $P(A \mid B')$ **(2 marks)**

The event C has $P(C) = 0.3$

The events B and C are mutually exclusive and the events A and C are independent.

c Find $P(A \cap C)$ **(2 marks)**
d Draw a Venn diagram to illustrate the events A, B and C, giving the probabilities for each region. **(4 marks)**
e Find $P((A' \cup C)')$ **(2 marks)**

(E/P) **10** Three events A, B and C are such that $P(A) = 0.4$, $P(B) = 0.7$, $P(C) = 0.4$ and $P(A \cap B) = 0.3$
Given that A and C are mutually exclusive and that B and C are independent, find:

a $P(B \cap C)$ **(1 mark)**
b $P(B \mid C)$ **(1 mark)**
c $P(A \mid B')$ **(1 mark)**
d $P((B \cap C) \mid A')$ **(1 mark)**

(E/P) **11** Fatima and Gayana are sometimes late for school. The events A and B are defined as follows:
A is the event that Fatima is late for school.
B is the event that Gayana is late for school.
$P(A) = 0.3$, $P(B) = 0.7$ and $P(A' \cap B') = 0.1$. On a randomly selected day, find the probability that:

a both Fatima and Gayana are late to school **(1 mark)**
b Fatima is late to school given that Gayana is late to school. **(2 marks)**

Their teacher suspects that Fatima and Gayana being late for school is linked in some way.

c Comment on his suspicion, showing your working. **(2 marks)**

12 José and Cristiana play darts on the same team. The events J and C are defined as follows:

J is the event that José wins his match.
C is the event that Cristiana wins her match.

$P(J) = 0.6$, $P(C) = 0.7$ and $P(J \cup C) = 0.8$

Find the probability that:

a both José and Cristiana win their matches **(1 mark)**

b José wins his match given that Cristiana loses hers **(2 marks)**

c Cristiana wins her match given that José wins his. **(2 marks)**

d Determine whether or not the events J and C are independent.
You must show all your working. **(2 marks)**

4.8 Tree diagrams

- A **tree diagram** can be used to show the outcomes of two or more events happening in succession.

Example 15 SKILLS EXECUTIVE FUNCTION

A bag contains seven green beads and five blue beads. A bead is taken from the bag at random and not replaced. A second bead is then taken from the bag.

Find the probability that:

a both beads are green

b the beads are different colours.

a

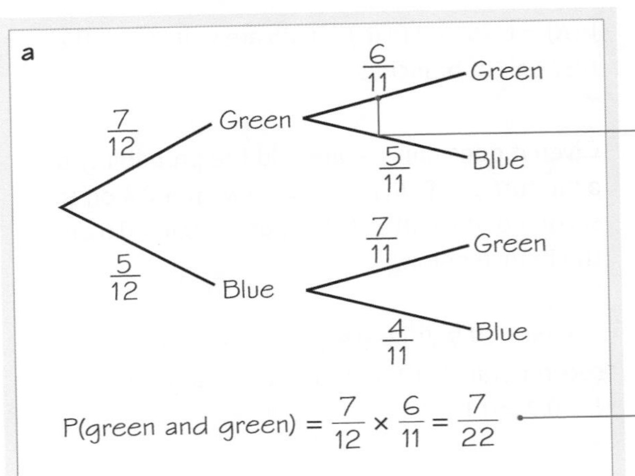

Draw a tree diagram to show the events.

As the first bead was not replaced, there are now only 6 green beads and 11 beads in total in the bag.

$$P(\text{green and green}) = \frac{7}{12} \times \frac{6}{11} = \frac{7}{22}$$

Multiply along the branch of the tree diagram.

b P(different colours)

$= P(\text{green then blue}) + P(\text{blue then green})$

$= \frac{7}{12} \times \frac{5}{11} + \frac{5}{12} \times \frac{7}{11} = \frac{35}{66}$

Multiply along each branch and add the two probabilities.

Conditional probabilities can be represented on a tree diagram.

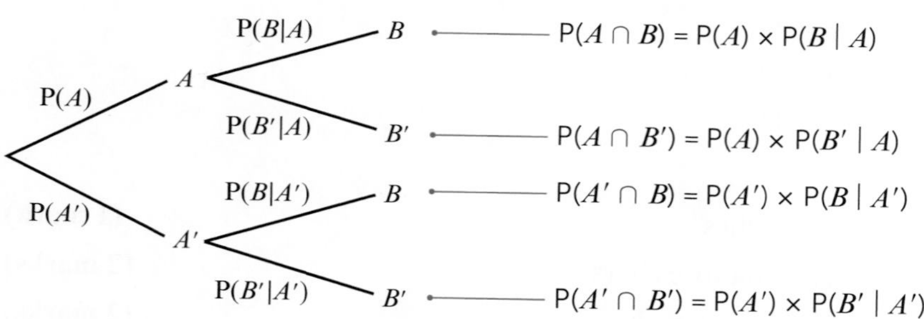

The probabilities on the second set of branches represent the conditional probabilities of B given that A has, or has not, happened.

Example 16 SKILLS EXECUTIVE FUNCTION; PROBLEM-SOLVING

The turnout of spectators at a Formula 1 race is dependent upon the weather. On a rainy day, the probability of a big turnout is 0.4, but if it doesn't rain, the probability of a big turnout increases to 0.9. The weather forecast gives a probability of 0.75 that it will rain on the day of the race.

a Draw a tree diagram to represent this information.

Find the probability that:

b there is a big turnout and it rains

c there is a big turnout.

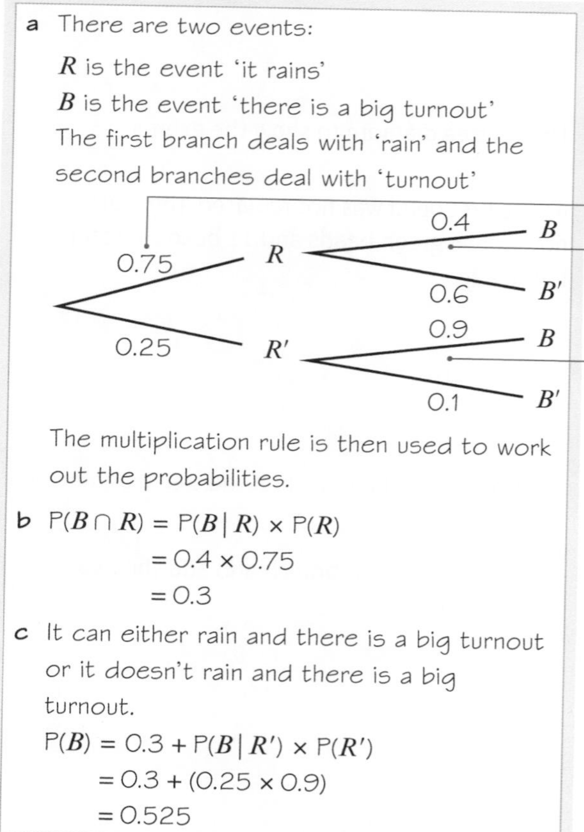

$P(R) = 0.75$ and $P(R') = 0.25$ are written on the first pair of branches.

Given it does rain, we are told the probability of a big turnout, $P(B|R) = 0.4$, so we put 0.4 on the second branch after R. We put $1 - 0.4 = 0.6$ on the branch below.

Similarly, $P(B|R') = 0.9$, so we put 0.9 on the second branch after R'. The other branch is $1 - 0.9 = 0.1$

Example 17 SKILLS PROBLEM-SOLVING

A bag contains 6 green beads and 4 yellow beads. A bead is taken from the bag at random, the colour is recorded and it is not replaced. A second bead is then taken from the bag and its colour recorded. Given that both beads are the same colour, find the probability that they are both yellow.

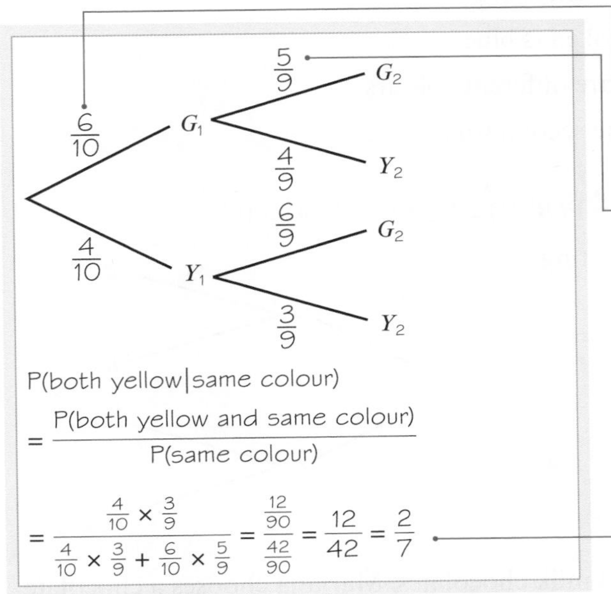

Initially there are 10 beads in the bag and 6 are green. $P(G_1) = \frac{6}{10}$.

Since a green bead is removed and not replaced, the total number of beads is reduced to 9 and there are just 5 green beads remaining.

P(both yellow|same colour)

$= \frac{\text{P(both yellow and same colour)}}{\text{P(same colour)}}$

$= \frac{\frac{4}{10} \times \frac{3}{9}}{\frac{4}{10} \times \frac{3}{9} + \frac{6}{10} \times \frac{5}{9}} = \frac{\frac{12}{90}}{\frac{42}{90}} = \frac{12}{42} = \frac{2}{7}$

Use $P(B|A) = \frac{P(B \cap A)}{P(A)}$

Exercise 4H SKILLS PROBLEM-SOLVING

1 Kaan takes part in two cycle races. The probability that he wins the first race is 0.6. The probability that he wins the second race is 0.7. Work out the probability that Kaan wins at least one race.

2 Chaiwat either walks to work or goes by bus. On any day that he goes to work, the probability that he walks is 0.6. When he walks, the probability that he is late is 0.1. When he goes by bus, the probability that he is late is 0.3.

a Complete a probability tree diagram.

b Calculate the probability that he goes to work by bus and is late.

c Calculate the probability that he is not late for work.

3 A bag contains 20 coins.

Ten are 25-cent coins

Six are 10-cent coins

Four are 5-cent coins

Sadia takes two of the coins at random from the bag.

Hint Draw a tree diagram.

a Work out the probability that Sadia takes two 5-cent coins.

b Work out the probability that the total value of the two coins is 20 cents or less.

4 A bag contains five red and four blue tokens. A token is chosen at random, the colour recorded and the token is not replaced. A second token is chosen and the colour recorded.

a Draw a tree diagram to illustrate this situation.

Find the probability that:

b the second token is red, given that the first token is blue

c the first token is red, given that the second token is blue

d the first token is blue, given that the tokens are different colours

e the tokens are the same colour, given that the second token is red.

5 A and B are two events such that $\text{P}(B|A) = 0.45$, $\text{P}(B|A') = 0.35$ and $\text{P}(A) = 0.7$

a Copy and complete the tree diagram representing this information.

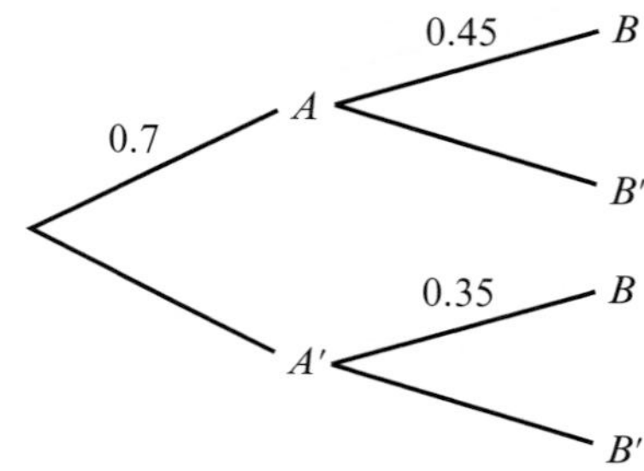

b Find:

i $\text{P}(A \cap B)$

ii $\text{P}(A' \cap B')$

iii $\text{P}(A \mid B)$

6 A box of 24 chocolates contains 10 dark and 14 milk chocolates. Mariana chooses a chocolate at random and eats it, followed by another one.

a Draw a tree diagram to represent this information.

Find the probability that Mariana eats:

b two dark chocolates

c one dark and one milk chocolate

d two dark chocolates, given that she eats at least one dark chocolate.

(P) **7** Chimamanda always goes to work by bus or by taxi. If she goes to work by bus one day, the probability she goes to work by taxi the next day is 0.4. If she goes to work by taxi one day, the probability she goes to work by bus the next day is 0.7.

Given that Chimamanda takes the bus to work on Monday, find the probability that she takes a taxi to work on Wednesday.

(P) **8** Aleena has two coins. One is fair, with a head on one side and a tail on the other. The second is a trick coin and has a tail on both sides. Aleena picks up one of the coins at random and flips it.

a Find the probability that it lands heads up.

b Given that it lands tails up, find the probability that she picked up the fair coin.

E **9** A bag contains 4 blue balls and 7 green balls. A ball is selected at random from the bag and its colour is recorded. The ball is not replaced. A second ball is selected at random and its colour is recorded.

a Draw a tree diagram to represent the information. **(3 marks)**

Find the probability that:

b the second ball selected is green **(2 marks)**

c both balls selected are green, given that the second ball selected is green. **(2 marks)**

E **10** In an engineering company, factories A, B and C are all producing tin sheets of the same type. Factory A produces 25% of the sheets, factory B produces 45% and the rest are produced by factory C. Factories A, B and C produce flawed sheets with probabilities 0.02, 0.07 and 0.04 respectively.

a Draw a tree diagram to represent this information. **(3 marks)**

b Find the probability that a randomly selected sheet is:

i produced by factory B and flawed **(2 marks)**

ii flawed. **(3 marks)**

c Given that a randomly selected sheet is flawed, find the probability that it was produced by factory A. **(3 marks)**

E/P **11** A genetic condition is known to be present in 4% of a population. A test is developed to help find whether or not someone has the genetic condition. If a person has the condition, the test is positive with probability 0.9. If a person does not have the condition, the test is positive with probability 0.02.

a Draw a tree diagram to represent this information. **(3 marks)**

A person is selected at random from the population and tested for this condition.

b Find the probability that the test is negative. **(3 marks)**

A doctor randomly selects a person from the population and tests for the condition.

c Given that the test is negative, find the probability that the person does have the condition. **(2 marks)**

d Comment on the effectiveness of this test. **(1 mark)**

E **12** On a randomly chosen day, the probabilities that Hussein travels to work by car, by bus or by train are 0.1, 0.6 and 0.3 respectively. The probabilities of being late when using these methods of travel are 0.55, 0.3 and 0.05 respectively.

a Draw a tree diagram to represent this information. **(3 marks)**

b Find the probability that on a randomly chosen day,

i Hussein travels by train and is late **(2 marks)**

ii Hussein is late. **(2 marks)**

c Given that Hussein is late, find the probability that he did not travel by car. **(4 marks)**

13 A box A contains 7 counters, of which 4 are green and 3 are blue.
A box B contains 5 counters, of which 2 are green and 3 are blue.
A counter is drawn at random from box A and placed in box B.
A second counter is drawn at random from box A and placed in box B.
A third counter is then drawn at random from the counters in box B.

a Draw a tree diagram to show this situation. **(4 marks)**

The event C occurs when the 2 counters drawn from box A are of the same colour.
The event D occurs when the counter drawn from box B is blue.

b Find P(C). **(3 marks)**

c Show that $P(D) = \frac{27}{49}$ **(3 marks)**

d Show that $P(C \cap D) = \frac{11}{49}$ **(2 marks)**

e Hence find $P(C \cup D)$. **(2 marks)**

f Given that all three counters drawn are the same colour, find the probability that they are all green. **(3 marks)**

E/P **14** A box of jelly beans contains 7 sweet flavours and 3 sour flavours. Two of the jelly beans are taken one after the other and eaten. Emilia wants to find the probability that both jelly beans eaten are sweet, given that at least one of them is. Her solution is shown below:

> P(both jelly beans are sweet) $= \frac{7}{10} \times \frac{7}{10} = \frac{49}{100}$
>
> P(at least one jelly bean is sweet)
>
> $= 1 - \text{P(neither are sweet)} = 1 - \frac{3}{10} \times \frac{3}{10} = \frac{91}{100}$
>
> P(both are sweet given at least one is sweet)
>
> $= \dfrac{\frac{49}{100}}{\frac{91}{100}} = \frac{49}{91}$

Identify Emilia's mistake and find the correct probability. **(4 marks)**

Chapter review 4

SKILLS CRITICAL THINKING; PROBLEM-SOLVING

1 A bag contains 4 yellow and 3 blue beads. Two beads are picked at random without replacement.

a Draw a probability tree diagram to show this information.

b Calculate the probability that both beads selected will be blue.

c Calculate the probability of picking one bead of each colour.

2 There are 15 coloured beads in a bag; seven beads are red, three are blue and five are green. Three beads are selected at random from the bag and replaced. Find the probability that:

a the first and second beads chosen are red and the third bead is blue or green **(3 marks)**

b one red, one blue and one green bead are chosen. **(3 marks)**

3 A baseball player has a batting average of 0.341. This means her probability of getting a hit when she bats is 0.341. She bats three times in one game. Estimate the probability that:

a she gets three hits

b she gets no hits

c she gets at least one hit.

(P) **4** The test scores for 250 students are shown in this grouped frequency table. One student is chosen at random.

Score, s	Frequency (Year 10)	Frequency (Year 11)
$20 \leqslant s < 25$	7	8
$25 \leqslant s < 30$	15	13
$30 \leqslant s < 35$	18	19
$35 \leqslant s < 40$	25	30
$40 \leqslant s < 45$	30	26
$45 \leqslant s < 50$	27	32

a Find the probability that the student is in Year 11.

b Find the probability that the student scored less than 35.

c Find the probability that the student is in Year 10 and scored between 25 and 34.

In order to pass the test, students must score 37 or more.

d Estimate the probability that a student chosen at random passes the test. State one assumption you have made in making your estimate.

(E/P) **5** The histogram shows the distribution of masses, in kg, of 50 newborn babies.

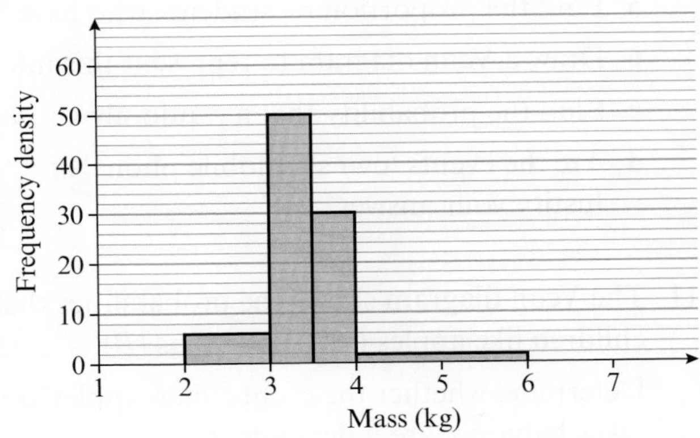

a Find the probability that a baby chosen at random has a mass greater than 3 kg. **(2 marks)**

b Estimate the probability that a baby chosen at random has a mass less than 3.75 kg. **(3 marks)**

(E) **6** A study was made of a group of 150 children to determine which of three cartoons they watch on television. The following results were obtained:

35 watch *Toontime*
54 watch *Fiesta*
62 watch *Skellingtons*
9 watch *Toontime* and *Fiesta*
14 watch *Fiesta* and *Skellingtons*
12 watch *Toontime* and *Skellingtons*
4 watch *Toontime*, *Fiesta* and *Skellingtons*

a Draw a Venn diagram to represent these data. **(4 marks)**

b Find the probability that a randomly selected child from the study watches:

i none of the three cartoons **(2 marks)**

ii no more than one of the cartoons. **(2 marks)**

(P) **7** The events A and B are such that $P(A) = \frac{1}{3}$ and $P(B) = \frac{1}{4}$. $P(A \text{ or } B \text{ or both}) = \frac{1}{2}$.

a Represent these probabilities on a Venn diagram.

b Show that events A and B are independent.

(E) **8** The Venn diagram shows the number of students who like either cricket (C), football (F) or swimming (S).

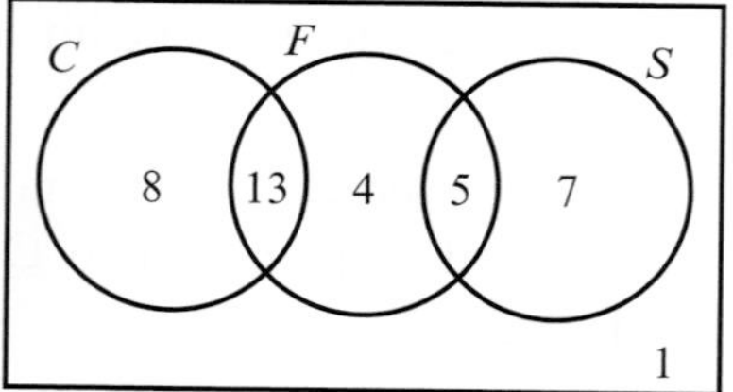

a Which two sports are mutually exclusive? **(1 mark)**

b Determine whether the events 'likes cricket' and 'likes football' are independent. **(3 marks)**

(E/P) **9** For events J and K, $P(J \text{ or } K \text{ or both}) = 0.5$, $P(K \text{ but not } J) = 0.2$ and $P(J \text{ but not } K) = 0.25$.

a Draw a Venn diagram to represent events J and K and the sample space $\mathscr{E}$. **(3 marks)**

b Determine whether or not events J and K are independent. **(3 marks)**

(E) **10** A survey of a group of students revealed that 85% have a mobile phone, 60% have a tablet and 5% have neither a phone nor a tablet.

a Find the proportion of students who have both devices. **(2 marks)**

b Draw a Venn diagram to represent this information. **(3 marks)**

c Find the probability that a randomly chosen student owns only a mobile phone. **(2 marks)**

d Are the events 'owns a mobile phone' and 'owns a tablet' independent? Justify your answer. **(3 marks)**

(E/P) **11** The Venn diagram shows the probabilities that a group of children like apples (A) or bananas (B).

Determine whether the events 'likes apples' and 'likes bananas' are independent. **(3 marks)**

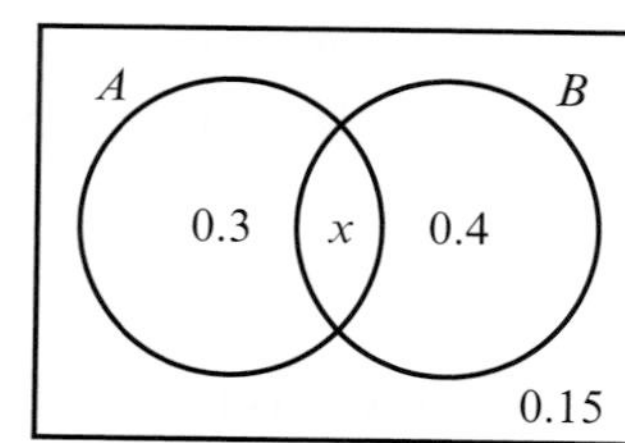

(E/P) **12** A computer game has three levels, and one of the objectives of every level is to collect a diamond. The probability that Yuna collects a diamond on the first level is $\frac{4}{5}$, the second level is $\frac{2}{3}$ and the third level is $\frac{1}{2}$. The events are independent.

a Draw a tree diagram to represent Yuna collecting diamonds on the three levels of the game. **(4 marks)**

b Find the probability that Yuna:

i collects all three diamonds **(2 marks)**

ii collects only one diamond. **(3 marks)**

c Find the probability that she collects at least two diamonds each time she plays. **(3 marks)**

(P) **13** In a factory, machines A, B and C produce electronic components (the parts for a piece of equipment). Machine A produces 16% of the components, machine B produces 50% of the components and machine C produces the rest. Some of the components are faulty. Machine A produces 4% faulty components, machine B produces 3% faulty components, and machine C produces 7% faulty components.

a Draw a tree diagram to represent this information.

b Find the probability that a randomly selected component is:

i produced by machine B and is faulty **ii** faulty.

(E) **14** A and B are two events such that $P(A) = 0.4$ and $P(B) = 0.35$. If $P(A \cap B) = 0.2$, find:

a $P(A \cup B)$ **(1 mark)**

b $P(A' \cap B')$ **(1 mark)**

c $P(B|A)$ **(2 marks)**

d $P(A'|B)$ **(2 marks)**

(E/P) **15** J, K and L are three events such that $P(J) = 0.25$, $P(K) = 0.45$ and $P(L) = 0.15$. Given that K and L are independent events, J and L are mutually exclusive and $P(J \cap K) = 0.1$,

a draw a Venn diagram to illustrate this situation. **(2 marks)**

b Find:

i $P(J \cup K)$ **(1 mark)**

ii $P(J' \cap L')$ **(1 mark)**

iii $P(J|K)$ **(2 marks)**

iv $P(K|J' \cap L')$ **(2 marks)**

(E/P) **16** Of 60 students in a high-school class, 35 study French and 45 study Spanish. If 27 students study both, find the probability that a student chosen at random:

a studies only one subject **(1 mark)**

b studies French, given that they study Spanish **(2 marks)**

c studies Spanish, given that they do not study French. **(2 marks)**

It is found that 75% of the students who study just French wear glasses and half of the students who study just Spanish wear glasses. Find the probability that a student chosen at random:

d studies one language and wears glasses **(2 marks)**

e wears glasses given that they study one language. **(2 marks)**

(E/P) **17** A bag contains 6 red balls and 9 green balls. A ball is chosen at random from that bag, its colour noted and the ball placed to one side. A second ball is chosen at random and its colour noted.

a Draw a tree diagram to illustrate this situation. **(2 marks)**

b Find the probability that:

i both balls are green **(1 mark)**

ii the balls are different colours. **(2 marks)**

Further balls are drawn from the bag and not replaced. Find the probability that:

c the third ball is red **(2 marks)**

d it takes just four selections to get four green balls. **(2 marks)**

(E) **18** In a tennis match, the probability that Ty wins the first set against Chimene is 0.7. If Ty wins the first set, the probability that he wins the second set is 0.8. If Ty loses the first set, the probability that he wins the second set is 0.4. A match is won when one player wins two sets.

a Find the probability that the game is over after two sets. **(2 marks)**

b Find the probability that Ty wins, given that the game is over after two sets. **(2 marks)**

If the game is tied at one set all, a tiebreaker is played and the probability of Ty winning it is 0.55.

c Find the probability of Ty winning the entire match. **(3 marks)**

(E/P) **19** The colours of the paws of 75 kittens are recorded. 26 kittens have all black paws and 14 kittens have all white paws. 15 have a combination of black and white paws. One kitten is chosen at random. Find the probability that the kitten has:

a neither white nor black paws **(1 mark)**

b a combination of black and white paws, given that they have some black paws. **(2 marks)**

Two kittens are now chosen. Find the probability that:

c both kittens have all black paws **(2 marks)**

d both kittens have some white paws. **(2 marks)**

(E/P) **20** Two events A and B are such that $P(A) = 0.4$ and $P(A \cap B) = 0.12$

If A and B are independent events, find:

a $P(B)$ **(1 mark)**

b $P(A' \cap B')$ **(1 mark)**

A third event C has $P(C) = 0.4$. Given that A and C are mutually exclusive and $P(B \cap C) = 0.1$,

c draw a Venn diagram to illustrate this situation. **(2 marks)**

d Find:

i $P(B \mid C)$ **(2 marks)**

ii $P(A \cap (B' \cup C))$ **(2 marks)**

(E/P) **21** In a football match, the probability that team A scores first is 0.6, and the probability that team B scores first is 0.35

a Suggest a reason why these probabilities do not add up to 1. **(1 mark)**

The probability that team A scores first and wins the match is 0.48

b Find the probability that team A scores first and does not win the match. **(3 marks)**

If team B scores first, the probability that team A will win the match is 0.3

c Given that team A won the match, find the probability that they did not score first. **(3 marks)**

Challenge

SKILLS PROBLEM-SOLVING

1 The members of a cycling club are married couples. For any married couple in the club, the probability that the husband is retired is 0.7 and the probability that the wife is retired 0.4. Given that the wife is retired, the probability that the husband is retired is 0.8

Two married couples are chosen at random.

Find the probability that only one of the two husbands and only one of the two wives are retired.

2 $P(A) = 0.6$ and $P(B) = 0.2$

a Given that $P(A \cap B') = p$, find the range of possible values of p.

$P(C) = 0.7$ and $P(A \cap B \cap C) = 0.1$

b Given $P(A \cap B' \cap C) = q$, find the range of possible values of q.

3 The **discrete random variable** X has probability function:

$P(X = x) = kx,\ x = 1, 2, 3, 4, 5$

Find:

a the value of k

b $P(X = 5 | X > 2)$

c $P(X \text{ is odd} | X \text{ is prime})$

Summary of key points

1 A **Venn diagram** can be used to represent events graphically. Frequencies or probabilities can be placed in the regions of the Venn diagram.

2 For **mutually exclusive** events, $P(A \text{ or } B) = P(A) + P(B)$

3 For **independent** events, $P(A \text{ and } B) = P(A) \times P(B)$

4 A **tree diagram** can be used to show the outcomes of two (or more) events happening in succession.

5 The event (A and B) can be written as $A \cap B$. The '∩' symbol is the symbol for **intersection**. The event (A or B) can be written as $A \cup B$. The '∪' symbol is the symbol for **union**. The event (not A) can be written as A'. This is also called the **complement** of A.

6 The probability that B occurs given that A has already occurred is written as $P(B|A)$. For independent events, $P(A|B) = P(A|B') = P(A)$, and $P(B|A) = P(B|A') = P(B)$.

7 Addition rule:

$P(A \cup B) = P(A) + P(B) - P(A \cap B)$

8 Conditional probability:

$P(A \text{ given } B) = P(A|B) = \dfrac{P(A \cap B)}{P(B)}$

9 Multiplication rule:

$P(A \cap B) = P(A|B) \times P(B)$ or $P(B|A) \times P(A)$

10 A and B are independent if:

$P(A | B) = P(A)$ or $P(B|A) = P(B)$ or $P(A \cap B) = P(A) \times P(B)$

11 A and B are mutually exclusive if:

$P(A \cap B) = 0$

Review exercise 1

1 a Give two reasons to justify use the of mathematical models.

It has been suggested that there are seven stages involved in creating a mathematical model. They are summarised below, with stages 3, 4 and 7 missing.

Stage 1. The recognition of a real–world problem

Stage 2. A mathematical model is devised

Stage 3.

Stage 4.

Stage 5. Comparisons are made against the devised model.

Stage 6. Statistical concepts are used to test how well the model describes the real-world problem.

Stage 7.

b Write down the missing stages.

← Statistics 1 Sections 1.1, 1.2

2 Data are coded using $y = \frac{x - 120}{5}$

The mean of the coded data is 24 and the standard deviation is 2.8. Find the mean and standard deviation of the original data. ← Statistics 1 Sections 2.2, 2.5, 2.6

3 The number of patients, x, seen by a doctor each week is coded using $y = 1.4x - 20$

The coded numbers of patients have a mean of 60.8 and standard deviation 6.60

Find the mean and standard deviation of x. ← Statistics 1 Sections 2.2, 2.5, 2.6

(E/P) 4 The daily total sunshine, s, in Amman is recorded.

The data are coded using $x = 10s + 1$ and the following summary statistics are obtained.

$n = 30 \qquad \Sigma x = 947 \qquad S_{xx} = 33\,065.37$

Find the mean and standard deviation of the daily total sunshine. **(4)**

← Statistics 1 Sections 2.2, 2.5, 2.6

5 The coded mean of employee annual earnings (USDx) for a store is 18.

The coding used was $y = \frac{x - 720}{1000}$

Work out the uncoded mean earnings.

← Statistics 1 Sections 2.2, 2.6

(E) 6 A teacher standardises the test marks of his class by adding 12 to each one and then reducing the mark by 20%.

If the standardised marks are represented by t and the original marks by m:

a write down a formula for the coding the teacher has used. **(1)**

The following summary statistics are calculated for the standardised marks:

$n = 28 \qquad \bar{t} = 52.8 \qquad S_{tt} = 7.3$

b Calculate the mean and standard deviation of the original marks gained. **(3)**

← Statistics 1 Sections 2.5, 2.6

7 The following histogram shows the variable t which represents the time taken, in minutes, by a group of people to swim 500m.

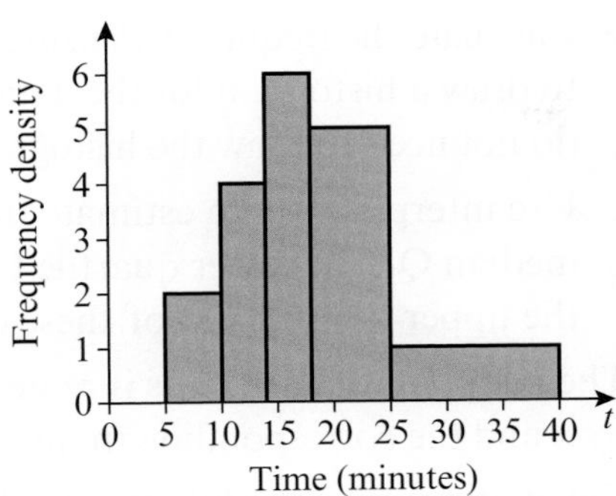

a Copy and complete the frequency table.

t	5–10	10–14	14–18	18–25	25–40
Frequency	10	16	24		

b Estimate the number of people who took longer than 20 minutes to swim 500 m.

c Find an estimate of the mean time taken.

d Find an estimate for the standard deviation of t.

e Find an estimate for the median and quartiles for t.

One measure of skewness is found using:

$$\frac{3(\text{mean} - \text{median})}{\text{standard deviation}}$$

f Evaluate this measure and describe the skewness of the data.

← Statistics 1 Sections 2.2, 2.5, 3.1, 3.5

E/P

8 The table shows average monthly temperature, t (°C), and the number of ice creams, c, in 100s, a riverside snack shop sold each month.

t	7	8	10	45	14	17	20	21	15	13	9	5
c	4	7	13	27	30	35	42	41	36	24	9	3

The following statistics were calculated for the data on temperature: mean = 15.3, standard deviation = 10.2 (both correct to 3 s.f.)

An outlier is an observation which lies ±2 standard deviations from the mean.

a Show that $t = 45$ is an outlier. **(1)**

b Give a reason whether or not this outlier should be omitted from the data. **(1)**

← Statistics 1 Sections 2.2, 2.5, 3.2

9 Summarised below are the distances, to the nearest km, travelled to work by a random sample of 120 commuters.

Distance (to the nearest km)	Number of commuters
0–9	10
10–19	19
20–29	43
30–39	25
40–49	8
50–59	6
60–69	5
70–79	3
80–89	1

a Describe this distribution's shape.

b Use linear interpolation to estimate the median.

The midpoint of each class was represented by x and its corresponding frequency f giving:

$$\sum fx = 3550 \text{ and } \sum fx^2 = 138\,020$$

c Estimate the mean and standard deviation of this distribution.

One coefficient of skewness is given by:

$$\frac{3(\text{mean} - \text{median})}{\text{standard deviation}}$$

d Evaluate this coefficient for this distribution.

e State whether or not the value of this coefficient is consistent with your description in part **a**. Justify your answer.

f State, with a reason, whether you should use the mean or the median to represent the data in this distribution.

g State the circumstance under which it would not matter whether you used the mean or the median to represent a set of data.

← Statistics 1 Sections 2.2, 2.3, 3.5

10 Over a period of time, the number of people x leaving a hotel each morning was recorded. The data are summarised in the stem and leaf diagram below.

		Totals
2	7 9 9	(3)
3	2 2 3 5 6	(5)
4	0 1 4 8 9	(5)
5	2 3 3 6 6 6 8	(7)
6	0 1 4 5	(4)
7	2 3	(2)
8	1	(1)

Key: 3|2 means 32 people leaving

For these data,

a write down the mode

b find the values of the three quartiles.

c Given that $\sum x = 1335$ and $\sum x^2 = 71\,801$ find the mean and standard deviation of these data.

One measure of skewness is found using

$$\frac{3(\text{mean} - \text{median})}{\text{standard deviation}}$$

d Evaluate this measure to show that the data is negatively skewed.

e Give two other reasons why the data is negatively skewed.

← Statistics 1 Sections 2.2, 2.5, 3.4, 3.5

11 The following table summarises the distances, to the nearest km, that 134 commuters travelled to work in Tokyo.

Distance (km)	Number of commuters
41–45	4
46–50	19
51–60	53
61–70	37
71–90	15
91–150	6

a Give a reason to justify the use of a histogram to represent these data.

b Calculate the frequency densities needed to draw a histogram for the data. (You do not need to draw the histogram.)

c Use interpolation to estimate the median Q_2, the lower quartile Q_1, and the upper quartile Q_3, of these data.

The midpoint of each class is represented by x and the corresponding frequency by f. Calculations give the following values:

$\sum fx = 8379.5$ and $\sum fx^2 = 557\,489.75$

d Calculate an estimate of the mean and an estimate of the standard deviation for these data.

One coefficient of skewness is given by

$$\frac{Q_3 - 2Q_2 + Q_1}{Q_3 - Q_1}$$

e Evaluate this coefficient and comment on the skewness of the data.

f Give another justification on your comment in part **e**.

← Statistics 1 Sections 2.3, 2.5, 3.1, 3.5

12 In a random sample, a teacher recorded, to the nearest minute, the time her students spent watching television one week. The times were summarised in a grouped frequency table and represented by a histogram.

One of the classes in the grouped frequency distribution was 20–29 and its associated frequency was 9. On the histogram, the height of the rectangle representing that class was 3.6 cm and the width was 2 cm.

a Give a reason to support the use of a histogram to represent these data.

b Write down the underlying feature associated with each of the bars in the histogram.

c Show that on this histogram each student was represented by $0.8\,\text{cm}^2$.

The total area under the histogram was $24\,\text{cm}^2$.

d Find the total number of students in the group. ← Statistics 1 Section 3.1

13 Aeroplanes fly from City A to City B. Over a long period of time the number of minutes delay in take-off from City A was recorded. The minimum delay was 5 minutes and the maximum delay was 63 minutes. One quarter of all delays were at most 12 minutes, and half were at most 28 minutes. Only one of the delays was longer than 45 minutes.

An outlier is an observation that falls either $1.5 \times$ the interquartile range above the upper quartile or $1.5 \times$ the interquartile range below the lower quartile.

a On graph paper, draw a box plot to represent the data.

b Comment on the distribution of delays. Justify your answer.

c Suggest how the distribution might be interpreted by a passenger who frequently flies from City A to City B.

← Statistics 1 Section 3.3

14 The following stem and leaf diagram shows the weekend earnings for a group of university students.

Males		Females
8	**0**	6
7 6 5	**1**	0 5 5 5 8 8
9 9 9 8 6 6	**2**	5 5 8 8 9
8 8 5 5 5	**3**	5 5
8 5	**4**	0

Key: 5|1|0 means £15 for males, £10 for females

a Write down the number of male students and the number of female students.

b Write down the largest amount of money earned by a male.

c Comment on whether males or females earned the most, in general.

← Statistics 1 Section 3.4

E **15** Students from schools A and B took part in a fun run for charity. The times, to the nearest minute, taken by the students from school A are summarised below.

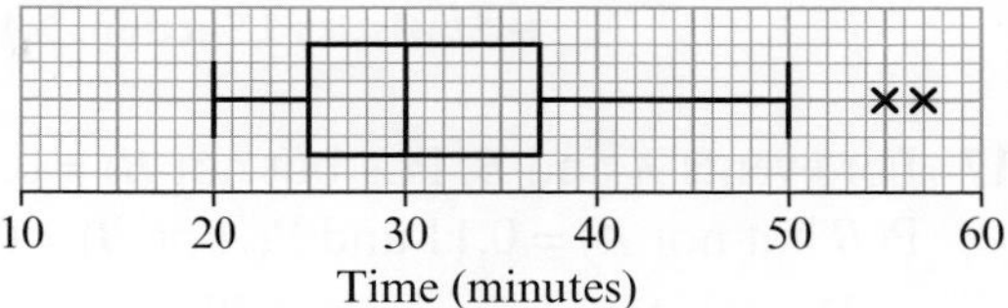

a i Write down the time by which 75% of the students in school A had completed the run. **(2)**

ii State the name given to this value. **(2)**

b Explain what you understand by the two crosses (×) on the box plot. **(2)**

For school B, the quickest time was 25 minutes, and the slowest time was 55 minutes. The three quartiles were 30, 37 and 50 respectively.

c On graph paper, draw a box plot to represent the data from school B. **(3)**

d Compare and contrast the two box plots. **(2)**

← Statistics 1 Sections 3.2, 3.3, 3.6

E/P **16** An ornithologist (a person who studies birds) is collecting data on the lengths, in cm, of snowy owls. She displays the information in a histogram as shown below.

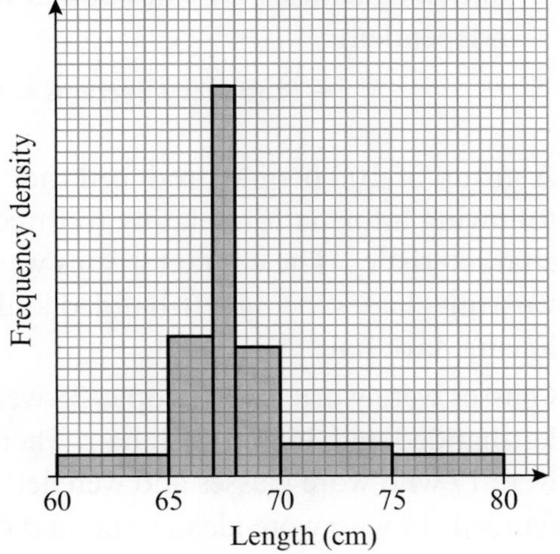

Given that there are 26 owls in the 65 to 67 cm class, estimate the probability that an owl, chosen at random is between 63 and 73 cm long. **(4)**

← Statistics 1 Sections 3.1, 4.1

E/P **17** For events A and B, P(A but not B) = 0.32, P(B but not A) = 0.11 and P(A or B) = 0.65

a Draw a Venn diagram to illustrate the complete sample space for the events A and B. **(3)**

b Write down the value of P(A) and the value of P(B). **(2)**

c Determine whether or not A and B are independent events. **(2)**

← Statistics 1 Sections 4.2, 4.3

E/P **18** The Venn diagram shows the number of children who like magazines (M), books (B) or television (T).

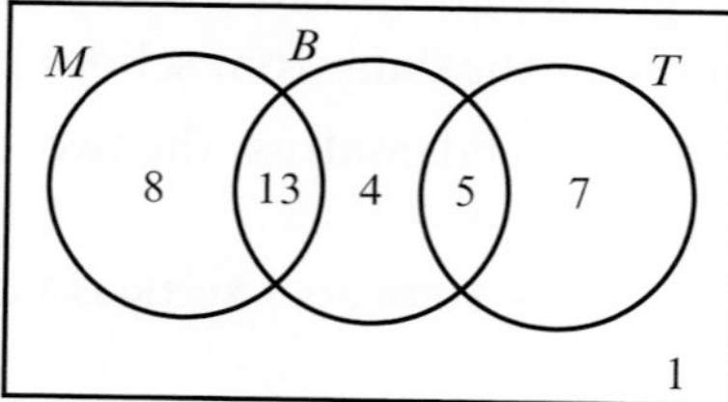

a Which two hobbies are mutually exclusive? **(1)**

b Determine whether or not the events 'likes magazines' and 'likes books' are independent. **(3)**

← Statistics 1 Sections 4.2, 4.3

E **19** A group of 100 people produced the following information relating to three characteristics. The characteristics were wearing glasses, being left-handed and having dark hair.

Glasses were worn by 36 people, 28 were left-handed and 36 had dark hair. There were 17 who wore glasses and were left-handed, 19 who wore glasses and had dark hair and 15 who were left-handed and had dark hair. Only 10 people wore glasses, were left-handed and had dark hair.

a Represent these data on a Venn diagram. **(3)**

A person was selected at random from this group.

Find the probability that this person:

b wore glasses, but was not left-handed and did not have dark hair **(1)**

c did not wear glasses, was not left-handed and did not have dark hair **(1)**

d had only two of the attributes **(2)**

e wore glasses given they were left-handed and had dark hair. **(2)**

← Statistics 1 Sections 4.2, 4.5, 4.6, 4.7

E **20** A survey of the reading habits of some students revealed that, on a regular basis, 25% read fiction books, 45% read non-fiction books and 40% do not read books at all.

a Find the proportion of students who read both fiction and non-fiction books. **(2)**

b Draw a Venn diagram to represent this information. **(3)**

A student is selected at random. Given that this student reads books on a regular basis,

c find the probability that this student only reads fiction books. **(2)**

← Statistics 1 Sections 4.2, 4.6, 4.7

E **21** For the events A and B, $P(A \cap B') = 0.34$, $P(A' \cap B) = 0.13$ and $P(A \cup B) = 0.62$.

a Draw a Venn diagram to illustrate the complete sample space for the events A and B. **(2)**

b Write down the values of P(A) and P(B). **(2)**

c Find $P(A|B')$. **(2)**

d Determine whether or not A and B are independent. **(2)**

← Statistics 1 Sections 4.4, 4.6, 4.7

E/P **22** Two events A and B are such that $P(B) = 0.3$ and $P(A \cap B) = 0.15$.
If A and B are independent, find:

a $P(A)$ **(1)**

b $P(A' \cap B')$ **(1)**

A third event C has $P(C) = 0.4$. Given that B and C are mutually exclusive and $P(A \cap C) = 0.1$,

c draw a Venn diagram to illustrate this situation. **(2)**

d Find:

i $P(A|C)$ **(2)**

ii $P(A \cap (B \cup C'))$ **(2)**

iii $P(A|(B \cup C'))$ **(2)**

← Statistics 1 Sections 4.4, 4.6, 4.7

E/P **23** At a college, there are 148 students studying either engineering, childcare or tourism. Of these students, 89 wear glasses and the others do not. There are 30 engineering students, of whom 18 wear glasses. There are 68 childcare students, of whom 44 wear glasses.

A student is chosen at random.

Find the probability that this student:

a is studying tourism **(1)**

b does not wear glasses, given that the student is studying tourism. **(2)**

Among the engineering students, 80% are right-handed. Corresponding percentages for childcare and tourism students are 75% and 70% respectively.

A student is again chosen at random.

c Find the probability that this student is right-handed. **(2)**

d Given that this student is right-handed, find the probability that the student is studying engineering. **(2)**

← Statistics 1 Sections 4.5, 4.7

E/P **24** The probability that Joanna oversleeps is 0.15. If she oversleeps, the probability that she is late to college is 0.75. If she gets up on time, the probability that she is late to college is 0.1.

a Find the probability that Joanna is late to college on any particular day. **(2)**

b Find the probability that Joanna overslept, given that she is late to college. **(2)**

← Statistics 1 Section 4.7

E **25** A bag contains nine blue balls and three red balls. A ball is selected at random from the bag and its colour is recorded. The ball is not replaced. A second ball is selected at random and its colour is recorded.

a Draw a tree diagram to represent the information. **(3)**

Find the probability that:

b the second ball selected is red **(1)**

c the balls are different colours. **(3)**

← Statistics 1 Section 4.8

E **26** A company assembles drills using components (the parts for a piece of equipment) from two sources. Goodbuy supplies 85% of the components and Amart supplies the rest. It is known that 3% of the components supplied by Goodbuy are faulty and 6% of those supplied by Amart are faulty.

a Represent this information on a tree diagram. **(2)**

An assembled drill is selected at random.

b Find the probability that it is not faulty. **(3)**

← Statistics 1 Section 4.8

E **27** A bag contains 3 blue counters and 5 red counters. One counter is drawn at random from the bag and not replaced. A second counter is then drawn.

a Draw a tree diagram to represent this situation. **(2)**

b Find the probability that:

i the second counter drawn is blue **(2)**

ii both counters selected are blue, given that the second counter is blue. **(2)**

← Statistics 1 Sections 4.7, 4.8

Challenge

1 The Venn diagram shows the number of sports club members liking three different sports.

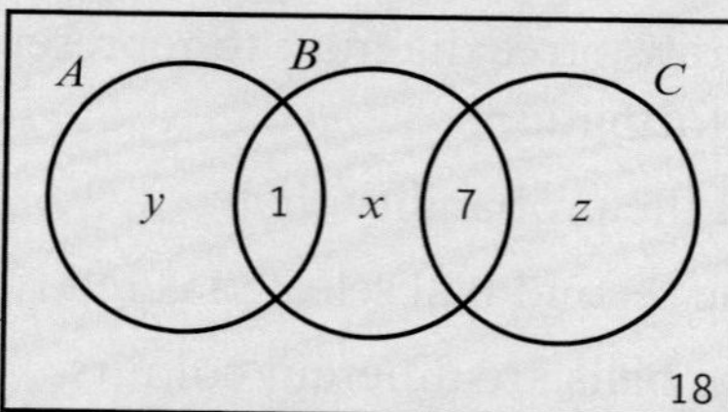

Given that there are 50 members in total, P(C) = 3P(A) and P(not B) = 0.76, find the values of x, y and z.

← Statistics 1 Section 4.2

2 P(A) = 0.7 and P(B) = 0.3

a Given that $P(A \cap B') = p$, find the range of possible values of p.

$P(C) = 0.5$ and $P(A \cap B \cap C) = 0.05$

b Given that $P(A' \cap B \cap C) = q$, find the range of possible values of q.

← Statistics 1 Sections 4.4, 4.6, 4.7

5 CORRELATION AND REGRESSION

4.1
4.2
4.3

Learning objectives

After completing this chapter you should be able to:

- Draw and interpret scatter diagrams → pages 96–99
- Decide if there is a relationship between variables → pages 96–99
- Use and interpret linear regression → pages 99–102
- Calculate least squares linear regression → pages 103–112
- Calculate and interpret the product moment correlation coefficient → pages 112–117
- Use coding to simplify calculation of the linear regression and the product moment correlation coefficient → pages 112–117

Prior knowledge check

1 Find the equation of the line with gradient m that passes through the point (x_1, y_1) when:

a $m = 3$ and $(x_1, y_1) = (2, 6)$

b $m = -6$ and $(x_1, y_1) = (3, 6)$

← International GCSE Mathematics

2 A straight line has equation $y = 0.34 - 3.21x$
Write down:

a the gradient of the line

b the y-intercept of the line

← International GCSE Mathematics

Climate scientists have demonstrated a strong correlation between greenhouse gas emissions and rising atmospheric temperatures. In places such as the Arctic, the rise in temperatures is causing the ice to melt and sea levels to rise, affecting the wildlife that lives there.

5.1 Scatter diagrams

- **Bivariate data are data which have pairs of values for two variables.**

You can represent bivariate data on a **scatter diagram**. This scatter diagram shows the results from an experiment on how breath rate affects pulse rate:

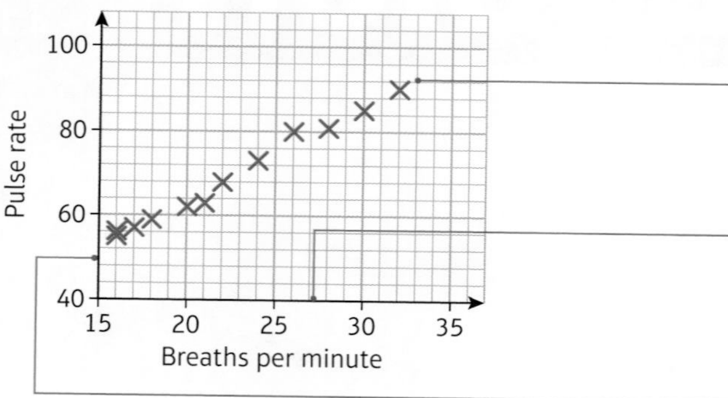

Each cross represents a data point. This person had a breath rate of 32 breaths per minute and a pulse rate of 89 beats per minute.

The researcher could control this variable. It is called the **independent** or **explanatory variable**. It is always plotted on the horizontal axis.

The researcher measured this variable. It is called the **dependent** or **response variable**. It is always plotted on the vertical axis.

The two different variables in a set of bivariate data are often related.

- **Correlation describes the nature of the linear relationship between two variables.**

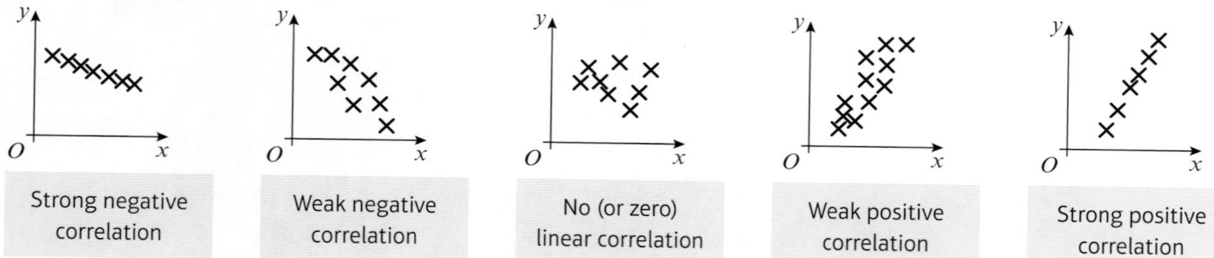

For negatively correlated variables, when one variable increases the other decreases.

For positively correlated variables, when one variable increases, the other also increases.

- **An independent (or explanatory) variable is one that is set independently of the other variable. It is plotted along the x-axis.**

Watch out You should only use correlation to describe data that shows a linear relationship. Variables with no linear correlation could still show a non-linear relationship.

- **A dependent (or response) variable is one whose values are determined by the values of the independent variable. It is plotted along the y-axis.**

In the study of a city, the population density, in people/hectare, and the distance from the city centre, in km, was investigated by picking a number of sample areas with the following results.

Area	A	B	C	D	E	F	G	H	I	J
Distance (km)	0.6	3.8	2.4	3.0	2.0	1.5	1.8	3.4	4.0	0.9
Population density (people/hectare)	50	22	14	20	33	47	25	8	16	38

a Draw a scatter diagram to represent these data.

b Describe the correlation between distance and population density.

c Interpret your answer to part **b**.

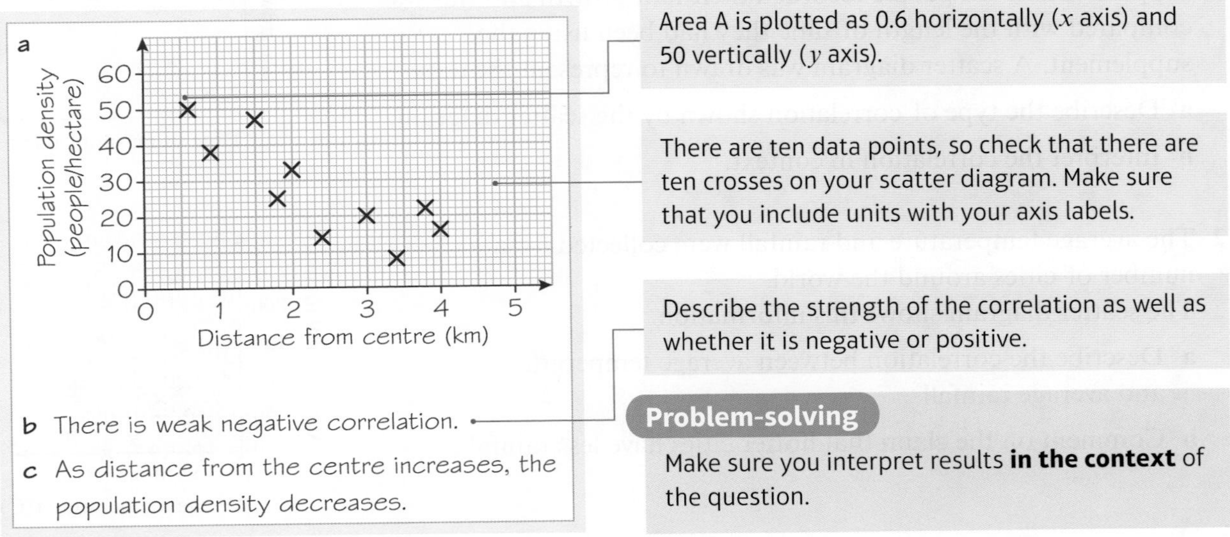

Two variables have a **causal relationship** if a change in one variable causes a change in the other. Just because two variables show correlation does not necessarily mean there is a causal relationship.

- **When two variables are correlated, you need to consider the context of the question and use your common sense to determine whether or not they have a causal relationship.**

Hideko wanted to see if there was a relationship between what people earn and the age at which they left education or training. She asked 14 friends to fill in an anonymous questionnaire and recorded the results in a scatter diagram.

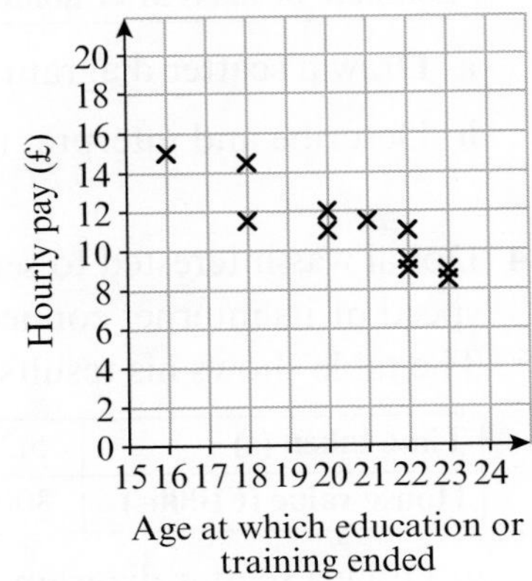

a Describe the type of correlation shown.

Hideko says that her data supports the conclusion that more education causes people to earn a lower hourly rate of pay.

b Give one reason why Hideko's conclusion might not be valid.

a Weak negative correlation.

b Respondents who left education later would have significantly less work experience than those who left education earlier. This could be the cause of the reduced income shown in her results.

You could also say that Hideko's conclusion is not valid because she used a small, opportunistic sample.

Exercise 5A SKILLS ANALYSIS

1 A lab technician researched the effectiveness of a herbal hair growth supplement. Seven people recorded their hair growth and this was compared with the length of time they had been using the supplement. A scatter diagram was drawn to represent the data.

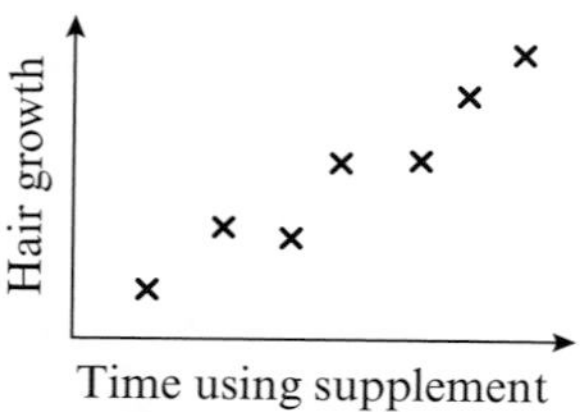

a Describe the type of correlation shown by the scatter diagram.

b Interpret the correlation in context.

2 The average temperature and rainfall were collected for a number of cities around the world.
The scatter diagram shows this information.

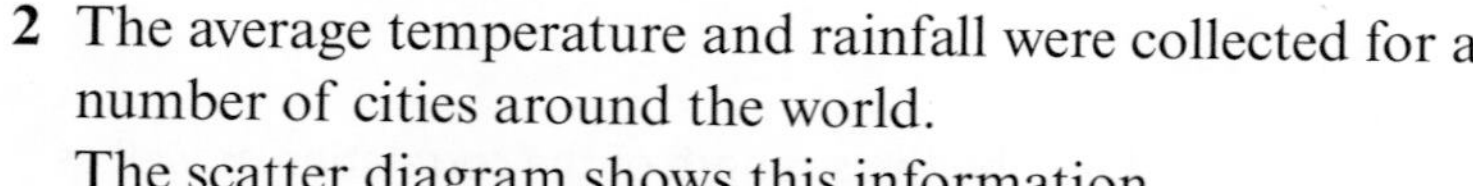

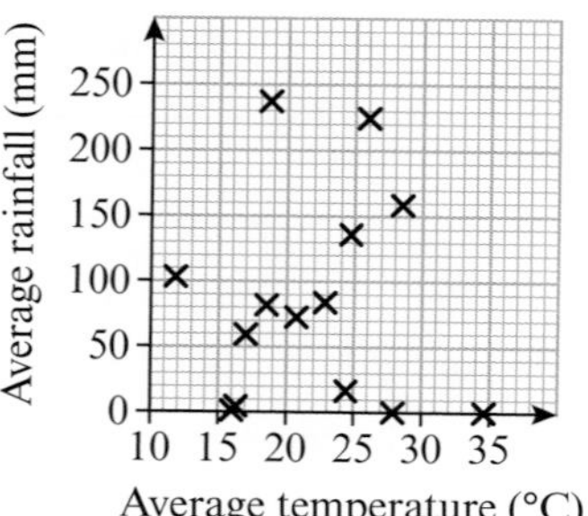

a Describe the correlation between average temperature and average rainfall.

b Comment on the claim that hotter cities have less rainfall.

3 Eight students were asked to estimate the mass of a bag of rice in grams. First they were asked to estimate the mass without touching the bag and then they were told to pick up the bag and estimate the mass again. The results are shown in the table below.

Student	A	B	C	D	E	F	G	H
Estimate of mass before holding the bag (g)	25	18	32	27	21	35	28	30
Estimate of mass after holding the bag (g)	16	11	20	17	15	26	22	20

a Draw a scatter diagram to represent the data.

b Describe and interpret the correlation between the two variables.

4 Donal was interested to see if there was a relationship between the value of a house and the speed of its internet connection, as measured by the time taken to download a 100 Mb file. The table shows his results.

Time taken (s)	5.2	5.5	5.8	6.0	6.8	8.3	9.3	13	13.6	16.0
House value (€1000s)	300	310	270	200	230	205	208	235	175	180

a Draw a scatter diagram to represent the data.

b Describe the type of correlation shown.

Donal says that his data shows that a slow internet connection reduces the value of a house.

c Give one reason why Donal's conclusion may not be valid.

(E) **5** The table shows the daily total rainfall, r mm, and daily total hours of sunshine, s, in Edinburgh, for a random sample of 11 days in August.

r	0	6.8	0.9	4.9	0.1	22.3	1.8	4.5	0.1	2	0.2
s	8.4	4.9	10.5	4.1	3.3	4.2	5.8	1.8	10.2	1	4.6

The median and quartiles for the rainfall data are: $Q_1 = 0.1$ $Q_2 = 1.8$ $Q_3 = 4.9$

An outlier is defined as a value which lies either 1.5 × the interquartile range above the upper quartile or 1.5 × the interquartile range below the lower quartile.

a Show that $r = 22.3$ is an outlier. **(1 mark)**

b Give a reason why you might:
i include this day's readings **ii** exclude this day's readings. **(2 marks)**

c Exclude this day's readings and draw a scatter diagram to represent the data for the remaining ten days. **(3 marks)**

d Describe the correlation between rainfall and hours of sunshine. **(1 mark)**

e Do you think there is a causal relationship between the amount of rain and the hours of sunshine on a particular day? Explain your reasoning. **(1 mark)**

5.2 Linear regression

When a scatter diagram shows correlation, you can draw a **line of best fit**. This is a linear model that approximates the relationship between the variables. One type of line of best fit that is useful in statistics is a **least squares regression line**. This is the straight line that minimises the sum of the squares of the vertical distances of each data point from the line.

Notation The least squares regression line is usually just called the **regression line**.

There are four data points on this scatter diagram.

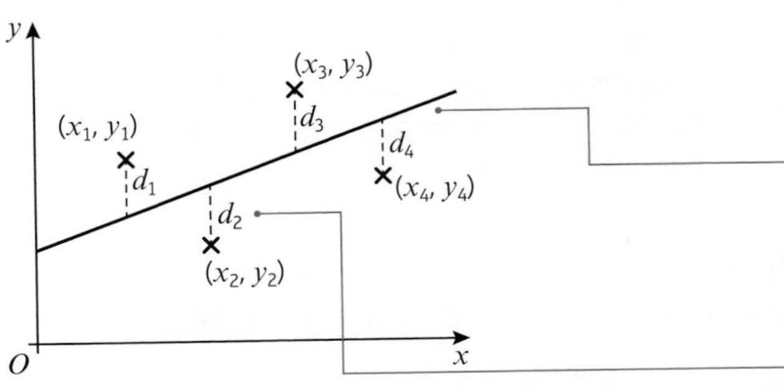

The regression line of y on x is the straight line that minimises the value of $d_1^2 + d_2^2 + d_3^2 + d_4^2$. In general, if each data point is a distance d_i from the line, the regression line minimises the value of Σd_i^2.

The point (x_2, y_2) is a vertical distance d_2 from the line.

- The regression line of y on x is written in the form $y = a + bx$.
- The coefficient b tells you the change in y for each unit change in x.
  - If the data are positively correlated, b will be positive.
  - If the data are negatively correlated, b will be negative.

Watch out The order of the variables is important. The regression line of y on x will be different from the regression line of x on y.

Example 3 SKILLS ANALYSIS

The daily mean wind speed, w knots, and the daily maximum gust, g knots, were recorded for the first 15 days in May in Camborne, a small village near Cambridge, UK.

w	14	13	13	9	18	18	7	15	10	14	11	9	8	10	7
g	33	37	29	23	43	38	17	30	28	29	29	23	21	28	20

The data were plotted on a scatter diagram:

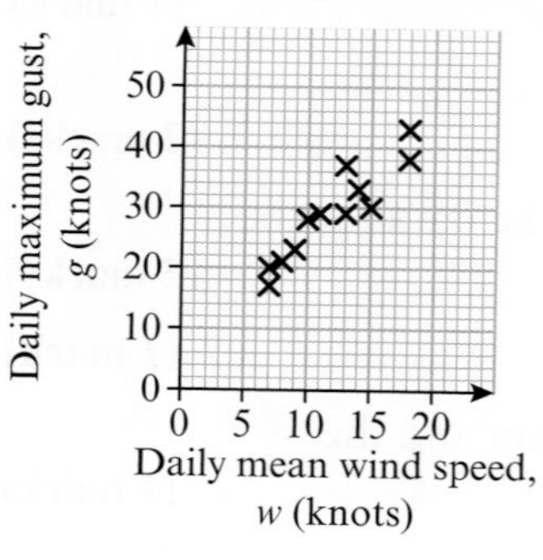

a Describe the correlation between daily mean wind speed and daily maximum gust.

The equation of the regression line of g on w for these 15 days is $g = 7.23 + 1.82w$

b Give an interpretation of the value of the gradient of this regression line.

c Justify the use of a linear regression line in this instance.

a There is a strong positive correlation between daily mean wind speed and daily maximum gust.

b If the daily mean wind speed increases by 10 knots the daily maximum gust increases by approximately 18 knots.

Make sure your interpretation refers to both the context and your numerical value of the gradient. Try to phrase your answer as a complete, clear sentence.

c The correlation suggests that there is a linear relationship between g and w so a linear regression line is a suitable model.

Problem-solving

A regression line is a valid model when the data shows linear correlation. The stronger the correlation, the more accurately the regression line will model the data.

If you know a value of the **independent variable** from a bivariate data set, you can use the regression line to make a prediction or estimate of the corresponding value of the **dependent variable**.

- **You should only use the regression line to make predictions for values of the dependent variable that are within the range of the given data.**

Notation This is called **interpolation**. Making a prediction based on a value outside the range of the given data is called **extrapolation**, and gives a much less reliable estimate.

SKILLS ANALYSIS

The head circumference, y cm, and gestation period, x weeks, for a random sample of eight newborn babies at a clinic were recorded.

Gestation period, x (weeks)	36	40	33	37	40	39	35	38
Head circumference, y (cm)	30.0	35.0	29.8	32.5	33.2	32.1	30.9	33.6

The scatter diagram shows the results.

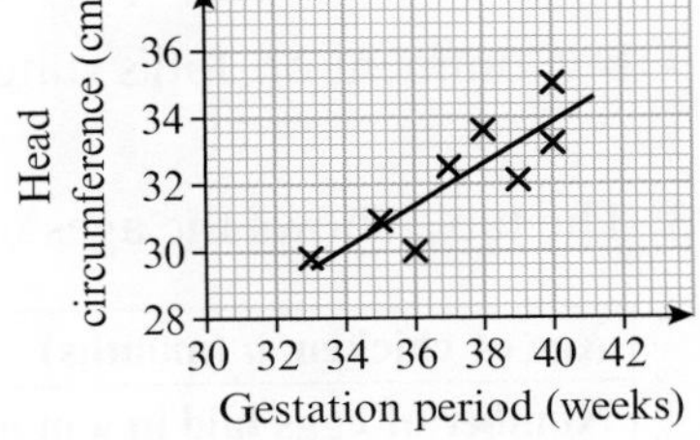

The equation of the regression line of y on x is $y = 8.91 + 0.624x$

The regression equation is used to estimate the head circumference of a baby born at 39 weeks and a baby born at 30 weeks.

a Comment on the reliability of these estimates.

A nurse wants to estimate the gestation period for a baby born with a head circumference of 31.6 cm.

b Explain why the regression equation given above is not suitable for this estimate.

a The prediction for 39 weeks is within the range of the data (interpolation) so is more likely to be accurate.

The prediction for 30 weeks is outside the range of the data (extrapolation) so is less likely to be accurate.

b The independent (explanatory) variable in this model is the gestation period, x. You should not use this model to predict a value of x for a given value of y.

You could also comment on the sample. The sample was randomly chosen which would improve the accuracy of the predictions, but the sample size is small which would reduce the accuracy of the predictions.

Watch out You should make predictions only for the **dependent** variable. If you needed to predict a value of x for a given value of y, you would need to use the regression line of x on y.

Exercise 5B

SKILLS ANALYSIS

1 An accountant monitors the number of items produced per month by a company, together with the total production costs. The table shows these data.

Number of items, n (1000s)	21	39	48	24	72	75	15	35	62	81	12	56
Production costs, p (€1000s)	40	58	67	45	89	96	37	53	83	102	35	75

a Draw a scatter diagram to represent these data.

The equation of the regression line of p on n is $p = 21.0 + 0.98n$

b Draw the regression line on your scatter diagram.

c Interpret the meaning of the numbers 21.0 and 0.98

The company expects to produce 74 000 items in June, and 95 000 items in July.

d Comment on the suitability of this regression line equation to predict the production costs in each of these months.

2 The relationship between the number of coats of paint applied to a boat and the resulting weather resistance was tested in a laboratory. The data collected are shown in the table.

Coats of paint, x	Protection, y (years)
1	4.4
2	5.9
3	7.1
4	8.8
5	10.2

a Draw a scatter diagram to represent the data.

The equation of the regression line is $y = 2.93 + 1.45x$

Joti says that a gradient of 1.45 means that if 10 coats of paint are applied then the protection will last 14.5 years.

b Comment on Joti's statement.

3 The table shows the ages of some chickens and the number of eggs that they laid in a month.

Age of chicken, a (months)	18	32	44	60	71	79	99	109	118	140
Number of eggs laid in a month, n	16	18	13	7	12	7	11	13	6	9

a Draw a scatter diagram to show this information.

Mehmet calculates the regression line of n on a as $n = 16.1 + 0.063a$

b Without further calculation, explain why Mehmet's regression equation is incorrect.

4 Aisha collected data on the number of bedrooms, x, and the value, y (€1000s), of the houses in her village. She calculated the regression equation of y on x to be $y = 190 + 50x$

She states that the value of the constant in her regression equation means that a house with no bedrooms in her village would be worth €190 000. Explain why this is not a reasonable statement.

(E) **5** The table below shows data on the number of visitors to Ireland in a month, V (in '000s), and the amount of money they collectively spend, M (€, millions), for each of eight months.

Number of visitors, V (in '000s)	2450	2480	2540	2420	2350	2290	2400	2460
Amount of money spent, M (€, millions)	1370	1350	1400	1330	1270	1210	1330	1350

The equation on the regression line of M on $V = -467 + 0.740V$ (3 s.f.)

a Give an interpretation of the gradient of the regression line. **(2 marks)**

b Use the regression line to estimate the amount of money spent when the number of visitors to Ireland in a month is 2 200 000. **(2 marks)**

c Comment on the reliability of your estimate in part **b**.
Give a reason for your answer. **(2 marks)**

5.3 Calculating least squares linear regression

When you are analysing bivariate data, you can use a least squares regression line to predict values of the dependent (response) variable for given values of the independent (explanatory) variable. If the response variable is y and the explanatory variable is x, you should use the regression line of $\boldsymbol{y}$ **on** $\boldsymbol{x}$, which can be written in the form $y = a + bx$

Watch out You should only use the regression line to make predictions for values of the dependent variable that are within the range of the given data.

The least squares regression line is the line that minimises the **sum of the squares of the residuals** of each data point.

The residual of a given data point is the difference between the observed value of the dependent variable and the predicted value of the dependent variable.

Notation The Greek letter epsilon (ε) is sometimes used to denote a residual.

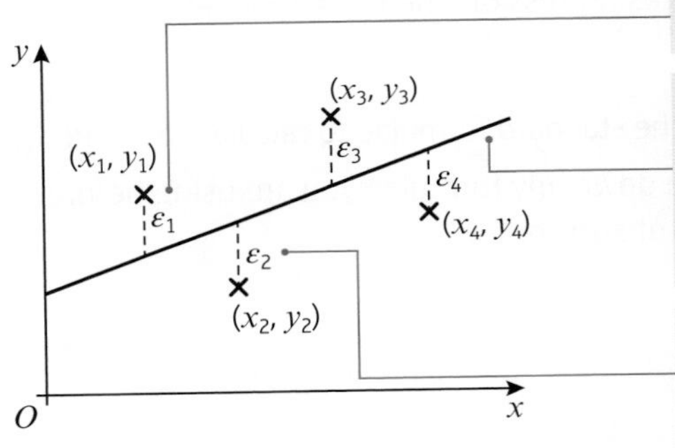

ε_1 is the residual of the data point (x_1, y_1)

The least squares regression line of y on x is the straight line that minimises the value of $\varepsilon_1^2 + \varepsilon_2^2 + \varepsilon_3^2 + \varepsilon_4^2$. In general, if each data point has residual ε_i then the regression line minimises the value of $\sum \varepsilon_i^2$

The observed value of the dependent variable, y_2, is **less** than the predicted value, so the residual of (x_2, y_2) will be **negative**.

You need to be able to find the equation of a least squares regression line either by using raw data or by using summary statistics.

- The equation of the regression line of y on x is:

$$y = a + bx$$

where $b = \frac{S_{xy}}{S_{xx}}$ and $a = \bar{y} - b\bar{x}$

S_{xy} and S_{xx} are known as summary statistics and you can calculate them using these formulae:

- $$\boldsymbol{S_{xy} = \sum xy - \frac{\sum x \sum y}{n}}$$

$$\boldsymbol{S_{xx} = \sum x^2 - \frac{(\sum x)^2}{n}}$$

$$\boldsymbol{S_{yy} = \sum y^2 - \frac{(\sum y)^2}{n}}$$

Example 5 SKILLS INTERPRETATION

The results from an experiment in which different masses were placed on a spring and the resulting length of the spring measured, are shown below.

Mass, x (kg)	20	40	60	80	100
Length, y (cm)	48	55.1	56.3	61.2	68

a Calculate S_{xx} and S_{xy}

(You may use $\sum x = 300$ $\sum x^2 = 22\,000$ $\bar{x} = 60$ $\sum xy = 18\,238$ $\sum y^2 = 16\,879.14$ $\sum y = 288.6$ $\bar{y} = 57.72$)

b Calculate the regression line of y on x.

c Use your equation to predict the length of the spring when the applied mass is:

i 58 kg

ii 130 kg

d Comment on the reliability of your predictions.

Online Explore the calculation of a least squares regression line using GeoGebra.

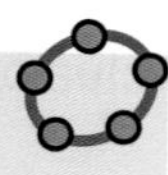

a $S_{xx} = \sum x^2 - \frac{(\sum x)^2}{n}$

$= 22\,000 - \frac{300^2}{5}$

$= 4000$

$S_{xy} = \sum xy - \frac{\sum x \sum y}{n}$

$= 18\,238 - \frac{300 \times 288.6}{5}$

$= 922$

Use the standard formulae to calculate S_{xx} and S_{xy}. Write down any formulae you are using before you substitute.

b $b = \frac{S_{xy}}{S_{xx}} = \frac{922}{4000} = 0.2305$

$a = \bar{y} - b\bar{x}$

$= 57.72 - 0.2305 \times 60$

$= 43.89$

$y = 43.89 + 0.2305x$

Use the formulae to calculate a and b.

Remember to write the equation at the end. The numbers should be given to a suitable degree of accuracy.

c **i** $y = 43.89 + 0.2305 \times 58$

$= 57.3$ cm (3 s.f.)

ii $y = 43.89 + 0.2305 \times 130$

$= 73.9$ cm (3 s.f.)

Substitute the given values into the equation of the regression line.

d Assuming the model is reasonable, the prediction when the mass is 58 kg is reliable since this is within the range of the data.

This is **interpolation**.

The prediction when the mass is 130 kg is less reliable since this is outside the range of the data.

This is **extrapolation**.

Example 6 SKILLS INTERPRETATION; ANALYSIS

A scientist working in agricultural research believes that there is a linear relationship between the amount of a food supplement given to hens and the hardness of the shells of the eggs they lay. As an experiment, controlled quantities of the supplement were added to the hens' normal diet for a period of two weeks and the hardness of the shells of the eggs laid at the end of this period was then measured on a scale from 1 to 10, with the following results:

Food supplement, f (g/day)	2	4	6	8	10	12	14
Hardness of shell, h	3.2	5.2	5.5	6.4	7.2	8.5	9.8

a Find the equation of the regression line of h on f.
(You may use $\sum f = 56$ $\sum h = 45.8$ $\bar{f} = 8$ $\bar{h} = 6.543$ $\sum f^2 = 560$ $\sum fh = 422.6$)

b Interpret what the values of a and b tell you.

a $S_{fh} = \sum fh - \frac{\sum f \sum h}{n}$

$= 422.6 - \frac{56 \times 45.8}{7} = 56.2$

$S_{ff} = \sum f^2 - \frac{(\sum f)^2}{n}$

$= 560 - \frac{56^2}{7} = 112$

$b = \frac{S_{fh}}{S_{ff}} = \frac{56.2}{112}$

$= 0.5017\ldots$ hardness units per g per day

$a = \bar{h} - b\bar{f}$

$= 6.543 - 0.5017\ldots \times 8$

$= 2.5287\ldots$ hardness units

$h = 2.53 + 0.502f$

b a estimates the shell strength when no supplement is given (when $f = 0$). Zero is only just outside the range of f so it is reasonable to use this value.
b estimates the rate at which the hardness increases with increased food supplement; in this case for every extra one gram of food supplement per day the hardness increases by 0.502 (3 s.f.) hardness units.

Watch out The variables given might not be x and y. Be careful that you use the correct values when you substitute into the formulae. It can sometimes help to write x next to the explanatory variable (f) in the table and y next to the response variable (h).

When dealing with a real problem do not forget to put the units of measurement for the two constants.

Make sure you give your answer in the context of the question. Don't just say that one value increases as the other increases – you need to comment on the **rate** of increase of hardness.

Example 7 SKILLS INTERPRETATION; ANALYSIS

A repair workshop finds it is having a problem with a pressure gauge it uses. It decides to have the gauge checked by a specialist firm. The following data were obtained.

Gauge reading, x (bars)	1.0	1.4	1.8	2.2	2.6	3.0	3.4	3.8
Correct reading, y (bars)	0.96	1.33	1.75	2.14	2.58	2.97	3.38	3.75

(You may use $\sum x = 19.2$ $\sum x^2 = 52.8$ $\sum y = 18.86$ $\sum y^2 = 51.30$ $\sum xy = 52.04$)

a Show that $S_{xy} = 6.776$ and find S_{xx}

It is thought that a linear relationship of the form $y = a + bx$ could be used to describe these data.

b Use linear regression to find the values of a and b, giving your answers to 3 significant figures.

c Draw a scatter diagram to represent these data and draw the regression line on your diagram.

d The gauge shows a reading of 2 bars. Using the regression equation, work out what the correct reading should be.

a $S_{xy} = \sum xy - \frac{\sum x \sum y}{n}$

$= 52.04 - \frac{19.2 \times 18.86}{8} = 6.776$

$S_{xx} = \sum x^2 - \frac{(\sum x)^2}{n}$

$= 52.8 - \frac{(19.2)^2}{8} = 6.72$

Quote the formula you are going to use before substituting the values.

b $b = \frac{S_{xy}}{S_{xx}} = \frac{6.776}{6.72} = 1.0083\ldots$

$a = \bar{y} - b\bar{x} = \frac{18.86}{8} - 1.0083\ldots \times \frac{19.2}{8}$

$= -0.0625$

Regression line is: $y = -0.0625 + 1.008x$

or $y = 1.008x - 0.0625$

c

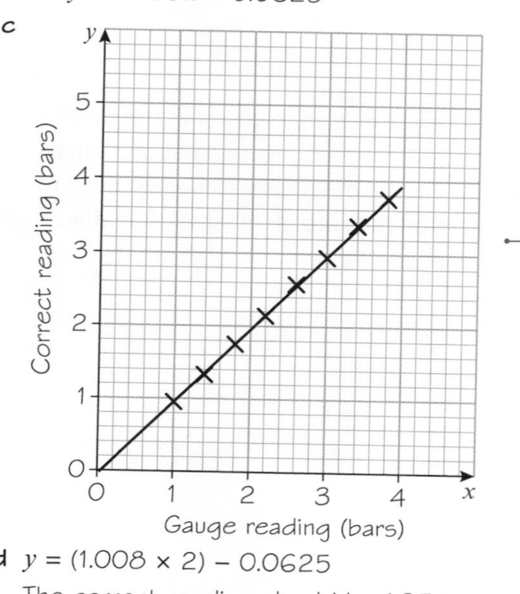

To draw the regression line either plot the point $(0, a)$ and use the gradient or find two points on the line.

In this case using $x = 1$ gives $y = 0.95$ and using $x = 3$ gives $y = 2.96$

d $y = (1.008 \times 2) - 0.0625$

The correct reading should be 1.95 bar (3 s.f.)

Exercise 5C

SKILLS INTERPRETATION; ANALYSIS

1 The equation of a regression line in the form $y = a + bx$ is to be found. Given that $S_{xx} = 15$, $S_{xy} = 90$, $\overline{x} = 3$ and $\overline{y} = 15$, work out the values of a and b.

2 Given that $S_{xx} = 30$, $S_{xy} = 165$, $\overline{x} = 4$ and $\overline{y} = 8$, find the equation of the regression line of y on x.

3 The equation of a regression line is to be found. The following summary data are given:

$S_{xx} = 40$ $\quad S_{xy} = 80$ $\quad \overline{x} = 6$ $\quad \overline{y} = 12$

Find the equation of the regression line in the form $y = a + bx$

4 Data are collected and summarised as follows:

$\sum x = 10$ $\quad \sum x^2 = 30$ $\quad \sum y = 48$ $\quad \sum xy = 140$ $\quad n = 4$

a Work out $\overline{x}$, $\overline{y}$, S_{xx} and S_{xy}

b Find the equation of the regression line of y on x in the form $y = a + bx$

5 For the data in the table,

x	2	4	5	8	10
y	3	7	8	13	17

Hint You can check your answer using the statistical functions on your calculator.

a calculate S_{xx} and S_{xy}

b find the equation of the regression line of y on x in the form $y = a + bx$

(P) 6 Research was done to see if there is a relationship between finger dexterity and the ability to do work on a production line. The data are shown in the table.

Dexterity score, x	2.5	3	3.5	4	5	5	5.5	6.5	7	8
Productivity, y	80	130	100	220	190	210	270	290	350	400

The equation of the regression line for these data is $y = -59 + 57x$

a Use the equation to estimate the productivity of someone with a dexterity of 6.

b Give an interpretation of the value of 57 in the equation of the regression line.

c State, giving a reason in each case, whether or not it would be reasonable to use this equation to work out the productivity of someone with a dexterity score of:

i 2 $\qquad$ ii 14

7 A field was divided into 12 plots of equal area. Each plot was fertilised with a different amount of fertiliser (h). The yield of grain (g) was measured for each plot. Find the equation of the regression line of g on h in the form $g = a + bh$, given the following summary data.

$\sum h = 22.09$ $\quad \sum g = 49.7$ $\quad \sum h^2 = 45.04$ $\quad \sum g^2 = 244.83$ $\quad \sum hg = 97.778$ $\quad n = 12$

(P) **8** Research was done to see if there was a relationship between the number of hours in the working week (w) and productivity (p). The data are shown in the two scatter diagrams below.

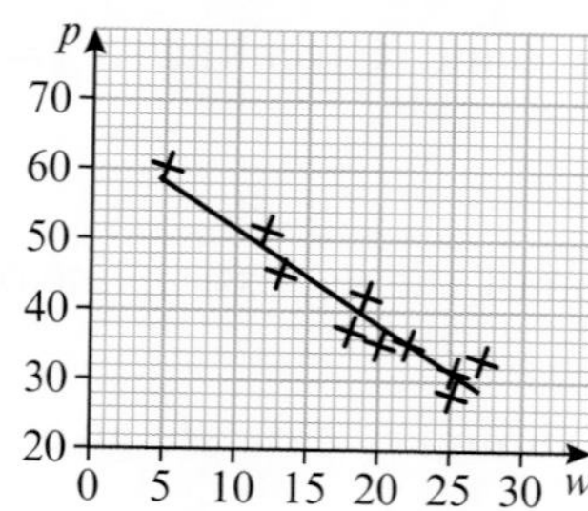

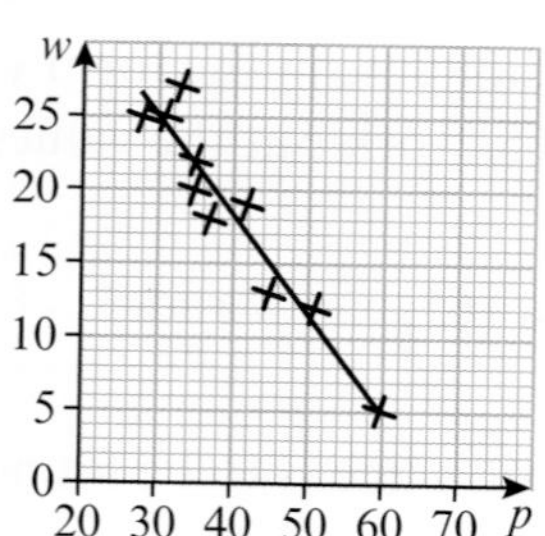

(You may use $\sum p = 397$ $\sum p^2 = 16\,643$ $\sum w = 186$ $\sum w^2 = 3886$ $\sum pw = 6797$)

a Calculate the equation of the regression line of p on w.
Give your answer in the form $p = a - bw$

b Rearrange this equation into the form $w = c + dp$

The equation of the regression line of w on p is $w = 45.0 - 0.666p$

c Comment on the fact that your answer to part **b** is different to this equation.

d Decide which equation you should use to predict:

i the productivity for a 23-hour working week

ii the number of hours in a working week that achieves a productivity score of 40.

(P) **9** In an experiment, the mass of chemical produced, y, and the temperature, x, are recorded.

x (°C)	100	110	120	130	140	150	160	170	180	190	200
y (mg)	34	39	41	45	48	47	41	35	26	15	3

Maya thinks that the data can be modelled using a linear regression line.

a Calculate the equation of the regression line of y on x.
Give your answer in the form $y = a + bx$

b Draw a scatter diagram for these data.

c Comment on the validity of Maya's model.

(E/P) **10** An accountant monitors the number of items produced per month by a company (n) together with the total production costs (p). The table shows these data.

Number of items, n (1000s)	21	39	48	24	72	75	15	35	62	81	12	56
Production cost, p (€1000s)	40	58	67	45	89	96	37	53	83	102	35	75

(You may use $\sum n = 540$ $\sum n^2 = 30\,786$
$\sum p = 780$ $\sum p^2 = 56\,936$
$\sum np = 41\,444$)

Watch out The number of items are given in 1000s. Be careful to choose the correct value to substitute into your regression equation.

a Calculate S_{nn} and S_{np} **(2 marks)**

b Find the equation of the regression line of p on n in the form $p = a + bn$ **(3 marks)**

c Use your equation to estimate the production costs of 40 000 items. **(2 marks)**

d Comment on the reliability of your estimate. **(1 mark)**

E/P **11** A printing company produces leaflets for different advertisers. The number of leaflets, n, measured in 100s, and printing costs, \$$p$, are recorded for a random sample of 10 advertisers. The table shows these data.

***n* (100s)**	1	3	4	6	8	12	15	18	20	25
***p* (\$)**	22.5	27.5	30	35	40	50	57.5	65	70	82.5

(You may use $\sum n = 112$ $\sum n^2 = 1844$ $\sum p = 480$ $\sum p^2 = 26\,725$ $\sum np = 6850$)

a Calculate S_{nn} and S_{np} **(2 marks)**

b Find the equation of the regression line of p on n in the form $p = a + bn$ **(3 marks)**

c Give an interpretation of the value of b. **(1 mark)**

An advertiser is planning to print t hundred leaflets. A rival printing company charges 5 cents per leaflet.

d Find the range of values of t for which the first printing company is cheaper than the rival. **(2 marks)**

E/P **12** The relationship between the number of coats of paint applied to a boat and the resulting weather resistance was tested in a laboratory. The data collected are shown in the table.

Coats of paint, x	1	2	3	4	5
Protection, y (years)	1.4	2.9	4.1	5.8	7.2

a Find an equation of the regression line of y on x as a model for these results, giving your answer in the form $y = a + bx$ **(2 marks)**

b Interpret the value b in your model. **(1 mark)**

c Explain why this model would not be suitable for predicting the number of coats of paint that had been applied to a boat that had remained weather resistant for 7 years. **(1 mark)**

d Use your answer to part **a** to predict the number of years of protection when 7 coats of paint are applied. **(2 marks)**

In order to improve the reliability of its results, the laboratory made two further observations:

Coats of paint, x	6	8
Protection, y (years)	8.2	9.9

e Using all 7 data points:

i produce a refined model

ii use your new model to predict the number of years of protection when 7 coats of paint are applied

iii give two reasons why your new prediction might be more accurate than your original prediction. **(5 marks)**

Challenge

SKILLS PROBLEM-SOLVING

A doctor recorded the length of time taken, y minutes, to travel to work when leaving home x minutes after 08:00, on seven randomly selected mornings. He then drew a scatter diagram to investigate a correlation. The linear regression line for his scatter diagram was $y = 18.5 + 0.546x$

The doctor needs to arrive at work no later than 09:40. The number of minutes the doctor arrives early to work, when leaving home x minutes after 07:00, is denoted z.

Show that $z = (100 - a) - (1 + b)x$ and hence estimate, to the nearest minute, the latest time that the doctor can leave home without arriving late to work.

Sometimes the original data are coded to make it easier to manage. You can calculate the equation of the original regression line from the coded one by substituting the coding formula into the equation of the coded regression line.

Example 8

SKILLS PROBLEM-SOLVING; ANALYSIS

Eight samples of carbon steel were produced with different percentages, $c\%$, of carbon in them. Each sample was heated in a furnace until it melted and the temperature, m in °C, at which it melted was recorded.

The results were coded such that $x = 10c$ and $y = \frac{m - 700}{5}$

The coded results are shown in the table.

Percentage of carbon, x	1	2	3	4	5	6	7	8
Melting point, y	35	28	24	16	15	12	8	6

a Calculate S_{xy} and S_{xx}
(You may use $\sum x^2 = 204$ and $\sum xy = 478$)

b Find the regression line of y on x.

c Estimate the melting point of carbon steel which contains 0.25% carbon.

a $S_{xy} = \sum xy - \frac{\sum x \sum y}{n}$

$= 478 - \frac{36 \times 144}{8} = -170$

$S_{xx} = \sum x^2 - \frac{(\sum x)^2}{n} = 204 - \frac{36^2}{8} = 42$

b $b = \frac{S_{xy}}{S_{xx}} = \frac{-170}{42} = -4.047...$

$a = \overline{y} - b\overline{x}$

$= \frac{144}{8} + 4.047... \times \frac{36}{8} = 36.214...$

$y = 36.2 - 4.05x$

$\sum x = 1 + 2 + 3 + 4 + 5 + 6 + 7 + 8 = 36$
$\sum y = 35 + 28 + 24 + 16 + 15 + 12 + 8 + 6 = 144$

$\overline{y} = \frac{\sum y}{n}$ and $\overline{x} = \frac{\sum x}{n}$

c Method 1

If $c = 0.25$, then $x = 10 \times 0.25 = 2.5$

$y = 36.214... - 4.047... \times 2.5 = 26.095...$

$y = \frac{m - 700}{5}$

$m = 5y + 700$

$= 5 \times 26.095... + 700 = 830$ (3 s.f.)

Method 2

$y = 36.214... - (4.047...)x$

$\frac{m - 700}{5} = 36.214... - 4.047... \times 10c$

$m - 700 = 181.07... - (202.38...)c$

$m = 881.07... - (202.38...)c$

$= 881.07... - (202.38...) \times 0.25$

$= 830$ (3 s.f.)

The estimate for the melting point is 830 °C (3 s.f.)

Watch out y and x are coded values. You can either code the given value of c, then reverse the coding for the resulting value of y (Method 1), or you can convert your regression equation in y and x to an equation in m and c (Method 2).

You can find an equation for the regression line of m on c by substituting $y = \frac{m - 700}{5}$ and $x = 10c$ into the regression line of y on x, then rearranging into the form $m = p + qc$

Write a conclusion in the context of the question and give units. If possible, you should check that your answer makes sense. If you substituted $x = 0.25$ into the regression line of y on x you would get a melting point of 35 °C, which is clearly wrong.

Exercise 5D

SKILLS PROBLEM-SOLVING; ANALYSIS

1 Given that the coding $p = x + 2$ and $q = y - 3$ has been used to get the regression equation $p + q = 5$, find the equation of the regression line of y on x in the form $y = a + bx$

2 Given the coding $x = p - 10$ and $y = s - 100$ and the regression equation $x = y + 2$, work out the equation of the regression line of s on p.

3 Given that the coding $g = \frac{x}{3}$ and $h = \frac{y}{4} - 2$ has been used to get the regression equation $h = 6 - 4g$, find the equation of the regression line of y on x.

4 The regression line of t on s is found by using the coding $x = s - 5$ and $y = t - 10$. The regression equation of y on x is $y = 14 + 3x$. Work out the regression line of t on s.

5 A regression line of c on d is worked out using the coding $x = \frac{c}{2}$ and $y = \frac{d}{10}$

a Given that $S_{xy} = 120$, $S_{xx} = 240$,, $\bar{x} = 5$, and $\bar{y} = 6$, calculate the regression line of y on x.

b Find the regression line of d on c.

(E/P) **6** Some data on the coverage area, $a\,\text{m}^2$, and cost, \$$c$, of five boxes of flooring were collected.

The results were coded such that $x = \frac{a-8}{2}$ and $y = \frac{c}{5}$

The coded results are shown in the table.

x	1	5	10	16	17
y	9	12	16	21	23

a Calculate S_{xy} and S_{xx} and use them to find the equation of the regression line of y on x. **(4 marks)**

b Find the equation of the regression line of c on a. **(2 marks)**

c Estimate the cost of a box of flooring which covers an area of $32\,\text{m}^2$. **(2 marks)**

(E/P) **7** A farmer collected data on the annual rainfall, x cm, and the annual yield of potatoes, p tonnes per acre.

The data for annual rainfall were coded using $v = \frac{x-4}{8}$ and the following statistics were found:

$S_{vv} = 10.21$ $\quad S_{pv} = 15.26$ $\quad S_{pp} = 23.39$ $\quad \bar{p} = 9.88$ $\quad \bar{v} = 4.58$

a Find the equation of the regression line of p on v in the form $p = a + bv$ **(3 marks)**

b Using your regression line, estimate the annual yield of potatoes per acre when the annual rainfall is 42 cm. **(2 marks)**

5.4 The product moment correlation coefficient

The **product moment correlation coefficient** (**PMCC**) measures the **linear correlation** between two variables. The PMCC can take values between 1 and −1, where 1 is perfect positive linear correlation and −1 is perfect negative linear correlation.

Watch out The PMCC was designed to analyse **continuous data** that comes from a population having a **bivariate normal distribution**. (That is, when considered separately, both the x and y data sets are normally distributed.)

Previously, you used the summary statistics S_{xx}, S_{yy} and S_{xy} to calculate the coefficients of a regression line equation. You can also use these summary statistics to calculate the product moment correlation coefficient.

- The product moment correlation coefficient, r, is given by

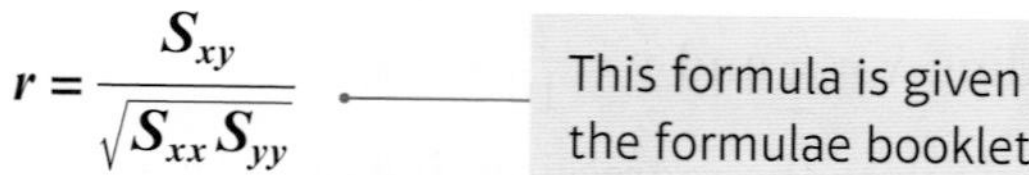

$$r = \frac{S_{xy}}{\sqrt{S_{xx}S_{yy}}}$$

This formula is given in the formulae booklet.

Online Explore linear correlation between two variables, measured by the PMCC, using GeoGebra.

Sometimes the original data are coded to make it easier to manage. Coding affects different statistics in different ways. As long as the coding is **linear**, the product moment correlation coefficient will be unaffected by the coding.

Examples of linear coding of a data set x_i are $p_i = ax_i + b$ and $p_i = \frac{x_i - a}{b}$

You can think of linear coding as a change in scale on the axes of a scatter diagram.

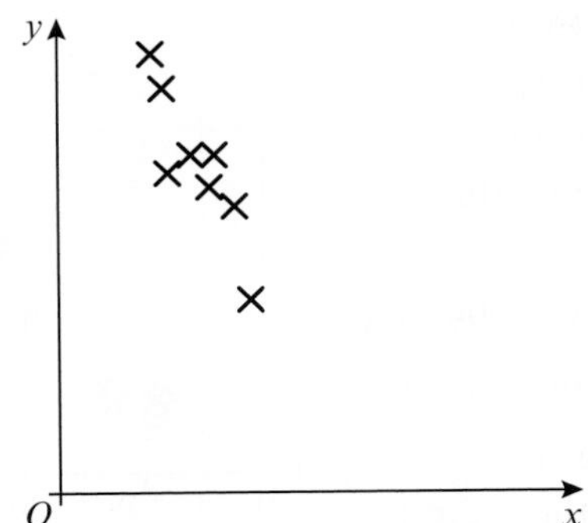

Raw data are often tightly grouped or contain very small or very large values. Changing the scale (which is equivalent to linear coding) can make the scatter diagram easier to read.

The degree of linear correlation is unaffected by the change of scale. The value of r for the uncoded and coded values will be the same.

It is important to understand the limitations of the PMCC. You can determine the strength of the linear relationship between the variables by looking at the value of the PMCC

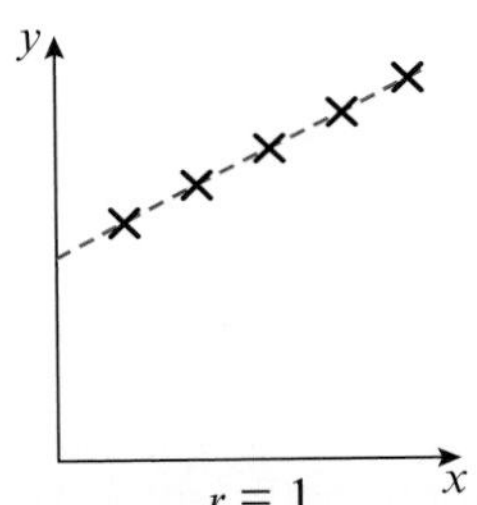

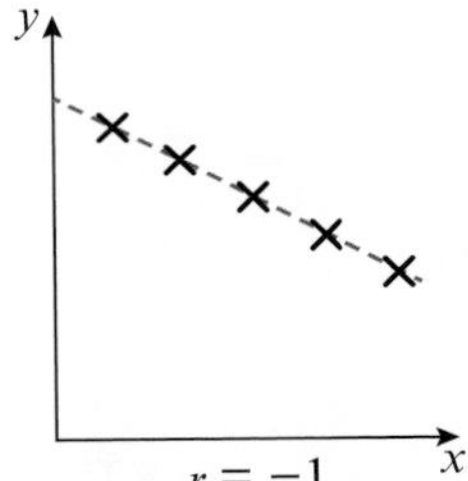

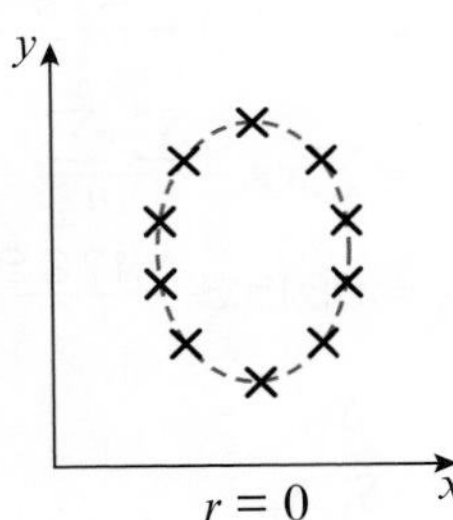

If $r = 1$, there is a perfect positive linear correlation between the variables. All points fit a straight line with a positive gradient.

If $r = -1$, there is a perfect negative linear correlation between the two variables. All points fit a straight line with a negative gradient.

If r is zero or close to zero there is no linear correlation. This does not, however, exclude any other sort of relationship.

- **Values of r between 1 and 0 indicate a greater or lesser degree of positive correlation. The closer to 1 the better the correlation, the closer to 0 the worse the correlation.**
- **Values of r between −1 and 0 indicate a greater or lesser degree of negative correlation. The closer to −1 the better the correlation, the closer to 0 the worse the correlation.**

Even if two variables are associated and have a linear correlation, it does not necessarily mean that a change in one of the variables causes a change in the other variable.

For example, just because of the number of cars on the road has increased and the number of TVs bought has decreased, it does not mean there is a correlation between these two variables. A certain amount of critical thought is required when answering these types of questions.

Example 9 SKILLS INTERPRETATION; PROBLEM-SOLVING

The number of vehicles, x millions, and the number of accidents, y thousands, were recorded in 15 different countries. The following summary statistics were calculated and a scatter diagram of the data is given to the right:

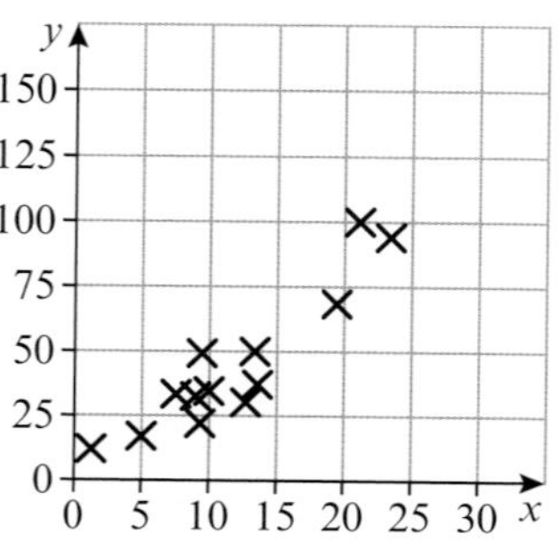

$\sum x = 176.9 \quad \sum y = 679 \quad \sum x^2 = 2576.47 \quad \sum y^2 = 39\,771 \quad \sum xy = 9915.3$

a Calculate the product moment correlation coefficient between x and y.

b With reference to your answer to part **a** and the scatter diagram, comment on the suitability of a linear regression model for these data.

a $S_{xx} = \sum x^2 - \frac{(\sum x)^2}{n}$

$= 2576.47 - \frac{176.9^2}{15} = 490.23$

$S_{yy} = \sum y^2 - \frac{(\sum y)^2}{n}$

$= 39771 - \frac{679^2}{15} = 9034.93$

$S_{xy} = \sum xy - \frac{\sum x \sum y}{n}$

$= 9915.3 - \frac{176.9 \times 679}{15} = 1907.63$

$r = \frac{S_{xy}}{\sqrt{S_{xx}S_{yy}}}$

$= \frac{1907.63}{\sqrt{490.23 \times 9034.93}} = 0.906$ (3 s.f.)

b From the scatter diagram, the data appear to be linearly distributed and the correlation coefficient calculated in part **a** is close to 1, so a linear regression model appears suitable for these data.

Use the standard formula given in the formulae booklet.

The value of the correlation coefficient is 0.906. This is a positive correlation.

The greater the number of vehicles the higher the number of accidents.

Example 10 SKILLS INTERPRETATION; PROBLEM-SOLVING

Data are collected on the amount of a dietary supplement, d grams, given to a sample of 8 cows and their milk yield, m litres. The data were coded using $x = \frac{d}{2} - 6$ and $y = \frac{m}{20}$. The following summary statistics were obtained:

$\sum d^2 = 4592 \quad S_{dm} = 90.6 \quad \sum x = 44 \quad S_{yy} = 0.05915$

a Use the formula for S_{yy} to show that $S_{mm} = 23.66$

b Find the value of the product moment correlation coefficient between d and m.

a $S_{yy} = \sum\left(\frac{m}{20}\right)^2 - \frac{\left(\sum\frac{m}{20}\right)^2}{8}$ — Substitute the code for y into the formula for S_{yy}

$0.05915 = \frac{1}{400}\sum m^2 - \frac{\frac{1}{400}\left(\sum m\right)^2}{8}$

$= \frac{1}{400}\left(\sum m^2 - \frac{\left(\sum m\right)^2}{8}\right)$

$= \frac{1}{400}S_{mm}$

Problem-solving

If you take a factor of $\frac{1}{20^2} = \frac{1}{400}$ out of each term on the right-hand side you are left with the formula for S_{mm}

Hence $S_{mm} = 0.05915 \times 400 = 23.66$ — Substitute and simplify to find the value of S_{mm}

b $\sum x = \sum\left(\frac{d}{2} - 6\right) \Rightarrow 44 = \frac{1}{2}\sum d - 8 \times 6$

Hence $\sum d = 184$ — Substitute the code into $\sum x$ and rearrange to find $\sum d$

$S_{dd} = 4592 - \frac{184^2}{8} = 360$ — Find S_{dd} using the standard formula.

$r = \frac{90.6}{\sqrt{360 \times 23.66}} = 0.982$ (3 s.f.)

Exercise 5E

SKILLS INTERPRETATION; PROBLEM-SOLVING

1 Given that $S_{xx} = 92$, $S_{yy} = 112$ and $S_{xy} = 100$, find the value of the product moment correlation coefficient between x and y.

2 Given the following summary data,

$\sum x = 367 \quad \sum y = 270 \quad \sum x^2 = 33\,845 \quad \sum y^2 = 12\,976 \quad \sum xy = 17\,135 \quad n = 6$

calculate the product moment correlation coefficient, r, using the formula

$$r = \frac{S_{xy}}{\sqrt{S_{xx}S_{yy}}}$$

(E) 3 The ages, a years, and heights, h cm, of seven members of a team were recorded. The data were summarised as follows:

$\sum a = 115 \quad \sum a^2 = 1899 \quad S_{hh} = 571.4 \quad S_{ah} = 72.1$

a Find S_{aa} **(1 mark)**

b Find the value of the product moment correlation coefficient between a and h. **(1 mark)**

c Describe and interpret the correlation between the age and height of these seven people based on these data. **(2 marks)**

(E) **4** In research on the quality of lamb produced by different breeds of sheep, data were obtained about the leanness, L, and taste, T, of the lamb. The data are shown in the table.

Leanness, L	1.5	2.6	3.4	5.0	6.1	8.2
Taste, T	5.5	5.0	7.7	9.0	10.0	10.2

a Find S_{LL}, S_{TT} and S_{LT} **(3 marks)**

b Calculate the product moment correlation coefficient between L and T using the values found in part **a**. **(2 marks)**

A scatter diagram is drawn for the data.

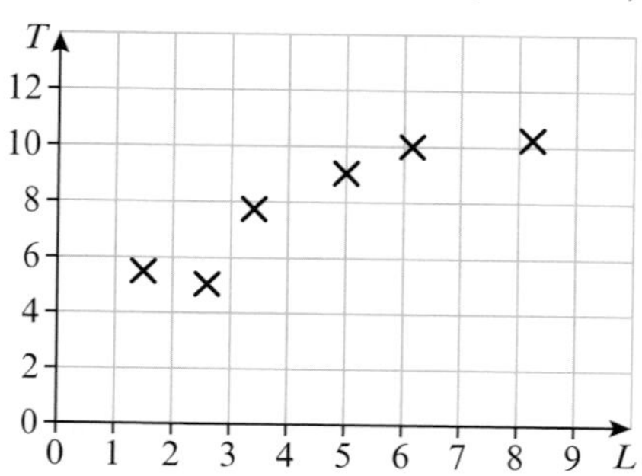

c With reference to your answer to part **b** and the scatter diagram, comment on the suitability of a linear regression model for these data. **(2 marks)**

(E) **5** Eight children had their IQ measured and then took a general knowledge test. Their IQ, x, and their marks, y, for the test were summarised as follows:

$\sum x = 973 \quad \sum x^2 = 120\,123 \quad \sum y = 490 \quad \sum y^2 = 33\,000 \quad \sum xy = 61\,595$

a Calculate the product moment correlation coefficient. **(3 marks)**

b Describe and interpret the correlation coefficient between IQ and general knowledge. **(2 marks)**

6 Two variables, x and y, were coded using $A = x - 7$ and $B = y - 100$
The product moment correlation coefficient between A and B is found to be 0.973
Find the product moment correlation coefficient between x and y.

7 The following data are to be coded using the coding $p = x$ and $q = y - 100$

x	0	5	3	2	1
y	100	117	112	110	106

a Complete a table showing the values of p and q.

b Use your values of p and q to find the product moment correlation coefficient between p and q.

c Hence write down the product moment correlation coefficient between x and y.

8 The PMCC is to be worked out for the following data set using coding.

x	50	40	55	45	60
y	4	3	5	4	6

a Using the coding $p = \frac{x}{5}$ and $t = y$, find the values of S_{pp}, S_{tt} and S_{pt}

b Calculate the product moment correlation coefficient between p and t.

c Write down the product moment correlation coefficient between x and y.

(E) **9** A shopkeeper thinks that the more newspapers he sells in a week the more sweets he sells. He records the amount of money (m dinars) that he takes in newspaper sales and also the amount of money he takes in sweet sales (s dinars) each week for seven weeks. The data are shown in the following table.

Newspaper sales, m (dinars)	380	402	370	365	410	392	385
Sweet sales, s (dinars)	560	543	564	573	550	544	530

a Use the coding $x = m - 365$ and $y = s - 530$ to find S_{xx}, S_{yy} and S_{xy} **(4 marks)**

b Calculate the product moment correlation coefficient for m and s. **(1 mark)**

c State, with a reason, whether or not what the shopkeeper thinks is correct. **(1 mark)**

(E/P) **10** A student vet collected 8 blood samples from a horse with an infection. For each sample, the vet recorded the amount of drug, f, given to the horse and the amount of antibodies present in the blood, g. She coded the data using $f = 10x$ and $g = 5(y + 10)$ and drew a scatter diagram of x against y.

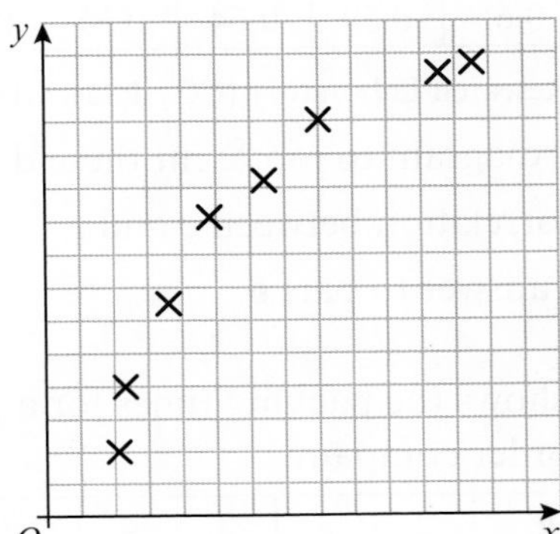

$\sum g^2 = 74458.75$

$S_{fg} = 5667.5$

$\sum y = 70.9$

$S_{xx} = 111.48$

Unfortunately, she forgot to label the axes on her scatter diagram and left the summary data calculations incomplete.

A second student was asked to complete the analysis of the data.

Problem-solving

Substitute the code into the formula for S_{xx}

a Show that $S_{ff} = 11\,148$ **(3 marks)**

b Find the value of the product moment correlation coefficient between f and g. **(4 marks)**

c With reference to the scatter diagram, comment on the result in part **b**. **(1 mark)**

(E/P) **11** Ji-yoo, a market gardener, measures the amount of fertiliser, x litres, that she adds to the compost for a random sample of 7 chilli plant beds. She also measures the yield of chillies, y kg. The data are shown in the table below:

x, litres	1.1	1.3	1.4	1.7	1.9	2.1	2.5
y, kg	6.2	10.5	12	15	17	18	19

$\left(\sum x = 12 \quad \sum x^2 = 22.02 \quad \sum y = 97.7 \quad \sum y^2 = 1491.69 \quad \sum xy = 180.37\right)$

a Show that the product moment correlation coefficient for these data is 0.946, correct to 3 significant figures. **(4 marks)**

The equation of the regression line of y on x is given as $y = -1.2905 + 8.8945x$

b Calculate the residuals. **(3 marks)**

Ji-yoo thinks that because the PMCC is close to 1, a linear relationship is a good model for these data.

c With reference to the residuals, evaluate Ji-yoo's conclusion. **(2 marks)**

Chapter review 5

SKILLS ANALYSIS; PROBLEM-SOLVING

1 A survey of British towns recorded the number of serious road accidents in a week (x) in each town, together with the number of fast food restaurants (y). The data showed a strong positive correlation. Katie states that this shows that building more fast food restaurants in her town will cause more serious road accidents. Explain whether the data supports Katie's statement.

2 The following table shows the mean CO_2 concentration in the atmosphere, c (ppm), and the increase in average temperature t (°C), for the period 1994–2015.

Year	2015	2013	2011	2009	2007	2005	2003	2001	1999	1997	1995	1994
c (ppm)	401	397	392	387	384	381	376	371	368	363	361	357
t (°C)	0.86	0.65	0.59	0.64	0.65	0.68	0.61	0.54	0.41	0.47	0.45	0.24

Source: Earth System Research Laboratory (CO_2 data); GISS Surface Temperature Analysis, NASA (temperature data)

a Draw a scatter diagram to represent these data.

b Describe the correlation between c and t.

c Interpret your answer to part **b**.

(E) 3 The table below shows the packing times for a particular employee for a random sample of orders in a mail order company.

Number of items, n	2	3	3	4	5	5	6	7	8	8	8	9	11	13
Time, t (min)	11	14	16	16	19	21	23	25	24	27	28	30	35	42

A scatter diagram was drawn to represent the data.

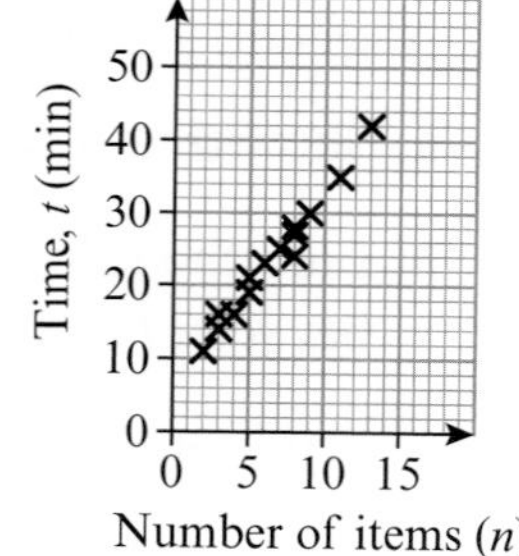

a Describe the correlation between number of items packed and time taken. **(1 mark)**

The equation of the regression line of t on n is $t = 6.3 + 2.64n$

b Give an interpretation of the value 2.64 **(1 mark)**

(E) 4 The table shows average monthly temperature, t (°C), and the number of pairs of gloves, g, a shop sells each month.

t (°C)	6	6	50	10	13	16	18	19	16	12	9	7
g	81	58	50	42	19	21	4	2	20	33	58	65

The following statistics were calculated for the data on temperature:
mean = 15.2, standard deviation = 11.4

An outlier is an observation which lies ±2 standard deviations from the mean.

a Show that $t = 50$ is an outlier. **(1 mark)**

b Give a reason whether or not this outlier should be omitted from the data. **(1 mark)**

The equation of the regression line of t on g for the remaining data is $t = 18.4 - 0.18g$

c Give an interpretation of the value −0.18 in this regression equation. **(1 mark)**

(E) **5** A student is investigating the relationship between the price (y pence) of 100 g of chocolate and the percentage (x%) of cocoa solids in the chocolate.

The data obtained are shown in the table.

Chocolate brand	x (% cocoa)	y (pence)
A	10	35
B	20	55
C	30	40
D	35	100
E	40	60
F	50	90
G	60	110
H	70	130

a Draw a scatter diagram to represent these data. **(2 marks)**

The equation of the regression line of y on x is $y = 17.0 + 1.54x$

b Draw the regression line on your diagram. **(2 marks)**

The student believes that one brand of chocolate is overpriced and uses the regression line to suggest a fair price for this brand.

c Suggest, with a reason, which brand is overpriced. **(1 mark)**

d Comment on the validity of the student's method for suggesting a fair price. **(1 mark)**

(E) **6** Two variables s and t are thought to be connected by an equation of the form $t = a + bs$, where a and b are constants.

a Use the summary data

$\sum s = 553$ $\sum t = 549$ $\sum st = 31\,185$ $n = 12$ $\bar{s} = 46.0833$

$\bar{t} = 45.75$ $S_{ss} = 6193$

to work out the regression line of t on s. **(3 marks)**

b Find the value of t when s is 50. **(1 mark)**

(E/P) **7** Energy consumption is claimed to be a good predictor of Gross National Product. An economist recorded the energy consumption (x) and the Gross National Product (y) for eight countries. The data are shown in the table.

Energy consumption, x	3.4	7.7	12.0	75	58	67	113	131
Gross National Product, y	55	240	390	1100	1390	1330	1400	1900

a Calculate S_{xy} and S_{xx} **(2 marks)**

b Find the equation of the regression line of y on x in the form $y = a + bx$ **(3 marks)**

c Estimate the Gross National Product of a country that has an energy consumption of 100. **(1 mark)**

d Estimate the energy consumption of a country that has a Gross National Product of 3500. **(1 mark)**

e Comment on the reliability of your answer to **d**. **(1 mark)**

(E) **8** In an environmental survey on the survival of mammals, the tail length t (cm) and body length m (cm) of a random sample of six small mammals of the same species were measured.

These data are coded such that $x = \frac{m}{2}$ and $y = t - 2$

The data from the coded records are summarised below.

$\sum y = 13.5$ $\sum x = 25.5$ $\sum xy = 84.25$ $S_{xx} = 59.88$

a Find the equation of the regression line of y on x in the form $y = ax + b$ **(3 marks)**

b Hence find the equation of the regression line of t on m. **(2 marks)**

c Predict the tail length of a mammal that has a body length of 10 cm. **(2 marks)**

(E/P) **9** A mail order company pays for postage of its goods partly by destination and partly by total weight sent out on a particular day. The number of items sent out and the total weights were recorded over a seven-day period. The data are shown in the table.

Number of items, *n*	10	13	22	15	24	16	19
Weight, *w* (kg)	2800	3600	6000	3600	5200	4400	5200

a Use the coding $x = n - 10$ and $y = \frac{w}{400}$ to work out S_{xy} and S_{xx} **(4 marks)**

b Work out the equation of the regression line for y on x. **(3 marks)**

c Work out the equation of the regression line for w on n. **(2 marks)**

d Use your regression equation to estimate the weight of 20 items. **(2 marks)**

e State why it would be unwise to use the regression equation to estimate the weight of 100 items. **(1 mark)**

(E/P) **10** A farm food supplier monitors the number of hens kept (x) against the weekly consumption of hen food (y kg) for a sample of 10 small holders. He records the data and works out the regression line for y on x to be $y = 0.16 + 0.79x$

a Write down a practical interpretation of the figure 0.79 **(1 mark)**

b Estimate the amount of food that is likely to be needed by a small holder who has 30 hens. **(2 marks)**

c If food costs €12 for a 10 kg bag, estimate the weekly cost of feeding 50 hens. **(2 marks)**

(E/P) **11** Water voles are becoming very rare. A group of scientists decided to record details of the water voles in their area. The members measured the mass (y) to the nearest 10 grams, and the body length (x) to the nearest centimetre, of eight active healthy water voles. The data they collected are shown in the table.

Body length, *x* (cm)	140	150	170	180	180	200	220	220
Mass, *y* (grams)	150	180	190	220	240	290	300	310

a Draw a scatter diagram of these data. **(2 marks)**

b Give a reason to support the calculation of a regression line for these data. **(1 mark)**

c Use the coding $l = \frac{x}{10}$ and $w = \frac{y}{10}$ to work out the regression line of w on l. **(3 marks)**

d Find the equation of the regression line for y on x. **(2 marks)**

e Draw the regression line on the scatter diagram. **(1 mark)**

f Use your regression line to calculate an estimate for the mass of a water vole that has a body length of 210 cm. Write down, with a reason, whether or not this is a reliable estimate. **(2 marks)**

The members of the society remove any water voles that seem unhealthy from the river and take them into care until they are fit to be returned.
They find three water voles on one stretch of river which have the following measurements.

A: Mass 235 g and body length 180 mm
B: Mass 180 g and body length 200 mm
C: Mass 195 g and body length 220 mm

g Write down, with a reason, which of these water voles were removed from the river. **(1 mark)**

(E/P) **12** The annual turnover, \$$t$ million, of eight randomly selected Malaysian companies, and the number of staff employed in 100s, s, is recorded and the data shown in the table below:

***t* ($million)**	1.2	1.5	1.8	2.1	2.5	2.7	2.8	3.1
***s* (100s)**	1.1	1.4	1.7	2.2	2.4	2.6	2.9	3.2

($\sum t = 17.7$ $\quad \sum s = 17.5$ $\quad \sum t^2 = 42.33$ $\quad \sum s^2 = 42.07$ $\quad \sum ts = 42.16$)

a Calculate the equation of the regression line of s on t, giving your answer in the form $s = a + bt$. Give the values of a and b correct to 3 significant figures. **(3 marks)**

b Use your regression line to predict the number of employees in a Malaysian company with an annual turnover of \$2,300,000. **(2 marks)**

(E) **13** A small bus company provides a service for a small town and some neighbouring villages. In a study of their service, a random sample of 20 journeys was taken and the distances x, in kilometres, and journey times t, in minutes, were recorded. The average distance was 4.535 km and the average journey time was 15.15 minutes.

Using $\sum x^2 = 493.77$, $\sum t^2 = 4897$, $\sum xt = 1433.8$, calculate the product moment correlation coefficient for these data. **(3 marks)**

(E) **14** Wai wants to know if the 10 people in her group are as good at science as they are at art. She collected the end-of-term test marks for science (s), and art (a), and coded them using $x = \frac{s}{10}$ and $y = \frac{a}{10}$

The data she collected can be summarised as follows:

$$\sum x = 67 \quad \sum x^2 = 465 \quad \sum y = 65 \quad \sum y^2 = 429 \quad \sum xy = 434$$

a Work out the product moment correlation coefficient for x and y. **(3 marks)**

b Write down the product moment correlation coefficient for s and a. **(1 mark)**

c Write down whether or not it is true to say that the people in Wai's group who are good at science are also good at art. Give a reason for your answer. **(1 mark)**

(E) **15** Nimer thinks that oranges that are very juicy cost more than those that are not very juicy. He buys 20 oranges from different places, and measures the amount of juice (j ml), that each orange produces. He also notes the price (p) of each orange.

The data can be summarised as follows:

$\sum j = 979$ $\sum p = 735$ $\sum j^2 = 52\,335$ $\sum p^2 = 32\,156$ $\sum jp = 39\,950$

a Find S_{jj}, S_{pp} and S_{jp} **(3 marks)**

b Using your answers to part **a**, calculate the product moment correlation coefficient. **(1 mark)**

c Describe the type of correlation between the amount of juice and the cost, and state, with a reason, whether or not Nimer is correct. **(2 marks)**

(E/P) **16** A geography student collected data on GDP per capita, x (in \$1000s), and infant mortality rates, y (deaths per 1000), from a sample of eight countries. She coded the data using $p = x - 10$ and $q = \frac{y}{20}$ and drew a scatter diagram of p against q.

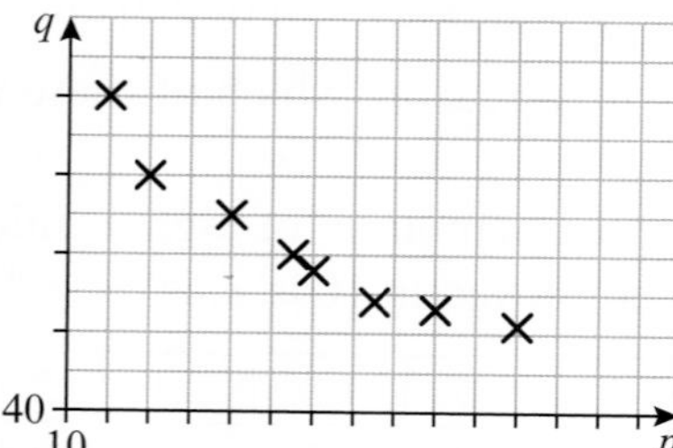

$\sum q^2 = 77.0375$

$S_{pq} = -11.625$

$\sum y = 491$

$S_{xx} = 85.5$

Unfortunately, she spilled coffee on her work and the only things still legible were her unfinished scatter diagram and a few summary data calculations.

a Show that $S_{pp} = S_{xx}$ **(3 marks)**

b Find the value of the product moment correlation coefficient between p and q. **(4 marks)**

c Write down the value of the correlation coefficient between x and y. **(1 mark)**

d With reference to the scatter diagram, comment on the result in part **b**. **(1 mark)**

Challenge

SKILLS INNOVATION

Two variables, x and y, are for a sample of ten pairs of values, summarised as follows:

$\sum x = 104.5$ $\sum y = 113.6$ $\sum x^2 = 1954.1$ $\sum y^2 = 2100.6$

The regression line of x and y has a gradient of 0.8

a Find $\sum xy$

b The equation of the regression line of y on x is given as $y = 0.725x + 3.50$
Find the product moment correlation coefficient between y and x.

Summary of key points

1. $S_{xx} = \sum(x - \bar{x})^2 = \sum x^2 - \frac{(\sum x)^2}{n}$

   $S_{yy} = \sum(y - \bar{y})^2 = \sum y^2 - \frac{(\sum y)^2}{n}$

   $S_{xy} = \sum(x - \bar{x})(y - \bar{y}) = \sum xy - \frac{\sum x \sum y}{n}$

2. An **independent** (or **explanatory**) **variable** is one that is set independently of the other variable. It is plotted along the x-axis.
3. A **dependent** (or **response**) **variable** is one whose values are determined by the values of the independent variable. It is plotted along the y-axis.
4. The equation of the regression line of y on x is:

   $y = a + bx$

   where $b = \frac{S_{xy}}{S_{xx}}$ and $a = \bar{y} - b\bar{x}$
5. Coding of the regression line is sometimes used to simplify calculations. To turn a coded regression line into an actual regression line you substitute the codes into the answer.
6. Interpolation is estimating the value of a dependent variable within the range of the data.
7. Extrapolation is estimating a value outside the range of data. Values estimated by extrapolation can be unreliable.
8. $r = \sqrt{\frac{S_{xy}}{S_{xx}S_{yy}}}$
9. r is a measure of linear relationship

   $r = 1 \Rightarrow$ perfect positive linear correlation

   $r = -1 \Rightarrow$ perfect negative linear correlation

   $r = 0 \Rightarrow$ no linear correlation
10. You can rewrite the variables x and y by using the coding $p = \frac{x - a}{b}$ and $q = \frac{y - c}{d}$
11. r is not affected by coding.

6 DISCRETE RANDOM VARIABLES

5.1
5.2
5.3
5.4

Learning objectives

After completing this chapter you should be able to:

- Understand what discrete random variables are and how they arise → pages 125-130
- Find the cumulative distribution function for a discrete random variable → pages 130-132
- Find the expected value of a discrete random variable → pages 133-136
- Find the variance of a discrete random variable → pages 136-138
- Find the expected value and variance of a function of x → pages 138-142
- Solve problems involving random variables → pages 142-143
- Use discrete uniform distribution as a model for the probability distribution of the outcomes of certain experiments → pages 144-146

Prior knowledge check

1 Write down all the possible outcomes when three fair coins are tossed. ← International GCSE Mathematics

2 $\frac{k}{1}+\frac{k}{2}+\frac{k}{3}+\frac{k}{4}=1$. Find the value of k. ← International GCSE Mathematics

3 Find the value of x and the value of y for these simultaneous equations:

$2x + y = 7$

$3x - y = 8$ ← International GCSE Mathematics

Discrete random variables are an important tool in probability. Bankers and stockmarket traders use random variables to model their risks on investments that have an element of randomness. By calculating the expected value of their profits, they can be confident of making money in the long term.

6.1 Discrete random variables

A **random variable** is a variable whose value depends on the outcome of a random event.

- The range of values that a random variable can take is called its **sample space**.
- A **variable** can take any of a range of specific values.
- The variable is **discrete** if it can take only certain numerical values.
- The variable is **random** if the outcome is not known until the experiment is carried out.

Notation Random variables are written using upper case letters, for example X or Y.

The particular values that the random variable can take are written using equivalent lower case letters, for example x or y.

The probability that the random variable X takes a particular value x is written as $P(X = x)$.

- **A probability distribution fully describes the probability of any outcome in the sample space.**

The probability distribution for a discrete random variable can be described in a number of different ways. For example, take the random variable X = 'score when a fair dice is rolled'. It can be described:

- as a **probability function**: $P(X = x) = \frac{1}{6}$, $x = 1, 2, 3, 4, 5, 6$
- using a table:

x	1	2	3	4	5	6
$P(X = x)$	$\frac{1}{6}$	$\frac{1}{6}$	$\frac{1}{6}$	$\frac{1}{6}$	$\frac{1}{6}$	$\frac{1}{6}$

- using a diagram:

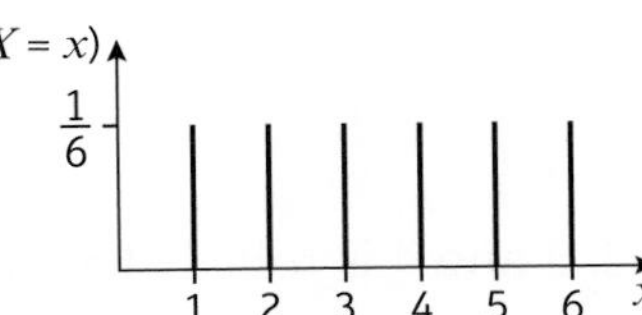

All of these representations show the probability that the random variable takes any given value in its sample space. When all of the probabilities are the same, as in this example, the distribution is known as a **discrete uniform distribution**.

Example 1

Write down whether or not each of the following is a discrete random variable.

a The average height of a group of students

b The number of times a coin is tossed before a head appears

c The number of months in a year

a Is not a discrete random variable as height is measured on a continuous scale

b Is a discrete random variable as it is a number that is the result of an experiment

c Is not a discrete random variable as it does not vary and is not the result of an experiment

Example 2

Three fair coins are tossed.

a Write down all the possible outcomes when the three coins are tossed.

A random variable, X, is defined as the number of heads that appear when the three coins are tossed.

b Write the probability distribution of X as:

i a table **ii** a probability function.

a HHH, HHT, HTH, HTT, THH, THT, TTH, TTT

These are the outcomes of the experiment.

b i

No. of heads, x	0	1	2	3
$P(X = x)$	$\frac{1}{8}$	$\frac{3}{8}$	$\frac{3}{8}$	$\frac{1}{8}$

X is the number of heads, so the sample space of X is {0, 1, 2, 3}

These are the values of the random variable.

ii

$$P(X = x) = \begin{cases} \frac{1}{8} & x = 0, 3 \\ \frac{3}{8} & x = 1, 2 \end{cases}$$

These are the values the random variable can take.

- **The sum of the probabilities of all outcomes of an event add up to 1. For a random variable X, you can write $\Sigma P(X = x) = 1$ for all x.**

Example 3

SKILLS CRITICAL THINKING

A biased four-sided dice with faces numbered 1, 2, 3 and 4 is rolled. The number on the bottom-most face is modelled as a random variable X.

a Given that $P(X = x) = \frac{k}{x}$, find the value of k.

b Write the probability distribution of X in table form.

c Find the probability that:

i $X > 2$ **ii** $1 < X < 4$ **iii** $X > 4$

a The probability distribution will be:

x	1	2	3	4
$P(X = x)$	$\frac{k}{1}$	$\frac{k}{2}$	$\frac{k}{3}$	$\frac{k}{4}$

$$\frac{k}{1} + \frac{k}{2} + \frac{k}{3} + \frac{k}{4} = 1$$

Since this is a probability distribution, $\Sigma P(X = x) = 1$

$$k\left(1 + \frac{1}{2} + \frac{1}{3} + \frac{1}{4}\right) = 1$$

$$k\left(\frac{12 + 6 + 4 + 3}{12}\right) = 1$$

$$k = \frac{12}{25}$$

Problem-solving

Write an equation and solve it to find the value of k. Then substitute this value of k into $P(X = x) = \frac{k}{x}$ for each x to find the probabilities.

b The probability distribution is:

x	1	2	3	4
$P(X = x)$	$\frac{12}{25}$	$\frac{6}{25}$	$\frac{4}{25}$	$\frac{3}{25}$

c **i** $X > 2$ is the same as getting 3 or 4

$P(X > 2) = \frac{4}{25} + \frac{3}{25} = \frac{7}{25}$

Consider all the values of x that satisfy this condition. Add the probabilities to find $P(X > 2)$.

ii $1 < X < 4$ is the same as getting 2 or 3

$P(1 < X < 4) = \frac{6}{25} + \frac{4}{25} = \frac{10}{25} = \frac{2}{5}$

iii There are no elements in the sample space that satisfy $X > 4$ so

$P(X > 4) = 0$

Watch out This random variable only **models** the behaviour of the dice. The outcomes from experiments in real life will never exactly fit the model, but the model provides a useful way of analysing possible outcomes.

Example 4

SKILLS CRITICAL THINKING

A fair spinner is spun until it lands on red or has been spun four times in total. Find the probability distribution of the random variable S, the number of times the spinner is spun.

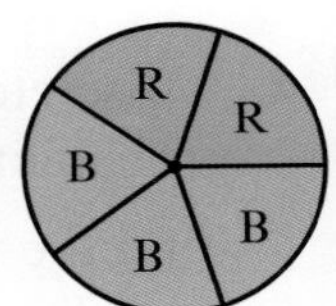

Problem-solving Read the definition of the random variable carefully. Here it is the number of spins.

$P(S = 1)$ is the probability that the spinner lands on red the first time:

$P(S = 1) = \frac{2}{5}$

On any given spin, $P(\text{Red}) = \frac{2}{5}$ and $P(\text{Blue}) = \frac{3}{5}$

If the spinner lands on red on the second spin it must have landed on blue on the first spin:

$P(S = 2) = \frac{3}{5} \times \frac{2}{5} = \frac{6}{25}$

Each spin is an independent event so P(Blue then red) = P(Blue) × P(Red)

Likewise for landing on red on the third spin:

$P(S = 3) = \frac{3}{5} \times \frac{3}{5} \times \frac{2}{5} = \frac{18}{125}$

B, B, R is the only outcome for which $S = 3$.

The experiment stops after 4 spins so:

$P(S = 4) = 1 - \left(\frac{2}{5} + \frac{6}{25} + \frac{18}{125}\right) = \frac{27}{125}$

The sample space of S is {1, 2, 3, 4}. So $P(S = 4) = 1 - P(S = 1, 2 \text{ or } 3)$.

x	1	2	3	4
$P(S = s)$	$\frac{2}{5}$	$\frac{6}{25}$	$\frac{18}{125}$	$\frac{27}{125}$

You have found $P(S = s)$ for all values in the sample space, so you have found the complete probability distribution. You can summarise it in a table.

Exercise 6A

SKILLS CRITICAL THINKING; PROBLEM-SOLVING

1 Write down whether or not each of the following is a discrete random variable. Give a reason for each answer.

a The height, X cm, of a seedling chosen randomly from a group of plants

b The number of times, R, a six appears when a fair dice is rolled 100 times

c The number of days, W, in a given week

2 A fair dice is rolled four times and the number of times it falls with a 6 on the top, Y, is noted. Write down the sample space of Y.

3 A bag contains two discs with the number 2 on them and two discs with the number 3 on them. A disc is drawn at random from the bag and the number noted. The disc is returned to the bag. A second disc is then drawn from the bag and the number noted.

a Write down all the possible outcomes of this experiment.

The discrete random variable X is defined as the sum of the two numbers.

b Write down the probability distribution of X as:

i a table **ii** a probability function.

4 A discrete random variable X has the probability distribution shown in the table.

Find the value of k.

x	1	2	3	4
$\mathrm{P}(X = x)$	$\frac{1}{3}$	$\frac{1}{3}$	k	$\frac{1}{4}$

E/P **5** The random variable X has a probability function

$$\mathrm{P}(X = x) = kx \qquad x = 1, 2, 3, 4$$

Show that $k = \frac{1}{10}$ **(2 marks)**

E/P **6** The random variable X has a probability function

$$\mathrm{P}(X = x) = \begin{cases} kx & x = 1, 3 \\ k(x-1) & x = 2, 4 \end{cases}$$

where k is a constant.

a Find the value of k. **(2 marks)**

b Find $\mathrm{P}(X > 1)$. **(2 marks)**

P **7** The discrete random variable X has a probability function

$$\mathrm{P}(X = x) = \begin{cases} 0.1 & x = -2, -1 \\ \beta & x = 0, 1 \\ 0.2 & x = 2 \end{cases}$$

a Find the value of β.

b Construct a table giving the probability distribution of X.

c Find $\mathrm{P}(-1 \leqslant X < 2)$.

(P) **8** A discrete random variable has a probability distribution shown in the table.

Find the value of a.

x	0	1	2
P($X = x$)	$\frac{1}{4} - a$	a	$\frac{1}{2} + a$

(P) **9** The random variable X can take any integer value from 1 to 50. Given that X has a discrete uniform distribution, find:

a $P(X = 1)$

b $P(X \geqslant 28)$

c $P(13 < X < 42)$

(E) **10** A discrete random variable X has the probability distribution shown in this table.

x	0	1	2	3
P($X = x$)	$\frac{1}{8}$	$\frac{1}{4}$	$\frac{1}{2}$	$\frac{1}{8}$

Find:

a $P(1 < X \leqslant 3)$ **(1 mark)**

b $P(X < 2)$ **(1 mark)**

c $P(X > 3)$ **(1 mark)**

(E/P) **11** A biased coin is tossed until a head appears or it is tossed four times.

a If $P(\text{Head}) = \frac{2}{3}$, write down the probability distribution of S, the number of tosses, in table form. **(4 marks)**

b Find $P(S > 2)$. **(1 mark)**

(P) **12** A fair five-sided spinner is spun.

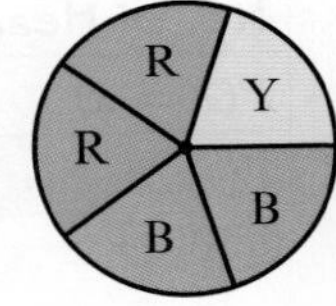

Given that the spinner is spun five times, write down, in table form, the probability distributions of the following random variables:

a X, the number of times red appears

b Y, the number of times yellow appears.

The spinner is now spun until it lands on blue, or until it has been spun five times. The random variable Z is defined as the number of spins in this experiment.

c Find the probability distribution of Z.

(E/P) **13** Marie says that a random variable X has a probability distribution defined by the following probability function:

$$P(X = x) = \frac{2}{x^2} \quad x = 2, 3, 4$$

a Explain how you know that Marie's function does not describe a probability distribution. **(2 marks)**

b Given that the correct probability function is in the form:

$$P(X = x) = \frac{k}{x^2}, \quad x = 2, 3, 4$$

where k is a constant, find the exact value of k. **(2 marks)**

Challenge

SKILLS CRITICAL THINKING

The independent random variables X and Y have probability distributions

$$\mathrm{P}(X = x) = \frac{1}{8}; \quad x = 1, 2, 3, 4, 5, 6, 7, 8 \qquad \mathrm{P}(Y = y) = \frac{1}{y}; \quad y = 2, 3, 6$$

Find $\mathrm{P}(X > Y)$.

Hint X and Y are independent so the value taken by one does not affect the probabilities for the other.

6.2 Finding the cumulative distribution function for a discrete random variable

- If a particular value of X is x, the probability that X is less than or equal to x is written as $\mathrm{F}(x)$.
- $\mathrm{F}(x)$ is found by adding together all the probabilities for those outcomes that are less than or equal to x. This is written as:

  $\mathrm{F}(x) = \mathrm{P}(X \leqslant x)$
- Like a probability distribution, a **cumulative distribution** function can be written as a table.

Example 5

Two fair coins are tossed. X is the number of heads showing on the two coins. Draw a table to show the cumulative distribution function for X.

The sample space is HH HT TH TT

No. of Heads x	0	1	2
$\mathrm{P}(X = x)$	0.25	0.5	0.25
$\mathrm{F}(x)$	0.25	0.75	1

$\mathrm{F}(0) = \mathrm{P}(0) = 0.25$
$\mathrm{F}(1) = \mathrm{P}(0) + \mathrm{P}(1) = 0.25 + 0.5 = 0.75$
$\mathrm{F}(2) = \mathrm{P}(0) + \mathrm{P}(1) + \mathrm{P}(2)$ or use $\mathrm{F}(1) + \mathrm{P}(2)$
$= 0.25 + 0.5 + 0.25 = 1$

Example 6

SKILLS REASONING/ARGUMENTATION

The discrete random variable X has a cumulative distribution function $\mathrm{F}(x)$ defined by:

$$\mathrm{F}(x) = \frac{(x + k)}{8}; \quad x = 1, 2, 3$$

a Find the value of k.

b Draw the distribution table for the cumulative distribution function.

c Write down $\mathrm{F}(2.6)$

d Find the probability distribution of X.

a $F(3) = 1$

So,

$\frac{3+k}{8} = 1$

$3 + k = 8$

$k = 5$

All values of x are less than or equal to 3.
So $F(3) = 1$ since all probabilities must add up to 1.

b $F(2) = \frac{2+5}{8} = \frac{7}{8}$

$F(1) = \frac{1+5}{8} = \frac{6}{8}$

x	1	2	3
F(X)	$\frac{3}{4}$	$\frac{7}{8}$	1

c $F(2.6) = F(2) = \frac{7}{8}$

F(2.6) means $P(X \leqslant 2.6)$ but X doesn't take any values between 2 and 3. So $X \leqslant 2.6$ is the same as $X \leqslant 2$ and thus $F(2.6) = F(2)$

d $P(1) = F(1) = \frac{3}{4}$

$P(2) = F(2) - F(1) = \frac{7}{8} - \frac{3}{4} = \frac{1}{8}$

$P(3) = F(3) - F(2) = 1 - \frac{7}{8} = \frac{1}{8}$

Therefore the distribution is:

x	1	2	3
$P(X = x)$	$\frac{3}{4}$	$\frac{1}{8}$	$\frac{1}{8}$

Watch out Remember X is a discrete random variable so you do not interpolate.

Exercise 6B

SKILLS REASONING/ARGUMENTATION

1 A discrete random variable X has a probability distribution given in the table.

x	1	2	3	4	5	6
$P(X = x)$	0.1	0.1	0.15	0.25	0.3	0.1

a Draw a table showing the cumulative distribution function $F(x)$.

b Write down $F(5)$

c Write down $F(2.2)$

2 A discrete random variable has a cumulative distribution function $F(x)$ given in the table

x	0	1	2	3	4	5	6
$F(x)$	0	0.1	0.2	0.45	0.5	0.9	1

a Show, by drawing a table, the probability distribution of X.

b Write down $P(X < 5)$

c Find $P(2 \leqslant X < 5)$

3 The random variable X has a probability function

$$P(X = x) = \begin{cases} kx & x = 1, 3, 5 \\ k(x-1) & x = 2, 4, 6 \end{cases}$$

where k is a constant.

a Find the value of k.

b Draw a table giving the probability distribution of X.

c Find $P(2 \leqslant X < 5)$

d Find $F(4)$

e Find $F(1.6)$

4 The discrete random variable X has a probability function

$$P(X = x) = \begin{cases} 0.1 & x = -2, -1 \\ \alpha & x = 0, 1 \\ 0.3 & x = 2 \end{cases}$$

a Find the value of α.

b Draw a table giving the probability distribution of X.

c Write down the value of $F(0.3)$

5 The discrete random variable X has a probability function $P(x)$ defined by

$$P(X = x) = \begin{cases} 0 & x = 0 \\ \dfrac{1+x}{6} & x = 1, 2, 3, 4, 5 \\ 1 & x > 5 \end{cases}$$

a Find $P(X \leqslant 4)$

b Show that $P(X = 4)$ is $\frac{1}{6}$

c Find the probability distribution for X.

6 The discrete random variable X has a cumulative distribution function $F(x)$ defined by

$$F(x) = \begin{cases} 0 & x = 0 \\ \dfrac{(x+k)^2}{16} & x = 1, 2 \text{ and } 3 \\ 1 & x > 5 \end{cases}$$

a Find the value of k.

b Find the probability distribution for X.

6.3 Expected value of a discrete random variable

If you take a set of observations from a discrete random variable, you can find the mean of those observations. As the number of observations increases, this value will get closer and closer to the **expected value** of the discrete random variable.

Watch out The expected value is a theoretical quantity, and gives information about the probability distribution of a random variable.

- **The expected value of the discrete random variable X is denoted $\mathrm{E}(X)$ and defined as $\mathrm{E}(X) = \sum x\mathrm{P}(X = x)$**

Notation The expected value is sometimes referred to as the **mean**, and is denoted by μ.

Example 7 SKILLS REASONING/ARGUMENTATION

A fair six-sided dice is rolled. The number that appears on the uppermost face is modelled by the random variable X.

a Write down the probability distribution of X.

b Use the probability distribution of X to calculate $\mathrm{E}(X)$.

a

x	1	2	3	4	5	6
$\mathrm{P}(X = x)$	$\frac{1}{6}$	$\frac{1}{6}$	$\frac{1}{6}$	$\frac{1}{6}$	$\frac{1}{6}$	$\frac{1}{6}$

Since the dice is fair, each side is equally likely to end facing up, so the probability of any face ending up as the uppermost is $\frac{1}{6}$

b The expected value of X is:

$$\mathrm{E}(X) = \sum x\mathrm{P}(X = x) = \frac{1}{6} + \frac{2}{6} + \ldots + \frac{6}{6}$$

$$= \frac{21}{6} = \frac{7}{2} = 3.5$$

Substitute values from the probability distribution into the formula then simplify.

If you know the probability distribution of X then you can calculate the expected value. Notice that in Example 7 the expected value is 3.5, but $\mathrm{P}(X = 3.5) = 0$. The expected value of a random variable does not have to be a value that the random variable can actually take. Instead this tells us that in the long run, we would expect the **average** of all rolls to get close to 3.5.

Example 8 SKILLS CRITICAL THINKING

The random variable X has a probability distribution as shown in the table.

x	1	2	3	4	5
$\mathrm{P}(x)$	0.1	p	0.3	q	0.2

a Given that $\mathrm{E}(X) = 3$, write down two equations involving p and q.

b Find the value of p and the value of q.

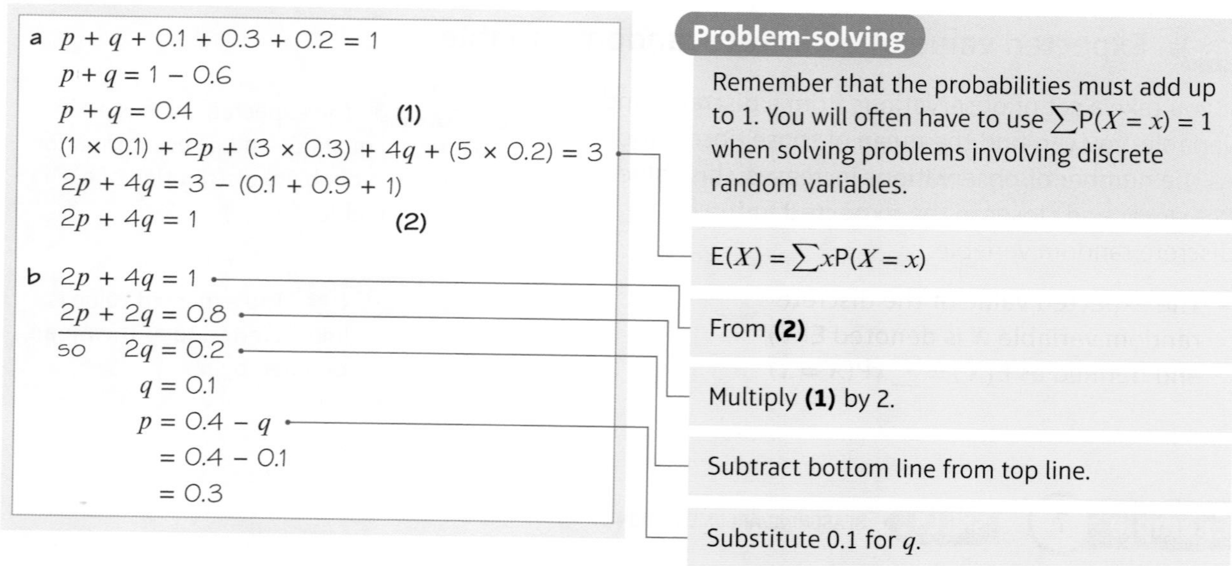

a $p + q + 0.1 + 0.3 + 0.2 = 1$

$p + q = 1 - 0.6$

$p + q = 0.4$ **(1)**

$(1 \times 0.1) + 2p + (3 \times 0.3) + 4q + (5 \times 0.2) = 3$

$2p + 4q = 3 - (0.1 + 0.9 + 1)$

$2p + 4q = 1$ **(2)**

b $2p + 4q = 1$

$2p + 2q = 0.8$

so $2q = 0.2$

$q = 0.1$

$p = 0.4 - q$

$= 0.4 - 0.1$

$= 0.3$

Problem-solving

Remember that the probabilities must add up to 1. You will often have to use $\sum P(X = x) = 1$ when solving problems involving discrete random variables.

$E(X) = \sum xP(X = x)$

From **(2)**

Multiply **(1)** by 2.

Subtract bottom line from top line.

Substitute 0.1 for q.

If X is a discrete random variable, then X^2 is also a discrete random variable. You can use this rule to determine the expected value of X^2.

- **$E(X^2) = \sum x^2P(X = x)$**

Hint Any function of a random variable is also a random variable

Example 9

A discrete random variable X has the following probability distribution:

x	1	2	3	4
$P(X = x)$	$\frac{12}{25}$	$\frac{6}{25}$	$\frac{4}{25}$	$\frac{3}{25}$

a Write down the probability distribution for X^2

b Find $E(X^2)$

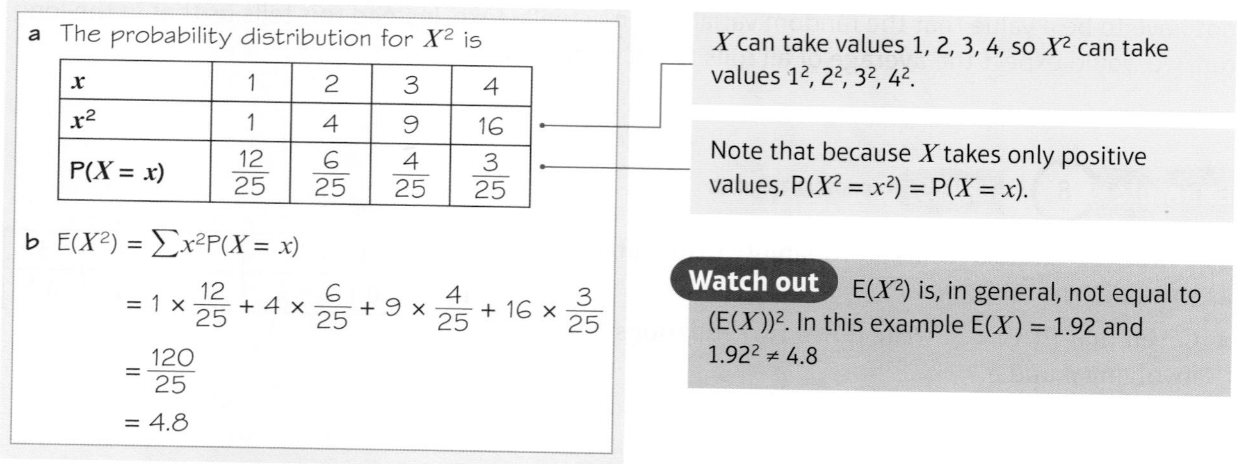

a The probability distribution for X^2 is

x	1	2	3	4
x^2	1	4	9	16
$P(X = x)$	$\frac{12}{25}$	$\frac{6}{25}$	$\frac{4}{25}$	$\frac{3}{25}$

b $E(X^2) = \sum x^2P(X = x)$

$= 1 \times \frac{12}{25} + 4 \times \frac{6}{25} + 9 \times \frac{4}{25} + 16 \times \frac{3}{25}$

$= \frac{120}{25}$

$= 4.8$

X can take values 1, 2, 3, 4, so X^2 can take values $1^2, 2^2, 3^2, 4^2$.

Note that because X takes only positive values, $P(X^2 = x^2) = P(X = x)$.

Watch out $E(X^2)$ is, in general, not equal to $(E(X))^2$. In this example $E(X) = 1.92$ and $1.92^2 \neq 4.8$

Exercise 6C SKILLS CRITICAL THINKING; REASONING/ARGUMENTATION

1 For each of the following probability distributions, write out the distribution of X^2 and calculate both E(X) and E(X^2).

a

x	2	4	6	8
P($X = x$)	0.3	0.3	0.2	0.2

b

x	−2	−1	1	2
P($X = x$)	0.1	0.4	0.1	0.4

Hint Note that, for example, $P(X^2 = 4) = P(X = 2) + P(X = -2)$

2 The score on a biased dice is modelled by a random variable X with probability distribution:

x	1	2	3	4	5	6
P($X = x$)	0.1	0.1	0.1	0.2	0.4	0.1

Find E(X) and E(X^2).

3 The random variable X has a probability function:

$$P(X = x) = \frac{1}{x}; \qquad x = 2, 3, 6$$

a Construct tables giving the probability distributions of X and X^2.

b Work out E(X) and E(X^2).

c State whether or not $(E(X))^2 = E(X^2)$.

4 The random variable X has a probability function given by

$$P(X = x) = \begin{cases} 2^{-x} & x = 1, 2, 3, 4 \\ 2^{-4} & x = 5 \end{cases}$$

a Construct a table giving the probability distribution of X.

b Calculate E(X) and E(X^2).

c State whether or not $(E(X))^2 = E(X^2)$.

E/P **5** The random variable X has the following probability distribution:

x	1	2	3	4	5
P($X = x$)	0.1	a	b	0.2	0.1

Given that E(X) = 2.9, find the value of a and the value of b. **(5 marks)**

6 The discrete random variable X has probability function:

$$P(X = x) = \begin{cases} a(1 - x) & x = -2, -1, 0 \\ b & x = 5 \end{cases}$$

Given that E(X) = 1.2, find the value of a and the value of b.

E/P 7 A biased six-sided dice has a $\frac{1}{8}$ chance of landing on any of the numbers 1, 2, 3 or 4. The probabilities of landing on 5 or 6 are unknown. The outcome is modelled as a random variable, X. Given that $E(X) = 4.1$, find the probability distribution of X. **(5 marks)**

E/P 8 A company makes phone covers. One out of every 50 phone covers is faulty, but the company doesn't know which ones are faulty until a buyer complains. Suppose the company makes a \$3 profit on the sale of any working phone cover, but suffers a loss of \$8 for every faulty phone cover due to replacement costs. Calculate the expected profit for each phone cover, regardless of whether or not it is faulty. **(5 marks)**

Challenge

SKILLS PROBLEM-SOLVING

Three fair six-sided dice are rolled. The discrete random variable X is defined as the largest value of the three values shown. Find $E(X)$.

6.4 Variance of a discrete random variable

If you take a set of observations from a discrete random variable, you can find the variance of those observations. As the number of observations increases, this value will get closer and closer to the **variance** of the discrete random variable.

Notation The variance is sometimes denoted by σ^2, where σ is the standard deviation.

- **The variance of X is usually written as $\text{Var}(X)$ and is defined as $\text{Var}(X) = E((X - E(X))^2)$**

The random variable $(X - E(X))^2$ is the squared deviation from the expected value of X. It is large when X takes values that are very different to $E(X)$.

- **Sometimes it is easier to calculate the variance using the formula $\text{Var}(X) = E(X^2) - (E(X))^2$**

From the definition you can see that $\text{Var}(X) \geqslant 0$ for any random variable X. The variance of a discrete random variable is a measure of spread for a distribution of a random variable that determines the degree to which the values of a random variable differ from the expected value. In other words, the larger the value of $\text{Var}(X)$, the more likely it is to take values significantly different to its expected value.

Example 10 SKILLS PROBLEM-SOLVING

A fair six-sided dice is rolled. The number on the uppermost face is modelled by the random variable X.

Find Var(X)

Method 1

We have that $E(X) = 3.5$

This was calculated in Example 7.

The distributions of X, X^2 and $(X - E(X))^2$ are given by

x	1	2	3	4	5	6
x^2	1	4	9	16	25	36
$(x - E(X))^2$	6.25	2.25	0.25	0.25	2.25	6.25
$P(X = x)$	$\frac{1}{6}$	$\frac{1}{6}$	$\frac{1}{6}$	$\frac{1}{6}$	$\frac{1}{6}$	$\frac{1}{6}$

So the variance is

$$\text{Var}(X) = \sum(x - E(X))^2 P(X = x)$$

$$= 6.25 \times \frac{2}{6} + 2.25 \times \frac{2}{6} + 0.25 \times \frac{2}{6}$$

Substitute values into the formula for variance.

$$= (6.25 + 2.25 + 0.25) \times \frac{1}{3} = \frac{35}{12}$$

Method 2

The expected value of X^2 is

$$E(X^2) = \sum x^2 P(X = x) = \frac{1}{6}(1 + 4 + \ldots + 36) = \frac{91}{6}$$

So using the alternative formula

$$\text{Var}(X) = E(X^2) - (E(X))^2 = \frac{91}{6} - \frac{49}{4} = \frac{35}{12}$$

It is usually quicker to use this method to find the variance of a random variable.

Exercise 6D SKILLS PROBLEM-SOLVING

1 The random variable X has a probability distribution given by:

x	−1	0	1	2	3
$P(X = x)$	$\frac{1}{5}$	$\frac{1}{5}$	$\frac{1}{5}$	$\frac{1}{5}$	$\frac{1}{5}$

a Find E(X)

b Find Var(X)

2 Find the expected value and variance of the random variable X with probability distributions given by the following tables:

a

x	1	2	3
$P(X = x)$	$\frac{1}{3}$	$\frac{1}{2}$	$\frac{1}{6}$

b

x	−1	0	1
$P(X = x)$	$\frac{1}{4}$	$\frac{1}{2}$	$\frac{1}{4}$

c

x	−2	−1	1	2
$P(X = x)$	$\frac{1}{3}$	$\frac{1}{3}$	$\frac{1}{6}$	$\frac{1}{6}$

3 Given that Y is the score when a single, unbiased, eight-sided dice is rolled, find E(Y) and Var(Y).

(P) **4** Two fair, cubical (six-sided) dice are rolled and S is the sum of their scores. Find:

a the distribution of S

b E(S)

c Var(S)

d the standard deviation, σ

Hint The standard deviation of a random variable is the square root of its variance.

(P) **5** Two fair, tetrahedral (four-sided) dice are rolled and D is the difference between their scores. Find:

a the distribution of D

b E(D)

c Var(D)

(E) **6** A fair coin is flipped repeatedly until a head appears or three flips have been made. The random variable T represents the number of flips of the coin.

a Show that the probability distribution of T is:

t	1	2	3
P($T = t$)	$\frac{1}{2}$	$\frac{1}{4}$	$\frac{1}{4}$

(3 marks)

b Find the expected value and variance of T. **(6 marks)**

(E/P) **7** The random variable X has a probability distribution given by:

x	1	2	3
P($X = x$)	a	b	a

where a and b are constants.

a Write down an expression for E(X) in terms of a and b. **(2 marks)**

b Given that Var(X) = 0.75, find the values of a and b. **(5 marks)**

6.5 Expected value and variance of a function of X

If X is a discrete random variable, and g is a function, then g(X) is also a discrete random variable. You can calculate the expected value of g(X) using the formula:

- $\text{E}(\text{g}(X)) = \sum \text{g}(x)\text{P}(X = x)$

This is a more general version of the formula for E(X^2). For simple functions, such as addition and multiplication by a constant, you can learn the following rules:

- **If X is a random variable and a and b are constants, then $\text{E}(aX + b) = a\text{E}(X) + b$**
- **If X and Y are random variables, then $\text{E}(X + Y) = \text{E}(X) + \text{E}(Y)$**

You can use a similar rule to simplify variance calculations for some functions of random variables:

- **If X is a random variable and a and b are constants, then $\text{Var}(aX + b) = a^2\text{Var}(X)$**

Example 11

SKILLS CRITICAL THINKING

A discrete random variable X has the probability distribution:

x	1	2	3	4
$P(X = x)$	$\frac{12}{25}$	$\frac{6}{25}$	$\frac{4}{25}$	$\frac{3}{25}$

a Write down the probability distribution for Y, where $Y = 2X + 1$

b Find $E(Y)$

c Compute $E(X)$ and verify that $E(Y) = 2E(X) + 1$

a The probability distribution for Y is:

x	1	2	3	4
y	3	5	7	9
$P(Y = y)$	$\frac{12}{25}$	$\frac{6}{25}$	$\frac{4}{25}$	$\frac{3}{25}$

When $x = 1$, $y = 2 \times 1 + 1 = 3$
$x = 2$, $y = 2 \times 2 + 1 = 5$
etc.

Notice how the probabilities relating to X are still being used, for example, $P(X = 3) = P(Y = 7)$.

b $E(Y) = \sum yP(Y = y)$

$= 3 \times \frac{12}{25} + 5 \times \frac{6}{25} + 7 \times \frac{4}{25} + 9 \times \frac{3}{25}$

$= \frac{121}{25}$

$= 4.84$

c $E(X) = \sum xP(X = x) = 1 \times \frac{12}{25} + 2 \times \frac{6}{25}$

$+ 3 \times \frac{4}{25} + 4 \times \frac{3}{25} = \frac{48}{25} = 1.92$

Therefore $2E(X) + 1 = 2 \times 1.92 + 1 = 4.84$

This confirms that $E(Y) = 2E(X) + 1$

If you know or are given $E(X)$ you can use the formula to find $E(Y)$ quickly.

Example 12

SKILLS CRITICAL THINKING

A random variable X has $E(X) = 4$ and $\text{Var}(X) = 3$. Find:

a $E(3X)$

b $E(X - 2)$

c $\text{Var}(3X)$

d $\text{Var}(X - 2)$

e $E(X^2)$

a $E(3X) = 3E(X) = 3 \times 4 = 12$

b $E(X - 2) = E(X) - 2 = 4 - 2 = 2$

c $\text{Var}(3X) = 3^2 \text{Var}(X) = 9 \times 3 = 27$

d $\text{Var}(X - 2) = \text{Var}(X) = 3$

e $E(X^2) = \text{Var}(X) + (E(X))^2 = 3 + 4^2 = 19$

Rearrange $\text{Var}(X) = E(X^2) - (E(X))^2$

Example 13 SKILLS CRITICAL THINKING; PROBLEM-SOLVING

Two fair 10-cent coins are tossed. The random variable X cents represents the total value of the coins that land heads up.

a Find $E(X)$ and $Var(X)$.

The random variables S and T are defined as follows:

$$S = X - 10 \text{ and } T = \frac{1}{2}X - 5$$

b Show that $E(S) = E(T)$.

c Find $Var(S)$ and $Var(T)$.

A large number of observations of S and T are taken.

d Comment on any likely differences or similarities.

a The probability distribution of X is:

x	0	10	20
$P(X = x)$	$\frac{1}{4}$	$\frac{1}{2}$	$\frac{1}{4}$

$E(X) = 10$ by inspection

$Var(X) = E(X^2) - (E(X))^2$

$Var(X) = 0^2 \times \frac{1}{4} + 10^2 \times \frac{1}{2} + 20^2 \times \frac{1}{4} - 10^2 = 50$

b $E(S) = E(X - 10) = E(X) - 10 = 10 - 10 = 0$

$E(T) = E\left(\frac{1}{2}X - 5\right) = \frac{1}{2}E(X) - 5 = \frac{1}{2} \times 10 - 5 = 0$

Use $E(aX + b) = aE(X) + b$

c $Var(S) = Var(X) = 50$

$Var(T) = \left(\frac{1}{2}\right)^2 Var(X) = \frac{50}{4} = 12.5$

Subtracting a constant doesn't change the variance, so $Var(S) = Var(X)$.

d The means of both sets of observations should be close to zero. The observed values of S will be more spread out than the observed values of T.

You could also say that the sum of the observed values of each random variable will be close to 0.

Example 14 SKILLS INNOVATION

The random variable X has the following probability distribution:

x	0°	30°	60°	90°
$P(X = x)$	0.4	0.2	0.1	0.3

Calculate $E(\sin X)$.

The distribution of $\sin X$ is:

$\sin x$	0	$\frac{1}{2}$	$\frac{\sqrt{3}}{2}$	1
$P(X = x)$	0.4	0.2	0.1	0.3

$$E(\sin X) = \sum \sin x \, P(X = x)$$

$$= 0 \times 0.4 + \frac{1}{2} \times 0.2 + \frac{\sqrt{3}}{2} \times 0.1 + 1 \times 0.3$$

Use the general formula for E(g(X)).

$$= \frac{8 + \sqrt{3}}{20} \approx 0.487$$

Exercise 6E SKILLS PROBLEM-SOLVING; INNOVATION

1 The random variable X has a probability distribution given by:

x	1	2	3	4
$P(X = x)$	0.1	0.3	0.2	0.4

a Write down the probability distribution for Y where $Y = 2X - 3$

b Find $E(Y)$

c Calculate $E(X)$ and verify that $E(2X - 3) = 2E(X) - 3$

2 The random variable X has a probability distribution given by:

x	−2	−1	0	1	2
$P(X = x)$	0.1	0.1	0.2	0.4	0.2

a Write down the probability distribution for Y where $Y = X^3$

b Calculate $E(Y)$

3 The random variable X has $E(X) = 1$ and $Var(X) = 2$. Find:

a $E(8X)$ **b** $E(X + 3)$ **c** $Var(X + 3)$

d $Var(3X)$ **e** $Var(1 - 2X)$ **f** $E(X^2)$

4 The random variable X has $E(X) = 3$ and $E(X^2) = 10$. Find:

a $E(2X)$ **b** $E(3 - 4X)$ **c** $E(X^2 - 4X)$

d $Var(X)$ **e** $Var(3X + 2)$

5 The random variable X has a mean μ and standard deviation σ.

Find, in terms of μ and σ:

a $E(4X)$ **b** $E(2X + 2)$ **c** $E(2X - 2)$

d $Var(2X + 2)$ **e** $Var(2X - 2)$

6 In a space-themed board game, players roll a fair, six sided dice each time they make it around the board. The board represents one turn around the galaxy. The score on the dice is modelled as a discrete random variable X.

a Write down $E(X)$.

Players collect 200 points, plus 100 times the score on the dice. The amount of points given to each player is modelled as a discrete random variable Y.

b Write Y in terms of X.

c Find the expected number of points a player receives each time they make it around the board.

(P) 7 Hiroki runs a pizza parlour that sells pizza in three sizes: small (20 cm diameter), medium (30 cm diameter) and large (40 cm diameter). Each pizza base is 1 cm thick. Hiroki has worked out that on average, customers order a small, medium or large pizza with probabilities $\frac{3}{10}$, $\frac{9}{20}$ and $\frac{5}{20}$ respectively. Calculate the expected amount of pizza dough needed per customer.

(E/P) 8 Two tetrahedral dice are rolled. The random variable X represents the result of subtracting the smaller score from the larger.

a Find $E(X)$ and $Var(X)$. **(7 marks)**

The random variables Y and Z are defined as $Y = 2^X$ and $Z = \frac{4X + 1}{2}$

b Show that $E(Y) = E(Z)$. **(3 marks)**

c Find $Var(Z)$. **(2 marks)**

Challenge

SKILLS INNOVATION

Show that $E((X - E(X))^2) = E(X^2) - (E(X))^2$

Hint You can assume that $E(X + Y) = E(X) + E(Y)$

6.6 Solving problems involving random variables

Suppose you have two random variables: a variable X, and a variable $Y = g(X)$. If g is one-to-one, and you know the mean and variance of Y, then it is possible to deduce the mean and variance of X.

Example 15 SKILLS PROBLEM-SOLVING

X is a discrete random variable. The discrete random variable Y is defined as $Y = \frac{X - 150}{50}$

Given that $E(Y) = 5.1$ and $Var(Y) = 2.5$, find:

a $E(X)$

b $Var(X)$.

a $Y = \frac{X - 150}{50}$

$X = 50Y + 150$ — Rearrange to get an expression for X in terms of Y.

$E(X) = E(50Y + 150)$

$= 50E(Y) + 150$

$= 255 + 150$

$= 405$

b $Var(X) = Var(50Y + 150)$ — Use your expression for X in terms of Y. Remember that the '+150' does not affect the variance, and that you have to multiply Var(Y) by 50^2 to get Var(X).

$= 50^2 Var(Y)$

$= 50^2 \times 2.5$

$= 6250$

Exercise 6F SKILLS PROBLEM-SOLVING

1 X is a discrete random variable. The random variable Y is defined by $Y = 4X - 6$
Given that $E(Y) = 2$ and $Var(Y) = 32$, find:

a $E(X)$

b $Var(X)$

c the standard deviation of X.

2 X is a discrete random variable. The random variable Y is defined by $Y = \frac{4 - 3X}{2}$

Given that $E(Y) = -1$ and $Var(Y) = 9$, find:

a $E(X)$

b $Var(X)$

c $E(X^2)$

(P) 3 The discrete random variable X has a probability distribution given by:

x	1	2	3	4
$P(X = x)$	0.3	a	b	0.2

The random variable Y is defined by $Y = 2X + 3$. Given that $E(Y) = 8$, find the values of a and b.

(E/P) 4 The discrete random variable X has a probability distribution given by:

x	90°	180°	270°
$P(X = x)$	a	b	0.3

The random variable Y is defined as $Y = \sin X°$

a Find the range of possible values of $E(Y)$. **(5 marks)**

b Given that $E(Y) = 0.2$, write down the values of a and b. **(2 marks)**

6.7 Using discrete uniform distribution as a model for the probability distribution of the outcomes of certain experiments

- **The probability distribution for the score S on a single roll of a dice is:**

s	1	2	3	4	5	6
$P(S = s)$	$\frac{1}{6}$	$\frac{1}{6}$	$\frac{1}{6}$	$\frac{1}{6}$	$\frac{1}{6}$	$\frac{1}{6}$

This is an example of a **discrete uniform distribution** over the set of values (1, 2, 3, 4, 5, 6). It is discrete because the values are discrete and it is uniform because all the probabilities are the same.

- **Conditions for discrete uniform distribution:**

  A discrete random variable X is defined over a set of n distinct values.

  Each value is equally likely, in other words: $P(X = x) = \frac{1}{n}$ for each x

- **In many cases, X is defined over the set (1, 2, 3 … n). In such cases, the mean and variance are given by the following:**

  For a discrete uniform distribution X over the values 1, 2, 3 … n

  $$E(X) = \frac{n+1}{2}$$

  $$\text{Var}(X) = \frac{(n+1)(n-1)}{12}$$

Watch out Remember, in order to use these formulas, the values for X must be 1, 2, 3, … n.

- **You do not need to prove these results, but you may find them useful for the examination when answering questions of this type.**

Example 16 SKILLS CREATIVITY

Digits are selected at random from a table of random numbers.

a Find the mean and standard deviation of a single digit.

b Find the probability that a particular digit lies within one standard deviation of the mean.

- In this example the digits will be the numbers 0 to 9 inclusive.
- Let R represent this random variable having a discrete uniform distribution over the set $\{0, 1, 2, \ldots 9\}$
- Let X represent a random variable having a discrete uniform distribution over the set $\{0, 1, 2, \ldots 10\}$
- There is a simple relationship between X and R, namely $R = X - 1$
- By introducing the random variable X, you can use the standard formula for X with $n = 10$

a $E(R) = E(X - 1)$
$= E(X) - 1$
$= \frac{n+1}{2} - 1$
$= \frac{10+1}{2} - 1$
$= 4.5$

Using the formula for the mean of series 1, 2, …, n

$\text{Var}(R) = \text{Var}(X - 1)$
$= \text{Var}(X)$
$= \frac{(n+1)(n-1)}{12}$
$= \frac{11 \times 9}{12}$
$= 8.25$

Using the formula for the variance of series 1, 2, …, n

Therefore:
$\sigma = \sqrt{8.25}$
$= 2.87$ (3 s.f.)

b Using the value of σ in **a**, the required probability is:
$P(4.5 - 2.87... < R < 4.5 + 2.87...)$
$= P(1.63 < R < 7.37)$
$= P(2 \leqslant R \leqslant 7)$
$= \frac{6}{10} = \frac{3}{5}$

Example 16 shows how you can use the formulae for the series {0, 1, 2, … n} and the formulae for the functions for X to get the answers. You could also get the answers by writing down the probability distribution and finding the mean and variance without any previous working out. This is an acceptable alternative for the examination, although a longer and more time-consuming method.

Exercise 6G SKILLS INNOVATION; CREATIVITY

1 X is a discrete uniform distribution over the numbers 1, 2, 3, 4 and 5. Work out the expectation and variance of X.

2 Seven similar balls are placed in a bag. The balls have the numbers 1 to 7 written on them. A ball is drawn out of the bag at random. The variable X represents the number on the ball.

a Find $E(X)$

b Work out $\text{Var}(X)$

3 A fair dice is thrown once and the random variable X represents the value on the upper face.

a Find the expectation and variance of X.

b Calculate the probability that X is within one standard deviation of the mean.

4 A card is selected at random from a pack of cards containing the even numbers 2, 4, 6 …, 20. The variable X represents the number on the card.

a Find $P(X > 15)$

b Find the expectation and variance of X.

5 A straight line is drawn on a piece of paper. The line is divided into four equal lengths and the segments are marked 1, 2, 3 and 4. In a party game, a person is blindfolded and asked to mark a point on the line and then the number of the segment is recorded. A discrete uniform distribution over the set (1, 2, 3, 4) is suggested as a model for this distribution. Comment on this suggestion.

6 The spinner shown is used in a fairground game. It costs 5 cents to have a go on the spinner.

The spinner is spun and the player wins the number of cents shown.

If X is the number which comes up on the next spin,

a name a suitable model for X

b find $E(X)$

c find $\text{Var}(X)$

d explain why a player should not expect to make money over a large number of spins.

Chapter review 6

SKILLS CRITICAL THINKING; PROBLEM-SOLVING

1 The random variable X has the following probability function:

$$P(X = x) = \frac{x}{15}; \qquad \text{time consuming } x = 1, 2, 3, 4, 5$$

a Construct a table giving the probability distribution of X.

b Find $P(3 < x \leqslant 5)$

2 The discrete random variable X has the probability distribution shown.

x	−2	−1	0	1	2	3
$P(X = x)$	0.2	q	0.3	0.1	0.2	0.1

a Find the value of q.

b Calculate $P(-1 \leqslant x < 2)$

E/P **3** The random variable X has probability function:

$$P(X = x) = \frac{(3x - 1)}{26}; \qquad x = 1, 2, 3, 4$$

a Construct a table giving the probability distribution of X. **(2 marks)**

b Find $P(2 < X \leqslant 4)$ **(2 marks)**

(E) **4** Sixteen counters are numbered 1 to 16 and placed in a bag. One counter is chosen at random and the number, X, recorded.

a Write down one condition on selecting a counter if X is to be modelled as a discrete uniform distribution. **(1 mark)**

b Find:

i $P(X = 5)$ **(1 mark)**

ii $P(X \text{ is prime})$ **(2 marks)**

iii $P(3 \leqslant X < 11)$ **(2 marks)**

(E/P) **5** The random variable Y has probability function:

$$P(Y = y) = \frac{y}{k}; \qquad y = 1, 2, 3, 4, 5$$

a Find the value of k. **(2 marks)**

b Construct a table giving the probability distribution of Y. **(2 marks)**

c Find $P(Y > 3)$. **(1 mark)**

(E/P) **6** Shashi rolls a biased six-sided dice four times. $P(\text{six}) = \frac{1}{4}$. The random variable T represents the number of times he rolls a six.

a Construct a table giving the probability distribution of T. **(3 marks)**

b Find $P(T < 3)$. **(2 marks)**

Shashi rolls the dice again, this time recording the number of rolls required to roll a six. He rolls the dice a maximum of five times. Let the random variable S represent the number of times he rolls the dice.

c Construct a table giving the probability distribution of S. **(3 marks)**

d Find $P(S > 2)$. **(2 marks)**

7 The random variable X has the probability function:

$$P(X = x) = \frac{x}{21}; \qquad x = 1, 2, 3, 4, 5, 6$$

a Construct a table giving the probability distribution of X.

Find:

b $P(2 < X \leqslant 5)$ **c** $E(X)$ **d** $\text{Var}(X)$

e $\text{Var}(3 - 2X)$ **f** $E(X^3)$

8 The discrete random variable X has the probability distribution given in the table below.

x	−2	−1	0	1	2	3
P(X = x)	0.1	0.2	0.3	r	0.1	0.1

Find:

a r **b** $P(-1 \leqslant X < 2)$ **c** $E(2X + 3)$ **d** $\text{Var}(2X + 3)$

9 A discrete random variable X has the probability distribution shown in the table below.

x	0	1	2
P($X = x$)	$\frac{1}{5}$	b	$\frac{1}{5} + b$

a Find the value of b.

b Show that $E(X) = 1.3$

c Find the exact value of $\text{Var}(X)$.

d Find the exact value of $P(X \leqslant 1.5)$

(E) **10** The discrete random variable X has a probability function:

$$P(X = x) = \begin{cases} k(1 - x) & x = 0, 1 \\ k(x - 1) & x = 2, 3 \\ 0 & \text{otherwise} \end{cases}$$

where k is a constant.

a Show that $k = \frac{1}{4}$ **(2 marks)**

b Find $E(X)$ and show that $E(X^2) = 5.5$ **(4 marks)**

c Find $\text{Var}(2X - 2)$ **(4 marks)**

11 A discrete random variable X has the probability distribution:

x	0	1	2	3
P($X = x$)	$\frac{1}{4}$	$\frac{1}{2}$	$\frac{1}{8}$	$\frac{1}{8}$

Find:

a $P(1 < X \leqslant 2)$

b $E(X)$

c $E(3X - 1)$

d $\text{Var}(X)$

e $E(\log(X + 1))$

12 A discrete random variable X has the probability distribution:

x	1	2	3	4
P($X = x$)	0.4	0.2	0.1	0.3

Find:

a $P(3 < X^2 < 10)$

b $E(X)$

c $\text{Var}(X)$

d $E\left(\frac{3 - X}{2}\right)$

e $E(\sqrt{X})$

f $E(2^{-x})$

(P) **13** The random variable X has the probability distribution:

x	1	2	3	4	5
P($X = x$)	0.1	p	q	0.3	0.1

a Given that $E(X) = 3.1$, write down two equations involving p and q.

Find:

b the value of p and the value of q

c $\text{Var}(X)$

d $\text{Var}(2X - 3)$

(E) **14** The random variable X has the probability function:

$$P(X = x) = \begin{cases} kx & x = 1, 2 \\ k(x - 2) & x = 3, 4, 5 \end{cases}$$

where k is a constant.

a Find the value of k. **(2 marks)**

b Find the exact value of E(X). **(1 mark)**

c Show that, to 3 significant figures, Var(X) = 2.02 **(2 marks)**

d Find, to 1 decimal place, Var(3 – 2X) **(1 mark)**

(E/P) **15** The discrete random variable X has a probability distribution given by:

x	-1	0	1	2
$P(X = x)$	0.1	0.3	a	b

The random variable Y is defined as $Y = 3X - 1$. Given that E(Y) = 1.1,

a find the values of a and b. **(5 marks)**

b Calculate E(X^2) and Var(X) using the values of a and b that you found in part **a**. **(3 marks)**

c Write down the value of Var(Y) **(1 mark)**

d Find $P(Y + 2 > X)$ **(2 marks)**

16 A discrete random variable is such that each of its values is assumed to be equally likely.

a Write down the name of this distribution.

b Give an example of such a distribution.

A discrete random variable X as defined above can take the values 0, 1, 2, 3 and 4.

Find:

c E(X)

d Var(X)

Challenge

SKILLS PROBLEM-SOLVING

Let n be a positive integer and suppose that X is a discrete random variable with $P(X = i) = \frac{1}{n}$, for $i = 1, \ldots, n$.

Show that $E(X) = \frac{n+1}{2}$ and $Var(X) = \frac{(n+1)(n-1)}{12}$

Hint You can make use of the following results:

$$\sum_{i=1}^{n} i = \frac{n(n+1)}{2}$$

$$\sum_{i=1}^{n} i^2 = \frac{n(n+1)(2n+1)}{6}$$

Summary of key points

1 For a random variable X:
- x is a particular value of X
- $P(X = x)$ or $P(x)$ refers to the probability that X is equal to a particular value of x

2 For a discrete random variable: the sum of all probabilities must add up to 1.
In symbols: $\sum P(X = x) = 1$

3 The cumulative frequency distribution $F(x) = P(X \leqslant x)$

4 Expected value of X: $E(X) = \sum xP(X = x) = \sum xP(x)$

5 Variance of X: $Var(X) = E(X^2) - [E(X)]^2$

6 $E(aX + b) = aE(X) + b$ and $Var(aX + b) = a^2 Var(X)$

7 Conditions for a discrete uniform distribution:
- A discrete random variable X is defined over a set of n distinct values
- Each value is equally likely

8 For a discrete uniform distribution X over the values 1, 2, 3, …, n:
- $E(X) = \frac{n+1}{2}$
- $Var(X) = \frac{(n+1)(n-1)}{12}$

7 THE NORMAL DISTRIBUTION

6.1

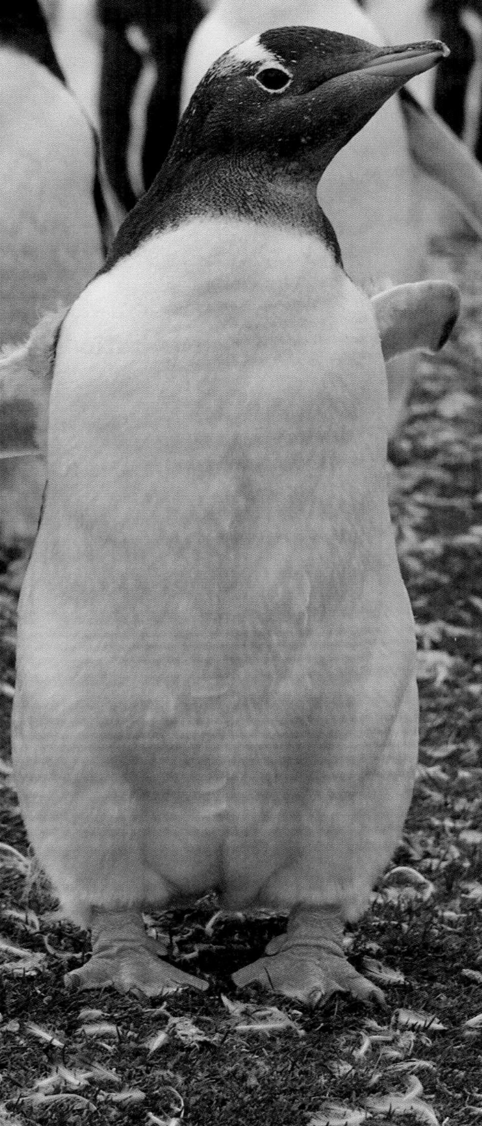

Learning objectives

After completing this chapter you should be able to:

- Understand the normal distribution curve and its characteristics → pages 152-155
- Use the tables to find the probabilities of the standard normal distribution Z → pages 155-158
- Use the tables to find the value of z given a probability → pages 158-161
- Understand the standard normal distribution and calculate μ and σ → pages 161-168

Prior knowledge check

1 The table below gives the probability distribution of the random variable Q.
Find the value of:

a t **b** $P(Q \leqslant 3)$ **c** $P(Q > 3)$

q	1	2	3	4	5
$P(Q = q)$	t	$2t$	$2t$	$2t$	t

← Statistics 1 Sections 6.1, 6.2

2 The probability that a plate made using a particular production process is faulty is given as 0.16. A sample of 20 plates is taken. Find:

a the probability that exactly two plates are faulty

b the probability that no more than three plates are faulty. ← Statistics 1 Section 4.8

Biologists use the normal distribution to model the distributions of physical characteristics, such as height and mass, in large populations.

7.1 The normal distribution

A **continuous random variable** can take any one of an unlimited number of values. The probability that a continuous random variable takes any one specific value is 0, but you can write the probability that it takes values within a given range. For example, when ten coins are flipped:

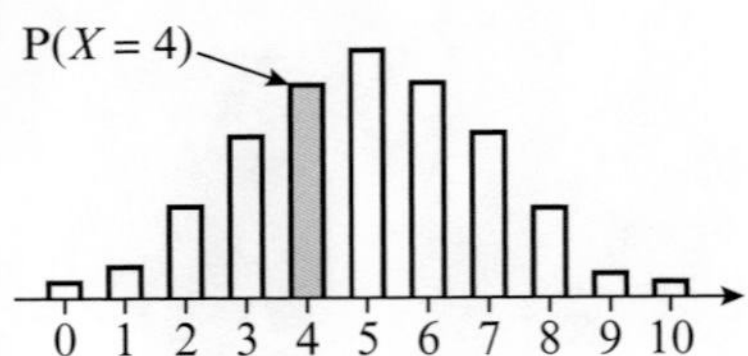

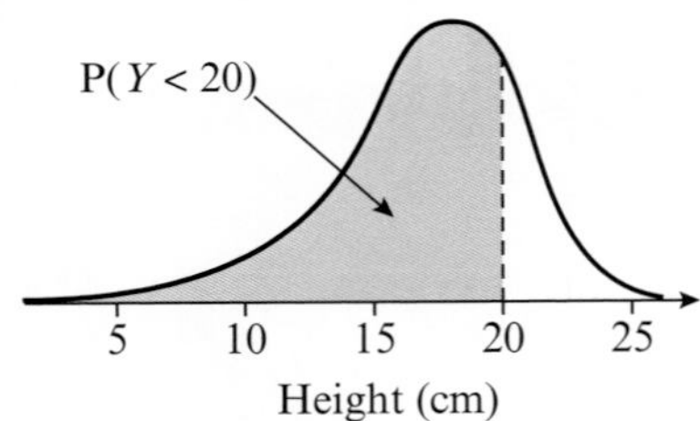

X = number of heads
Probability of getting 4 heads is written as $P(X = 4)$
X is a **discrete** random variable

Y = average vertical height of flipped coin
Probability that the average height is less than 20 cm is written as $P(Y < 20)$
Y is a **continuous** random variable

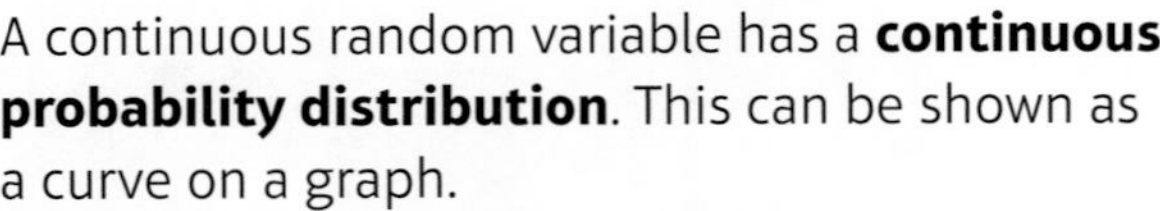

A continuous random variable has a **continuous probability distribution**. This can be shown as a curve on a graph.

- **The area under a continuous probability distribution curve is equal to 1.**

Links A discrete random variable can take only certain distinct values. The sum of the probabilities in a discrete probability distribution is equal to 1.

← Statistics 1 Section 6.1

The continuous variables generally encountered in real life are more likely to take values grouped around a central value than to take extreme values. The **normal distribution** is a continuous probability distribution that can be used to model many naturally occurring characteristics that behave in this way. Examples of continuous variables that can be modelled using the normal distribution are:

- heights of people within a given population
- weights of tigers in a jungle
- errors in scientific measurements
- size variations in manufactured objects

The histograms below show the distribution of heights of adult males in a particular city. As the class width reduces, the distribution gets smoother.

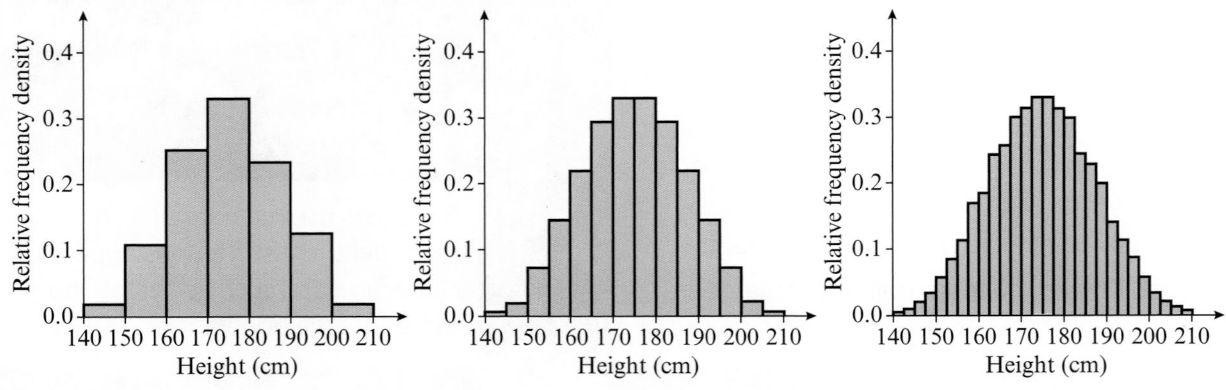

The distribution becomes bell-shaped and is symmetrical about the mean. You can model the heights of adult males in this city using a normal distribution, with mean 175 cm and standard deviation 12 cm.

Notation If X is a normally distributed random variable, you write $X \sim N(\mu, \sigma^2)$ where μ is the population mean and σ^2 is the population variance.

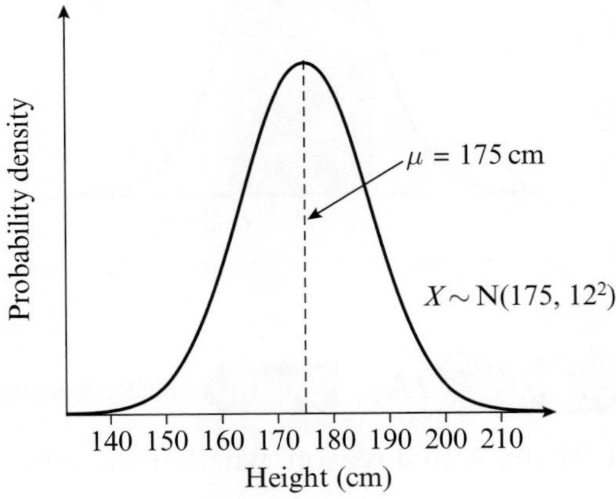

- **The normal distribution:**
  - **has parameters μ, the population mean, and σ^2, the population variance**
  - **is symmetrical (mean = median = mode)**
  - **has a bell-shaped curve with asymptotes at each end**
  - **has a total area under the curve equal to 1**
  - **has points of inflection at $\mu + \sigma$ and $\mu - \sigma$**

For a normally distributed variable:

- approximately 68% of the data lies within one standard deviation of the mean
- 95% of the data lies within two standard deviations of the mean
- nearly all of the data (99.7%) lies within three standard deviations of the mean

Watch out Although a normal random variable could take any value, in practice, observations a long way (more than 5 standard deviations) from the mean have probabilities close to 0.

Example 1 SKILLS PROBLEM-SOLVING

The diameters of a metal pin produced by a particular machine, X mm, are modelled as $X \sim N(8, 0.2^2)$. Find:

a $P(X > 8)$

b $P(7.8 < X < 8.2)$

a $P(X > 8) = 0.5$

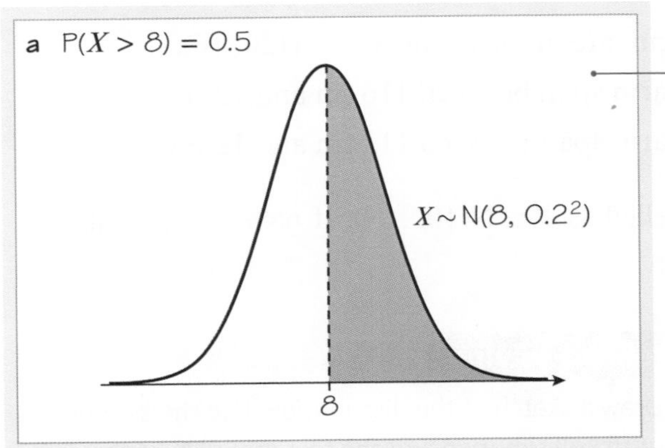

8 is the mean of the distribution. The normal distribution is **symmetrical**, so for any normally distributed random variable $P(X > \mu) = 0.5$

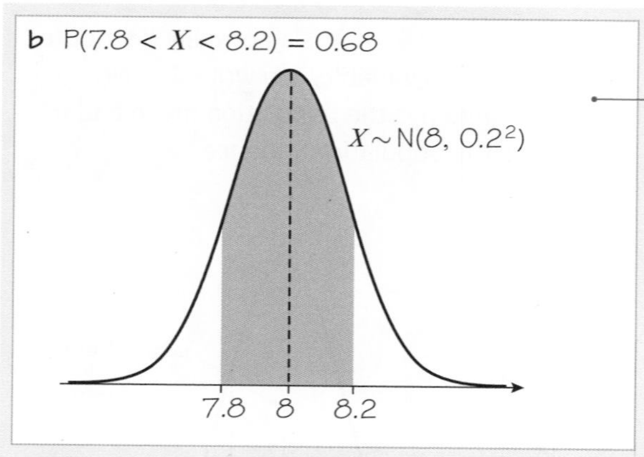

7.8 and 8.2 are each one standard deviation from the mean. For a normally distributed random variable, 68% of the data lies within one standard deviation of the mean. You can also write $P(\mu - \sigma < X < \mu + \sigma) = 0.68$

Exercise 7A

SKILLS PROBLEM-SOLVING

1 State, with a reason, whether these random variables are discrete or continuous:

a X, the lengths of a random sample of 100 sidewinder snakes in the Sahara desert

b Y, the scores achieved by 250 students in a university entrance exam

c C, the masses of honey badgers in a random sample of 1000

d Q, the shoe sizes of 200 randomly selected women in a particular town.

2 The lengths, X mm, of a bolt produced by a particular machine are normally distributed with mean 35 mm and standard deviation 0.4 mm. Sketch the distribution of X.

3 The distribution of incomes, in $000s per year, of employees at a bank is shown on the right.
State, with reasons, why the normal distribution is not a suitable model for these data.

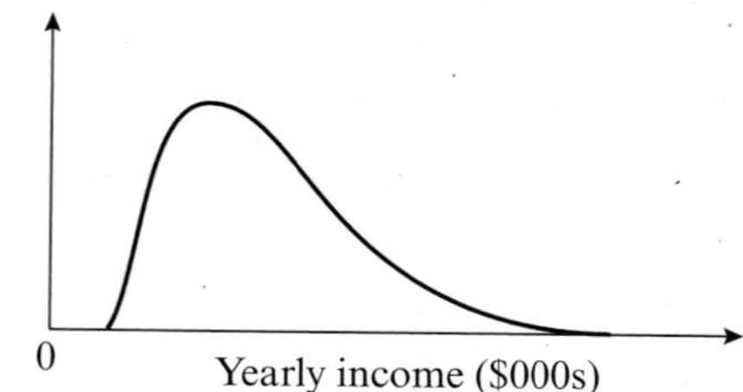

4 The arm spans of a group of Year 5 students, X cm, are modelled as $X \sim N(120, 16)$.

a State the proportion of students who have an arm span between 116 cm and 124 cm.

b State the proportion of students who have an arm span between 112 cm and 128 cm.

5 The lengths of a group of snakes, Y cm, are modelled as $Y \sim N(100, \sigma^2)$. If 68% of the snakes have a length between 93 cm and 107 cm, find σ^2.

(P) **6** The weights of a group of mice, D grams, are modelled as $D \sim N(\mu, 25)$. If 97.5% of the mice weigh less than 70 grams, find μ.

Problem-solving

Draw a sketch of the distribution. Use the symmetry of the distribution and the fact that 95% of the data lies within 2 standard deviations of the mean.

(P) **7** The masses of the sheep, M kg, on a farm are modelled as $M \sim N(\mu, \sigma^2)$. If 84% of the sheep weigh more than 52 kg and 97.5% of the sheep weigh more than 47.5 kg, find μ and σ^2.

(P) **8** The percentage scores, S, of a group of students in a test are modelled as a normal distribution with mean 45 and standard deviation 15. Find:

a $P(S > 45)$ **b** $P(30 < S < 60)$ **c** $P(15 < S < 75)$

Alexia states that since it is impossible to score above 100%, this is not a suitable model.

d State, with a reason, whether or not Alexia is correct.

(E) **9** The diagram shows the distribution of heights, in cm, of barn owls in the UK.

An ornithologist notices that the distribution is approximately normal.

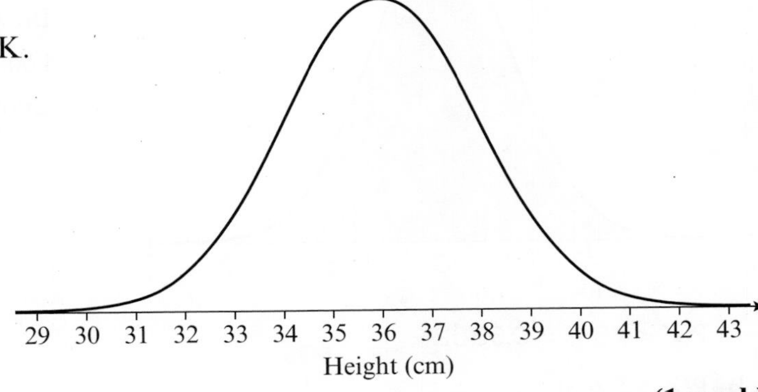

a State the value of the mean height. **(1 mark)**

b Estimate the standard deviation of the heights. **(2 marks)**

7.2 Using tables to find probabilities of the standard normal distribution Z

- **Tables are provided in this textbook and the exam to help you calculate probabilities for the standard normal distribution, Z.**
- **The standard normal variable is usually denoted by Z and has a mean of 0 and a standard deviation of 1. The common way of writing this is:**

$$Z \sim N(0, 1^2)$$

$\mu = 0$ and $\sigma^2 = 1$

$\sim$ means 'is distributed'

N for normal

Φ(a)is often used as shorthand for writing $P(A < a)$.

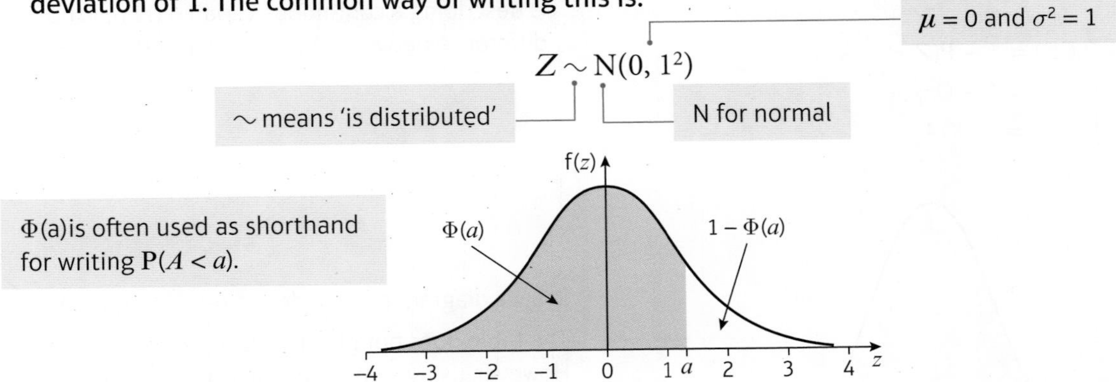

The total area under the curve = 1. (The sum of probabilities in a probability distribution always add up to 1). Thus, $P(Z < a)$ will just be the area under of the curve to the left of a.

You can use tables or calculators to find these probabilities. Normal distribution tables are found in the back of the book and will be provided in the Mathematical Formulae and Statistical Tables book in the exam. The tables give $P(Z < z)$ for different values of z.

For a continuous distribution, such as the normal distribution, there is no difference between $P(Z < z)$ and $P(Z \leq z)$.

Example 2 SKILLS INTERPRETATION

Use the normal distribution tables to find:

a $P(Z < 1.54)$ **b** $P(Z > 2.65)$

c $P(Z < -0.75)$ **d** $P(-1.20 < Z < 1.40)$

a $P(Z < 1.54)$

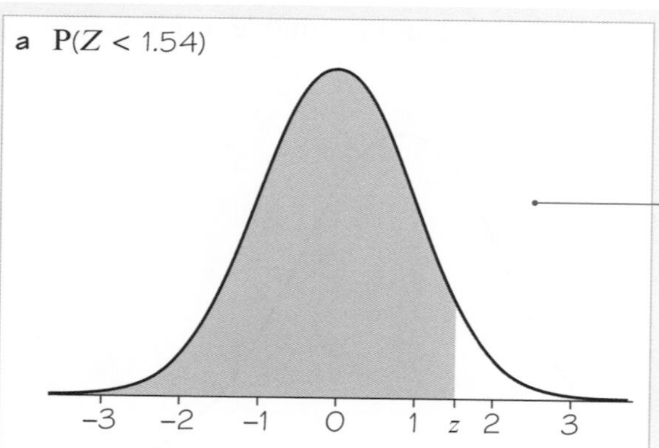

Draw a diagram and shade the region required. Look up the required z value – in this case 1.54 Quote the value in full from the table.

$P(Z < 1.54) = 0.9382$

b $P(Z > 2.65)$

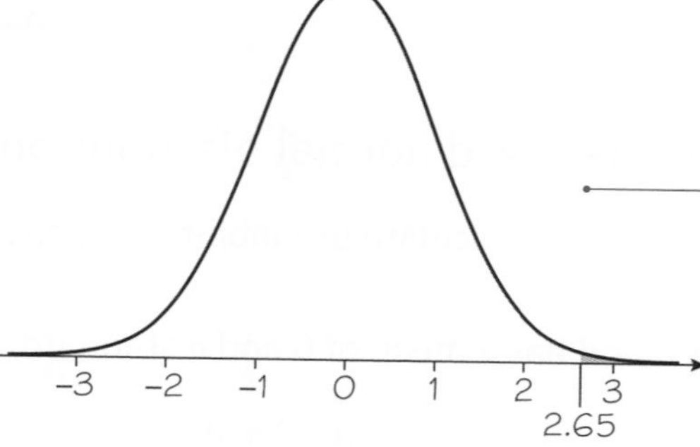

Draw the diagram and shade the region required. The table gives you $P(Z < 2.65)$. Therefore, you need to calculate '1 minus this probability'.

Watch out Because the normal distribution is describing a continuous variable there is no difference between $P(Z < 2.65)$ and $P(Z < 2.65)$

$P(Z > 2.65) = 1 - P(Z < 2.65)$
$= 1 - 0.996$
$= 0.004$

c $P(Z < -0.75)$

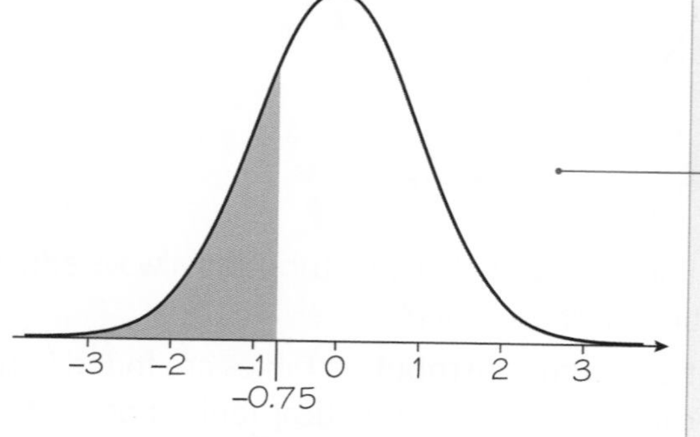

Draw a diagram and shade the region required. The table does not give the values of $z < 0$. However, using symmetry you can see the probability is the same as $P(Z > 0.75)$

$P(Z < -0.75) = P(Z > 0.75)$
$= 1 - 0.7734$
$= 0.2266$

Found from the main table.

d $P(-1.20 < Z < 1.40)$

Split the problem up into three graphs.

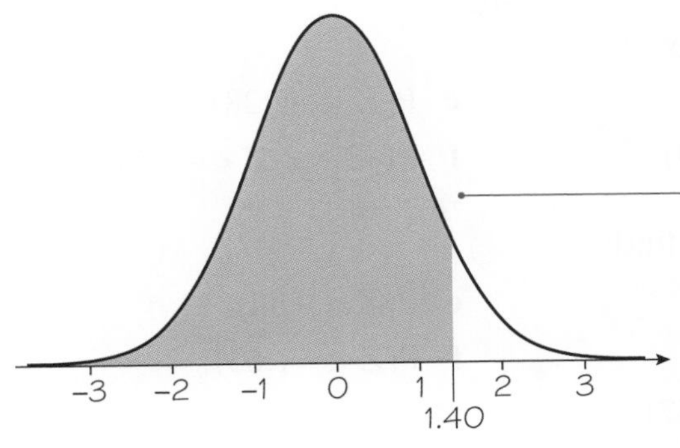

This graph shows the probability when $a < 1.40$

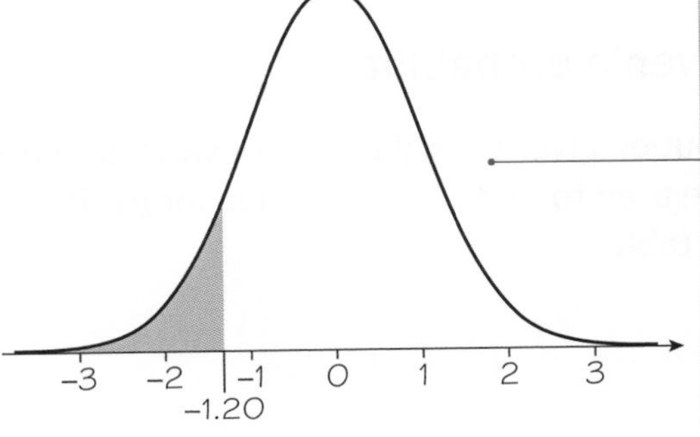

This graph shows the probability when $a < -1.20$

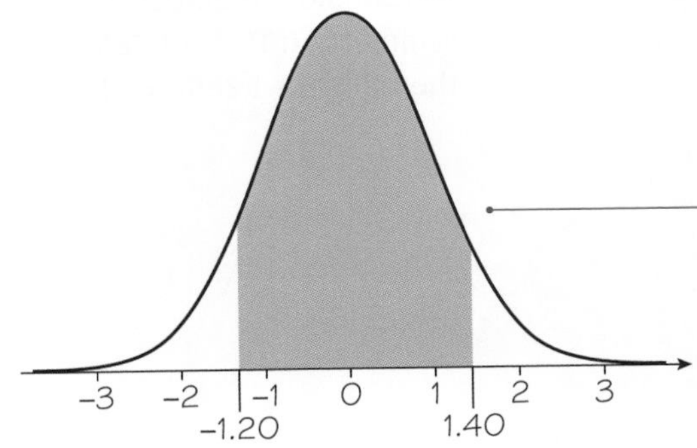

This graph shows the area that needs to be calculated. After visualising the problem you can calculate the probability by calculating $P(Z < 1.40) - P(Z < -1.20)$

$P(1.20 < Z < 1.40)$

$P(Z < 1.40) - P(Z < -1.20)$

$P(Z < 1.40) = 0.9192$ from the tables

$P(Z < -1.20) = 1 - P(Z < 1.20)$

$= 1 - 0.8849$ from the tables

Calculate the probabilities separately.

Therefore:

$P(Z < 1.40) - P(Z < -1.20)$

$= 0.9192 - 0.1151 = 0.8401$

Exercise 7B SKILLS INTERPRETATION

1 Use the normal distribution tables to find the following:

a $P(Z > 1.27)$ **b** $P(Z > -1.66)$ **c** $P(Z < -2.28)$

d $P(0 < Z < 1.31)$ **e** $P(1.30 < Z < 1.89)$ **f** $P(-2.8 < Z < -1.6)$

2 For the standard normal distribution $Z \sim N(0, 1^2)$, find:

a $P(Z < 2.12)$ **b** $P(Z < 1.36)$ **c** $P(Z > 0.84)$

d $P(Z < -0.38)$ **e** $P(-2.30 < Z < 0)$ **f** $P(Z < -1.63)$

g $P(-2.16 < Z < -0.85)$ **h** $P(-1.57 < Z < 1.57)$

7.3 Using tables to find the value of z given a probability

- The table of percentage points of the normal distribution gives the value of z for various values of $p = P(Z > z)$. Whenever possible, this table should be used to find z, given a value for $p = P(Z > z)$. However, sometimes you will need to use the main table.

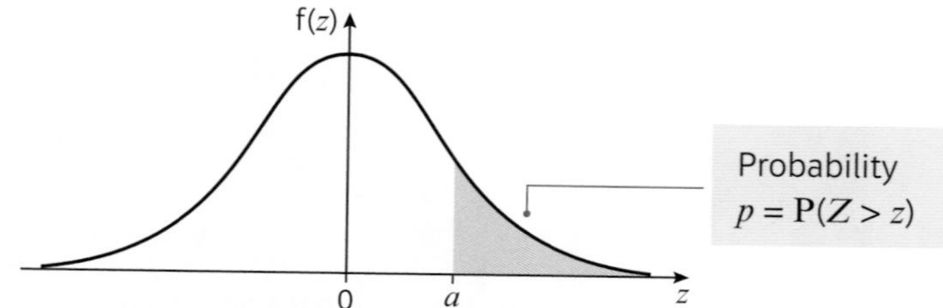

Probability $p = P(Z > z)$

You should remember that by symmetry, if $P(Z > 1.286) = 0.1$ then $P(Z < -1.286) = 0.1$ as well.

- If $P(Z < a)$ is greater than 0.5, then a will be > 0
- If $P(Z < a)$ is less than 0.5, then a will be < 0
- If $P(Z > a)$ is less than 0.5, then a will be > 0
- If $P(Z > a)$ is greater than 0.5, then a will be < 0

Example 3 SKILLS INTERPRETATION

Find the value of the constant a such that $P(Z < a) = 0.7517$

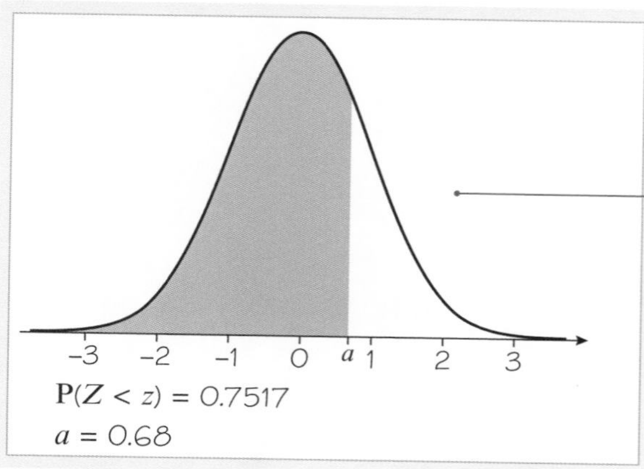

$P(Z < z) = 0.7517$

$a = 0.68$

Draw a diagram to help you visualise the curve.

Look in the main table to find the value that gives $P(Z < z) = 0.7517$.

This will give the value of a.

Example 4 SKILLS INTERPRETATION

Find the value of the constant a such that $P(Z > a) = 0.100$

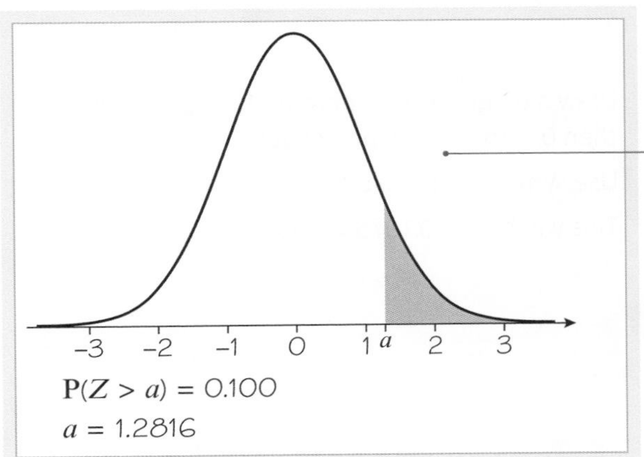

Draw a diagram. Also note that $P(Z > a)$ is less than 0.5, so a will be positive.

Check the table of percentages points of the normal distribution to see if $p = 0.100$ is listed.

Hint Always check the percentages points table first.

Example 5 SKILLS INTERPRETATION

Find the value of the constant a such that $P(Z > a) = 0.0322$

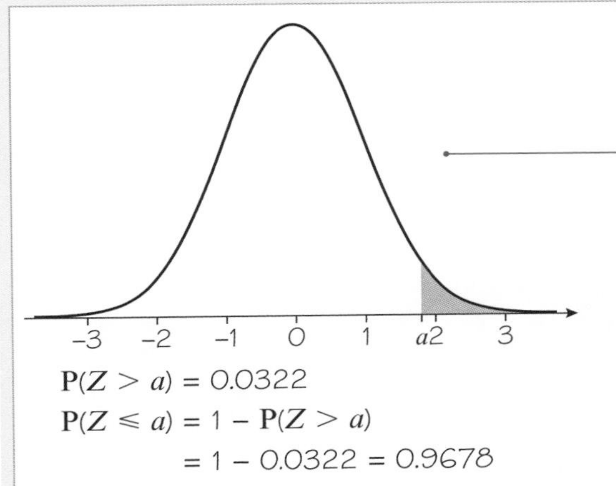

Draw a diagram. Also, note that if $P(Z > a)$ is less than 0.5, a will also be positive.

$p = 0.0322$ is not listed in the table of percentage points of the normal distribution.

Also, $p = 0.0322$ is not the in the main tables, so we need to calculate $1 – 0.0322$ and use the main table.

In the main table, find z so that $P(Z < z) = 0.9678$

Hint Find 0.9678 from the tables.

Example 6 SKILLS INTERPRETATION

Find the value of the constant a such that $P(Z < a) = 0.1075$

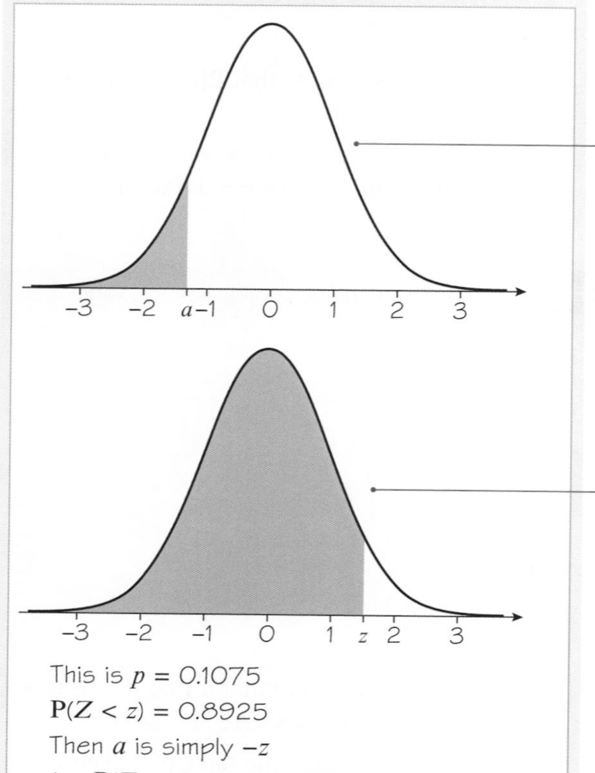

Draw a diagram. Also, note that if $P(Z < a)$ is less than 0.5, then a will be negative.

Use symmetry to help find a.

This will be $1 - 0.1075 = 0.8925$

Since $p = 0.1075$ is not in the main table, use the main table to find the value of z.

This is $p = 0.1075$

$P(Z < z) = 0.8925$

Then a is simply $-z$

$1 - P(Z < a) = 1 - 0.1075 = 0.8925$

$P(Z < z) = 0.8925$

$z = 1.24$

$a = -1.24$

Example 7 SKILLS INTERPRETATION

Use the tables to find $P(Z < a) = 0.75$

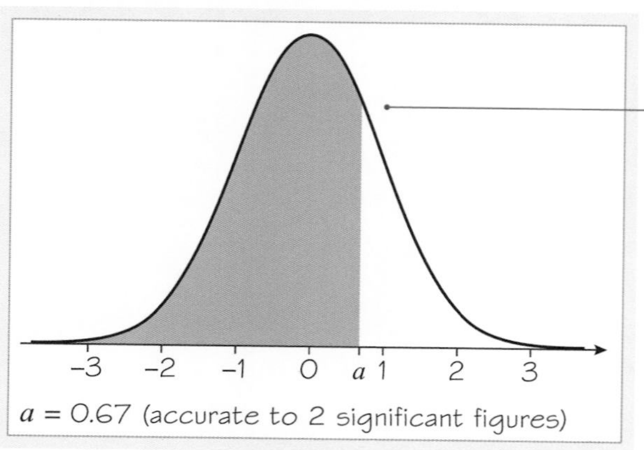

$a = 0.67$ (accurate to 2 significant figures)

Draw a diagram to help you visualise the curve.

When looking at the main table for 0.75 you will find when $a = 0.67$ the probability is 0.7486 and when $a = 0.68$ the probability is 0.7517. Use $a = 0.67$ as it is the value is closest to 0.75

Hint Watch out for questions like these in the exams.

Exercise 7C

SKILLS INTERPRETATION

1 Find the value of a in the following:

a $P(Z < a) = 0.3336$ **b** $P(Z > a) = 0.6879$

c $P(Z > a) = 0.1112$ **d** $P(-a < Z < a) = 0.5820$

2 For the standard normal distribution $Z \sim N(0, 1^2)$, find values of a such that:

a $P(Z < a) = 0.9082$ **b** $P(Z > a) = 0.0314$

c $P(Z > a) = 0.1500$ **d** $P(Z > a) = 0.9500$

e $P(0 < Z < a) = 0.3554$ **f** $P(0 < Z < a) = 0.4946$

g $P(-a < Z < a) = 0.80$ **h** $P(-a < Z < a) = 0.40$

Hint For parts **g** and **h** you will need to use the symmetry properties of the distribution.

7.4 The standard normal distribution

It is often useful to **standardise** normally distributed random variables. You do this by coding the data so that it can be modelled by the **standard normal distribution**.

- **The standard normal distribution has mean 0 and standard deviation 1.**

Notation The standard normal variable is written as $Z \sim N(0, 1^2)$

If $X \sim N(\mu, \sigma^2)$ is a normal random variable with mean μ and standard deviation σ, then you can code X using the formula:

$$Z = \frac{X - \mu}{\sigma}$$

Hint If $X = x$ then the corresponding value of Z will be $z = \frac{x - \mu}{\sigma}$. The mean of the coded data will be $\frac{\mu - \mu}{\sigma} = 0$ and the standard deviation will be $\frac{\sigma}{\sigma} = 1$

The resulting **z-values** will be normally distributed with mean 0 and standard deviation 1.

For the standard normal curve $Z \sim N(0, 1^2)$, the probability $P(Z < a)$ is sometimes written as $\Phi(a)$. You can find it by entering $\mu = 0$ and $\sigma = 1$ into the normal cumulative distribution function on your calculator, or by using the tables.

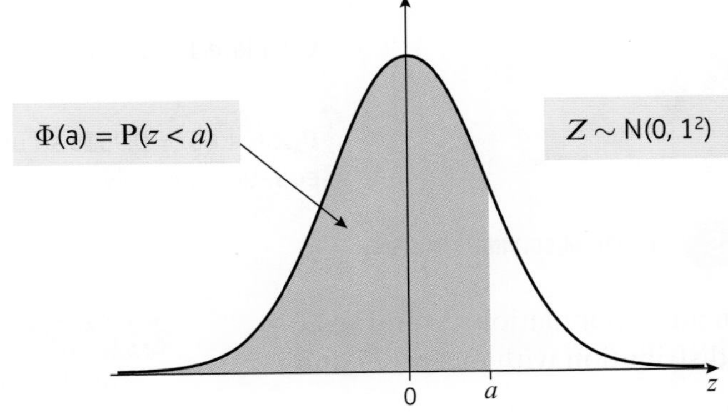

Example 8 SKILLS INTERPRETATION

The random variable $X \sim N(50, 4^2)$. Find:

a $P(X < 53)$ **b** $P(X \geqslant 55)$

a $z = \frac{53 - 50}{4} = 0.75$

$P(X < 53) = P(Z < 0.75)$
$= \Phi(0.75)$
$= 0.7734$

Code the data so that it is modelled by the standard normal distribution $N(0, 1^2)$.

Use $Z = \frac{X - \mu}{\sigma}$

b $P(X \geqslant 55) = 1 - P(X < 55)$

The distribution is continuous, so you can use $<$ and $\leqslant$ interchangeably.

$z = \frac{55 - 50}{4} = 1.25$

$P(X \geqslant 55) = 1 - P(Z < 1.25)$
$= 1 - \Phi(1.25)$
$= 1 - 0.8944$
(Using the table with $z = 1.25$)
$= 0.1056$

Example 9 SKILLS PROBLEM-SOLVING

The random variable $Y \sim N(20, 9)$.

Find the value of b such that $P(Y > b) = 0.0485$

$P(Y > b) = 0.0485$

Remember, $Y \sim N(20, 9)$ means that $\mu = 20$ and $\sigma = 3$ (The variance is 9 so the standard deviation is 3).

$P\left(Z > \frac{b - 20}{3}\right) = 0.0485$

Use $Z = \frac{Y - \mu}{\sigma}$

$P\left(Z < \frac{b - 20}{3}\right) = 1 - 0.0485$

$p = 0.0485$ is not in the table of percentage points.

$P\left(Z < \frac{b - 20}{3}\right) = 0.9515$

Calculate $1 - 0.0485$ and use the main table.

So,

$\frac{b - 20}{3} = 1.66$

$b - 20 = 4.98$

$b = 24.98$

$P(Z < 1.66) = 0.9515$ so use $Z = 1.66$ to form an equation and solve for b.

Example 10 SKILLS PROBLEM-SOLVING; ANALYSIS

The blood pressure of an adult population, S mmHg, is modelled as a normal distribution with mean 127 and standard deviation 16.

A medical researcher wants to study adults with blood pressures higher than the 95th percentile. Find the minimum blood pressure for an adult included in her study.

Notation mmHg is the standard unit for blood pressure.

$S \sim \mathrm{N}(127, 16^2)$
Using the percentage points table:
$\mathrm{P}(Z > 1.6449) = 0.05$
$\frac{s - 127}{16} = 1.6449$
$s = 153$ (3 s.f.)
The researcher should include adults with a blood pressure > 153 mmHg

Use the percentage points table with $p = 0.05$

Convert the value for Z back into a value for S. Remember that the denominator is σ, not σ^2.

You could also find the inverse normal function on your calculator with $\mu = 127$, $\sigma = 16$ and $p = 0.95$

Exercise 7D

SKILLS INTERPRETATION; PROBLEM-SOLVING

1 The random variable $X \sim \mathrm{N}(20, 4^2)$. Find:

a $\mathrm{P}(X \leqslant 26)$ **b** $\mathrm{P}(X > 30)$ **c** $\mathrm{P}(X \geqslant 17)$

2 Given that $X \sim \mathrm{N}(18, 10)$, find the following probabilities:

a $\mathrm{P}(X > 20)$ **b** $\mathrm{P}(X < 15)$

3 The random variable $X \sim \mathrm{N}(24, 3^2)$. Find:

a $\mathrm{P}(X \leqslant 29)$ **b** $\mathrm{P}(X \geqslant 22)$ **c** $\mathrm{P}(X < 16)$

4 The random variable $Y \sim \mathrm{N}(30, 25)$
Find the value of a such that $\mathrm{P}(Y > a) = 0.30$

5 The random variable $Y \sim \mathrm{N}(15, 9)$
Find the value of a such that $\mathrm{P}(Y > a) = 0.15$

6 The random variable $Y \sim \mathrm{N}(100, 225)$
Find the values of s and t such that:

a $\mathrm{P}(Y > s) = 0.975$

b $\mathrm{P}(Y < t) = 0.10$

c Write down $\mathrm{P}(s < Y < t)$

7 Given that $X \sim \mathrm{N}(80, 4^2)$,

a find the values a and b when:

i $\mathrm{P}(X > a) = 0.40$

ii $\mathrm{P}(X < b) = 0.5636$

b Write down $\mathrm{P}(b < X < a)$

8 The random variable $X \sim \mathrm{N}(0.8, 0.05^2)$. For each of the following values of X, write down the corresponding value of the standardised normal distribution, $Z \sim \mathrm{N}(0, 1^2)$.

a $x = 0.8$ **b** $x = 0.792$ **c** $x = 0.81$ **d** $x = 0.837$

9 The normal distribution $X \sim N(154, 12^2)$. Write in terms of $\Phi(z)$:

a $P(X < 154)$ **b** $P(X < 160)$

c $P(X > 151)$ **d** $P(140 < X < 155)$

Hint Write your answer to part **d** in the form $\Phi(z_1) - \Phi(z_2)$

(E) **10 a** Use the percentage points table to find a value of z such that $P(Z > z) = 0.025$ **(1 mark)**

b A pilot training programme takes only the top 2.5% of candidates on a test. Given that the scores can be modelled using a normal distribution with mean 80 and standard deviation 4, use your answer to part **a** to find the score necessary to get on the programme. **(2 marks)**

(E) **11 a** Use the percentage points table to find a value of z such that $P(Z < z) = 0.15$ **(1 mark)**

b A hat manufacturer makes a special 'little' hat which should fit 15% of its customers. Given that hat sizes can be modelled using a normal distribution with mean 57 cm and standard deviation 2 cm, use your answer to part **a** to find the size of a 'little' hat. **(2 marks)**

(E) **12 a** Use the percentage points table to find the values of z that correspond to the 10% to 90% interpercentile range. **(2 marks)**

A particular brand of light bulb has a life modelled as a normal distribution with mean 1175 hours and standard deviation 56 hours. The bulb life is considered 'standard' if its life falls into the 10% to 90% interpercentile range.

b Use your answer to part **a** to find the range of life to the nearest hour for a 'standard' bulb. **(2 marks)**

7.5 Finding μ and σ

You might need to find an unknown mean or standard deviation for a normally distributed variable.

Example 11 SKILLS INTERPRETATION

The random variable $X \sim N(\mu, 3^2)$.

Given that $P(X > 20) = 0.20$, find the value of μ.

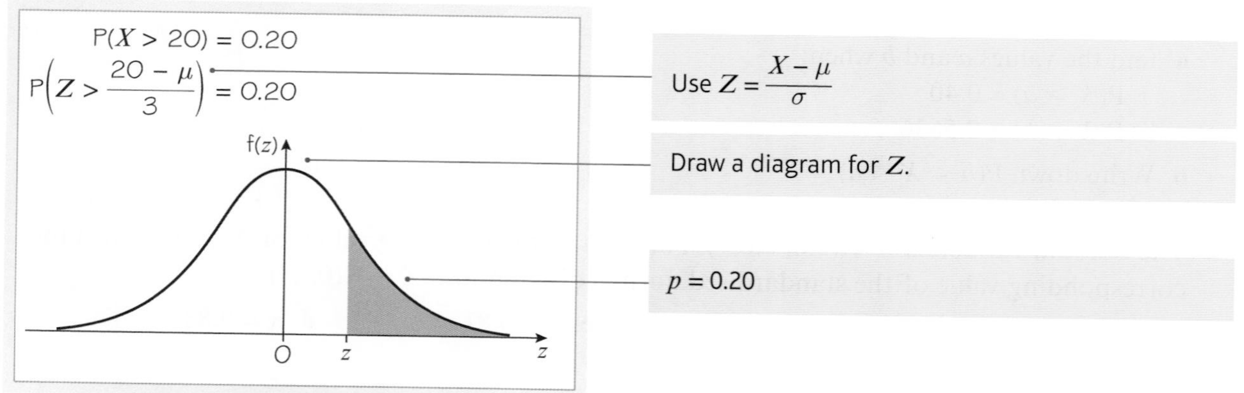

$z = 0.8416$

so $0.8416 = \dfrac{20 - \mu}{3}$

$\mu = 17.4752 = 17.5$ (3 s.f.)

You know one value of X and the corresponding value of Z so use the coding formula to find μ.

Problem-solving

You don't know μ, so you need to use the **standard normal distribution** or tables with $\mu = 0$, $\sigma = 1$ and $p = 0.8$ to find the value of z such that $P(Z > z) = 0.2$. You could also use the percentage points table.

Example 12 SKILLS PROBLEM-SOLVING; ANALYSIS

A machine makes metal sheets with width, X cm, modelled as a normal distribution such that $X \sim N(50, \sigma^2)$.

a Given that $P(X < 46) = 0.2119$, find the value of σ.

b Find the 90th percentile of the widths.

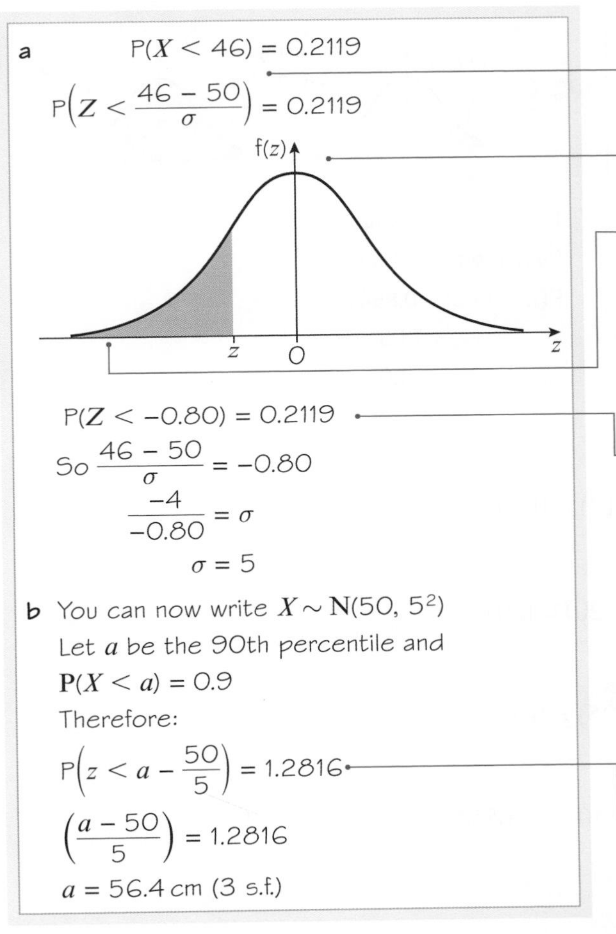

Use $Z = \dfrac{X - \mu}{\sigma}$

Draw a diagram for Z.

$p = 0.2119$

Use the inverse normal distribution function on your calculator with $\mu = 0$, $\sigma = 1$ and $p = 0.2119$
You can also find this value from the percentage points table by noting that $P(Z > 0.80) = 0.2119$
Or by noting that:
$P(Z < -0.80) = P(Z > 0.80)$
$P(Z > 0.80) = 1 - P(Z < 0.80)$
$= 1 - 0.7881$
$= 0.2119$

Online Use the Inverse Normal function on your calculator with the standard normal distribution. Alternatively you may use the statistical tables at the back of the book.

1.2816 found from the main table.

Example 13 SKILLS PROBLEM-SOLVING

The random variable $X \sim N(\mu, \sigma^2)$.
Given that $P(X > 35) = 0.025$ and $P(X < 15) = 0.1469$, find the value of μ and the value of σ.

$P(Z > z_1) = 0.025 \Rightarrow z_1 = 1.96$
$P(Z < z_2) = 0.1469 \Rightarrow z_2 = -1.05$

This shows $z_2 < 0$. Therefore, to find z_2 you will need to use symmetry.

So $-1.05 = \frac{15 - \mu}{\sigma}$

$-1.05\sigma + \mu = 15$ **(1)**

and $1.96 = \frac{35 - \mu}{\sigma}$

$1.96\sigma + \mu = 35$ **(2)**

(2) − (1): $3.01\sigma = 20$

$\sigma = 6.6445...$

Substituting into **(2)**:
$\mu = 35 - 1.96 \times 6.6445... = 21.976...$
So $\sigma = 6.64$ and $\mu = 22.0$ (3 s.f.)

Find z-values corresponding to a 'right-tail' of 0.025 and a 'left-tail' of 0.1469:
$p = 0.025$ gives $z = 1.96$ from the percentage points table.

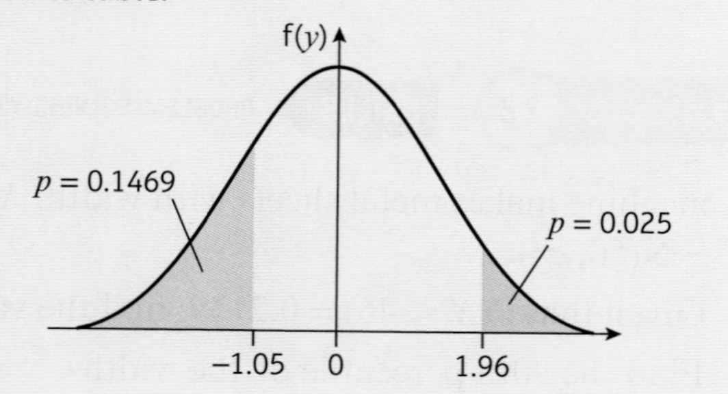

Use $\frac{X - \mu}{\sigma}$ to link X and Z values and form two simultaneous equations in μ and σ.

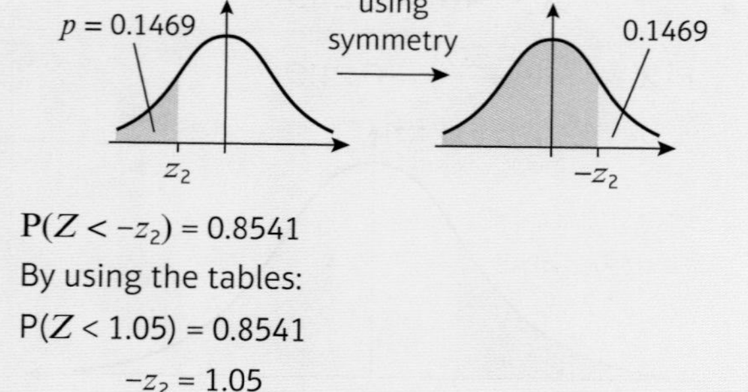

$P(Z < -z_2) = 0.8541$
By using the tables:
$P(Z < 1.05) = 0.8541$
$-z_2 = 1.05$
$z_2 = -1.05$

Exercise 7E SKILLS PROBLEM-SOLVING; ANALYSIS

1 The random variable $X \sim N(\mu, 5^2)$ and $P(X < 18) = 0.9032$
Find the value of μ.

2 The random variable $X \sim N(11, \sigma^2)$ and $P(X > 20) = 0.01$
Find the value of σ.

3 The random variable $Y \sim N(\mu, 40)$ and $P(Y < 25) = 0.15$
Find the value of μ.

4 The random variable $Y \sim N(50, \sigma^2)$ and $P(Y > 40) = 0.6554$
Find the value of σ.

(P) 5 The random variable $X \sim N(\mu, \sigma^2)$.
Given that $P(X < 17) = 0.8159$ and $P(X < 25) = 0.9970$, find the value of μ and the value of σ.

(P) **6** The random variable $Y \sim N(\mu, \sigma^2)$.
Given that $P(Y < 25) = 0.10$ and $P(Y > 35) = 0.005$, find the value of μ and the value of σ.

(P) **7** The random variable $X \sim N(\mu, \sigma^2)$.
Given that $P(X > 15) = 0.20$ and $P(X < 9) = 0.20$,
find the value of μ and the value of σ.

Hint Draw a diagram and use symmetry to find μ.

(P) **8** The random variable $X \sim N(\mu, \sigma^2)$.
The lower quartile of X is 25 and the upper quartile of X is 45.
Find the value of μ and the value of σ.

(P) **9** The random variable $X \sim N(0, \sigma^2)$.
Given that $P(-4 < X < 4) = 0.6$, find the value of σ.

(P) **10** The random variable $X \sim N(2.68, \sigma^2)$.
Given that $P(X > 2a) = 0.2$ and $P(X < a) = 0.4$, find the value of σ and the value of a.

(E/P) **11** A loom makes tablecloths with an average thickness of 2.5 mm. The thickness, T mm, can be modelled using a normal distribution. Given that 65% of tablecloths are less than 2.55 mm thick, find:

a the standard deviation of the thickness **(2 marks)**

b the proportion of tablecloths with thickness between 2.4 mm and 2.6 mm. **(3 marks)**

(E/P) **12** The masses of the penguins on an island are found to be normally distributed with mean μ, and standard deviation σ. Given that 10% of the penguins have a mass less than 18 kg and 5% of the penguins have a mass greater than 30 kg,

a sketch a diagram to represent this information **(2 marks)**

b find the value of μ and the value of σ. **(6 marks)**

10 penguins are chosen at random.

(E/P) **13** The length of an adult Dachshund dog is found to be normally distributed with mean μ and standard deviation σ. Given that 20% of Dachshunds have a length less than 16 inches and 10% have a length greater than 18 inches, find:

a the value of μ and the value of σ **(6 marks)**

b the interquartile range. **(2 marks)**

Challenge

SKILLS ANALYSIS

A normally distributed random variable $X \sim N(\mu, \sigma^2)$ has interquartile range q.

a Show that $\sigma = 0.742q$, where the coefficient of q is correct to 3 s.f.

b Explain why it is not possible to write μ in terms of q only.

Use of calculators

You may be able to find probabilities for a normal distribution using your calculator.

You will need to refer to the instructions for your particular calculator.

These calculators can be used in your S1 examination but you are advised to clearly state the probability you are finding and give your final answer to 3 significant figures.

For example, $P(X < 53) = 0.5 + 0.27337\ldots = 0.77337\ldots = 0.773$ (3 s.f.)

Chapter review 7

SKILLS PROBLEM-SOLVING; ANALYSIS

E **1** The heights of a large group of men are normally distributed with a mean of 178 cm and a standard deviation of 4 cm. A man is selected at random from this group.

a Find the probability that he is taller than 185 cm. **(2 marks)**

b Find the probability that three men, selected at random, are all less than 180 cm tall. **(3 marks)**

A manufacturer of door frames wants to ensure that fewer than 0.005 men have to bend down to pass through the frame.

c On the basis of this group, find the minimum height of a door frame to the nearest centimetre. **(2 marks)**

E **2** The weights of steel sheets produced by a factory are known to be normally distributed with mean 32.5 kg and standard deviation 2.2 kg.

a Find the percentage of sheets that weigh less than 30 kg. **(1 mark)**

Bob requires sheets that weigh between 31.6 kg and 34.8 kg.

b Find the percentage of sheets produced that satisfy Bob's requirements. **(3 marks)**

E/P **3** The time a smartphone battery lasts before needing to be recharged is assumed to be normally distributed with a mean of 48 hours and a standard deviation of 8 hours.

a Find the probability that a battery will last for more than 60 hours. **(2 marks)**

b Find the probability that the battery lasts less than 35 hours. **(1 mark)**

E **4** The random variable $X \sim N(24, \sigma^2)$. Given that $P(X > 30) = 0.05$, find:

a the value of σ **(2 marks)**

b $P(X < 20)$ **(1 mark)**

c the value of d so that $P(X > d) = 0.01$ **(2 marks)**

E **5** A machine puts liquid into plastic cups in such a way that the given volume of liquid is normally distributed with a mean of 120 ml. The cups have a capacity of 140 ml and the probability that the machine puts in too much liquid so that the cup overflows is 0.01.

a Find the standard deviation of the volume of liquid dispensed. **(2 marks)**

b Find the probability that the machine puts in less than 110 ml. **(1 mark)**

Ten percent of customers complain that the machine has not given enough liquid.

c Find the largest volume of liquid, to the nearest millilitre, that will lead to a complaint. **(2 marks)**

(E/P) **6** The random variable $X \sim N(\mu, \sigma^2)$. The lower quartile of X is 20 and the upper quartile is 40.

a Find μ and σ. **(3 marks)**

b Find the 10% to 90% interpercentile range. **(3 marks)**

(E/P) **7** The heights of seedlings are normally distributed. Given that 10% of the seedlings are taller than 15 cm and 5% are shorter than 4 cm, find the mean and standard deviation of the heights. **(4 marks)**

(E) **8** A psychologist gives a student two different tests. The first test has a mean of 80 and a standard deviation of 10, and the student scores 85.

a Find the probability of scoring 85 or more on the first test. **(2 marks)**

The second test has a mean of 100 and a standard deviation of 15.
The student scores 105 on the second test.

b Find the probability of a score of 105 or more on the second test. **(2 marks)**

c State, giving a reason, which of the student's two test scores was better. **(2 marks)**

(E/P) **9** Jam is sold in jars and the mean weight of the contents is 108 grams. Only 3% of jars have contents weighing less than 100 grams. Assuming that the weight of jam in a jar is normally distributed, find:

a the standard deviation of the weight of jam in a jar **(2 marks)**

b the proportion of jars where the contents weigh more than 115 grams. **(2 marks)**

(E) **10** The waiting time at a doctor's surgery is assumed to be normally distributed with standard deviation of 3.8 minutes. Given that the probability of waiting more than 15 minutes is 0.0446, find:

a the mean waiting time **(2 marks)**

b the probability of waiting less than 5 minutes. **(2 marks)**

(E/P) **11** The thickness of some plastic shelving produced by a factory is normally distributed. As part of the production process, the shelving is tested with two gauges (used for measuring). The first gauge is 7 mm thick and 98.61% of the shelving passes through this gauge. The second gauge is 5.2 mm thick and only 1.02% of the shelves pass through this gauge.
Find the mean and standard deviation of the thickness of the shelving. **(4 marks)**

Challenge

SKILLS
CRITICAL THINKING

1 The lifespan of televisions has a normal distribution with a mean of 58 months and a standard deviation of 10 months. A company gives a warranty of 36 months to replace any defective television with a new one. Suppose the company makes 2 million televisions per year. How many televisions may be replaced?

2 The times taken by a large number of people to travel between two cities can be modelled by a normal distribution with a mean of 5.2 hours. It is found that 62.5% of the people took more than 4.5 hours to travel between the two cities.

a If a number of extra people are taken into account, all of whom took exactly 5.2 hours to travel between the two cities, state with reasons what would happen to:

i the mean

ii the variance.

b Explain why the distribution would no longer be normal.

Summary of key points

1 Total area under the normal distribution curve = 1

2 The normal distribution is perfectly symmetrical, and therefore:

$P(Z < 0) = 0.5$

$P(Z > 0) = 0.5$

3 $P(Z \leqslant a)$ is denoted by $\Phi(a)$

4 You can use symmetry properties to find the probability for $a < 0$

$P(Z < -a) = 1 - P(Z < a)$

$P(Z > -a) = P(Z < a)$

5

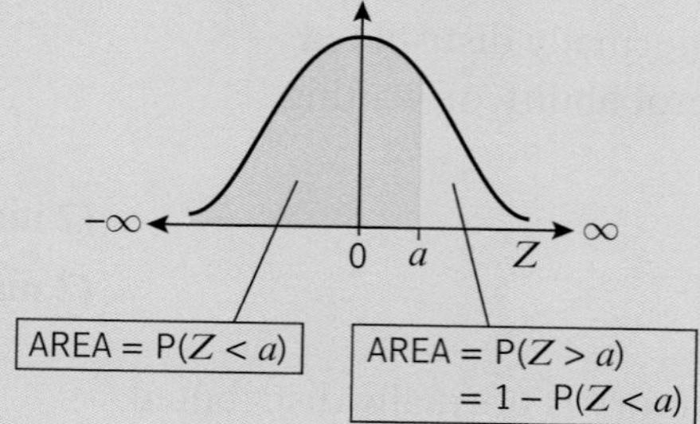

6 The random variable X that has a normal distribution with mean μ and deviation σ is represented by:

$X \sim N(\mu, \sigma^2)$

where σ^2 is the variance of the normal distribution.

7 If $X \sim N(\mu, \sigma^2)$ and $Z \sim N(0, 1^2)$ then

$$Z = \frac{X - \mu}{\sigma}$$

8 Normal distribution tables are found in the back of the book and will be provided in the Mathematical Formulae and Statistical Tables book in the exam.

9 Approximately 68% of the data lies within one standard deviation of the mean.

10 95% of the data lies within two standard deviations of the mean.

11 Nearly all of the data (99.7%) lies within three standard deviations of the mean.

Review exercise 2

(E) **1** The scatter diagrams below were drawn by a student.

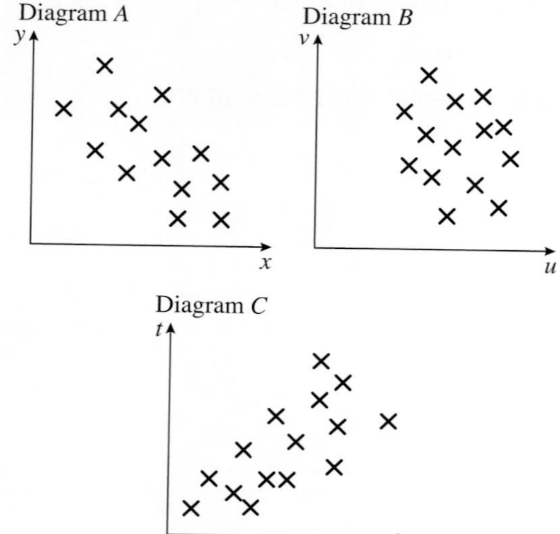

The student calculated the value of the product moment correlation coefficient for each of the sets of data.

The values were:

0.68 −0.79 0.08

Write down, with a reason, which value corresponds to which scatter diagram. **(3)**

← Statistics 1 Section 5.1

(E/P) **2** The table below shows the average monthly temperature, t (°C) and the number of ice creams, c, in 100s, a riverside snack barge sells each month.

t	7	8	10	45	14	17	20	21	15	13	9	5
c	4	7	13	27	30	35	42	41	36	24	9	3

The following statistics were calculated for the data on temperature: mean = 15.3, standard deviation = 10.2 (both correct to 3 s.f.)

An outlier is an observation which lies ±2 standard deviations from the mean.

a Show that $t = 45$ is an outlier. **(1)**

b Give a reason whether or not this outlier should be omitted from the data. **(1)**

This value is omitted from the data, and the equation of the regression line of c on t for the remaining data is calculated as $c = 2.81t - 13.3$

c Give an interpretation of the value of 2.81 in this regression equation. **(1)**

d State, with a reason, why using the regression line to estimate the number of ice creams sold when the average monthly temperature is 2 °C would not be appropriate. **(2)**

← Statistics 1 Section 5.2

(E/P) **3** A manufacturer stores drums of chemicals. During storage, evaporation takes place. A random sample of 10 drums was taken and the time in storage, x weeks, and the evaporation loss, y ml, are shown in the table below.

x	3	5	6	8	10	12	13	15	16	18
y	36	50	53	61	69	79	82	90	88	96

a On graph paper, draw a scatter diagram to represent these data. **(2)**

b Give a reason to support fitting a regression model of the form $y = a + bx$ to these data. **(1)**

c Find, to 2 decimal places, the value of a and the value of b.

(You may use $\sum x^2 = 1352$, $\sum y^2 = 53\,112$ and $\sum xy = 8354$) **(2)**

d Give an interpretation of the value of b. **(1)**

e Using your model, predict the amount of evaporation that would take place after:
i 19 weeks
ii 35 weeks. **(2)**

f Comment, with a reason, on the reliability of each of your predictions. **(2)**

← Statistics 1 Sections 5.1, 5.2, 5.3

E/P **4** A student is investigating the relationship between the price (y cents) of 100 g of chocolate and the percentage (x%) of the cocoa solids in the chocolate.

The following data are obtained:

Chocolate brand	x (% cocoa)	y (cents)
A	10	35
B	20	55
C	30	40
D	35	100
E	40	60
F	50	90
G	60	110
H	70	130

(You may use: $\sum x = 315$, $\sum x^2 = 15\,225$, $\sum y = 620$, $\Sigma y^2 = 56\,550$, $\sum xy = 28\,750$)

a Draw a scatter diagram to represent these data. **(2)**

b Show that $S_{xy} = 4337.5$ and find S_{xx} **(2)**

The student believes that a linear relationship of the form $y = a + bx$ could be used to describe these data.

c Use linear regression to find the value of a and the value of b, giving your answers to 3 significant figures. **(2)**

d Draw the regression line on your diagram. **(1)**

The student believes that one brand of chocolate is overpriced.

e Use the scatter diagram to:
i state which brand is overpriced
ii suggest a fair price for this brand.
Give reasons for both your answers. **(3)**

← Statistics 1 Sections 5.1, 5.2, 5.3

E **5** A long distance truck driver recorded the distance travelled, k kilometres, and the amount of fuel used, f litres, each day. Summarised below are data from the driver's records for a random sample of 8 days.

The data are coded such that $x = k - 250$ and $y = f - 100$.

The data collected can be summarised as follows:

$\sum x = 130$ $\quad \sum y = 48$
$\sum xy = 8880$ $\quad S_{xx} = 20\,487.5$

a Find the equation of the regression line of y on x in the form $y = a + bx$ **(2)**

b Hence find the equation of the regression line of f on k. **(3)**

c Predict the amount of fuel used on a journey of 235 kilometres. **(1)**

← Statistics 1 Sections 5.2, 5.3

E/P **6** A metallurgist measured the length, l mm, of a copper rod at various temperatures, t °C, and recorded the following results.

t	l
20.4	2461.12
27.3	2461.41
32.1	2461.73
39.0	2461.88
42.9	2462.03
49.7	2462.37
58.3	2462.69
67.4	2463.05

The results were then coded such that $x = t$ and $y = l - 2460$

a Calculate S_{xy} and S_{xx}
(You may use $\sum x^2 = 15965.01$ and $\sum xy = 757.467$) **(2)**

b Find the equation of the regression line of y on x in the form $y = a + bx$ **(2)**

c Estimate the length of the rod at 40 °C. **(1)**

d Find the equation of the regression line of l on t. **(2)**

e Estimate the length of the rod at 90 °C. **(1)**

f Comment on the reliability of your estimate in part **e**. **(1)**

← Statistics 1 Sections 5.2, 5.3

E/P **7** A young family were looking for a new three-bedroom semi-detached house. A local survey recorded the price, x, in £1000s, and the distance, y, in miles, from the nearest railway station of such houses. The following summary statistics were provided:

$S_{xx} = 113\,573 \qquad S_{yy} = 8.657$
$S_{xy} = -808.917$

a Use these values to calculate the product moment correlation coefficient. **(2)**

b Give an interpretation of your answer to part **a**. **(1)**

In another survey, the data for the same houses were supplied in km rather than miles.

c State the value of the product moment correlation coefficient in this case. **(1)**

← Statistics 1 Section 5.4

E/P **8** As part of a statistics project, Amika collected data relating to the length of time, to the nearest minute, spent by shoppers in a supermarket and the amount of money they spent. Her data for a random sample of 10 shoppers are summarised in the following table, where t represents time and m represents the amount spent over \$20.

t (minutes)	m (\$)
15	−3
23	17
5	−19
16	4
30	12
6	−9
32	27
23	6
35	20
27	6

a Write down the actual amount spent by the shopper who was in the supermarket for 15 minutes. **(1)**

b Calculate S_{tt}, S_{mm} and S_{tm}

(You may use $\sum t^2 = 5478$, $\sum m^2 = 2101$, and $\sum tm = 2485$) **(3)**

c Calculate the value of the product moment correlation coefficient between t and m. **(2)**

d Write down the value of the product moment correlation coefficient between t and the actual amount spent. Give a reason to justify your value. **(1)**

On another day, Amika collected similar data. For these data, the product moment correlation coefficient was 0.178

e Give an interpretation to both of these coefficients. **(2)**

f Suggest a practical reason why these two values are so different. **(1)**

← Statistics 1 Section 5.4

E **9** The masses of a reactant t mg and a product p mg in ten different instances of a chemistry experiment were recorded in a table.

t	p
1.2	3.8
1.9	7
3.2	11
3.9	12
2.5	9
4.5	12
5.7	13.5
4	12.2
1.1	2
5.9	13.9

(You may use $\sum t^2 = 141.51$, $\sum p^2 = 1081.74$ **and** $\sum tp = 386.32$**)**

a Draw a scatter diagram to represent these data. **(2)**

b State what is measured by the product moment correlation coefficient. **(1)**

c Calculate S_{tt}, S_{pp} and S_{tp} **(3)**

d Calculate the value of the product moment correlation coefficient r between t and p. **(2)**

← Statistics 1 Section 5.4

E/P **10** A fair coin is tossed 4 times.

Find the probability that:

a an equal number of heads and tails occur **(3)**

b all the outcomes are the same **(2)**

c the first tail occurs on the third toss. **(2)**

← Statistics 1 Section 6.1

E/P **11** The discrete random variable X has probability distribution given by:

x	−3	−2	0	1	3
$P(X = x)$	a	b	b	a	c

The random variable Y is defined as $Y = \frac{1 - 2X}{4}$. Given that $E(Y) = -0.05$ and $P(Y > 0) = 0.5$, find:

a the probability distribution of X **(7)**

b $P(-3X < 5Y)$. **(2)**

← Statistics 1 Sections 6.1, 6.2, 6.5

E **12** The random variable X has probability function:

$$P(X = x) = \frac{(2x - 1)}{36}; \quad x = 1, 2, 3, 4, 5, 6$$

a Construct a table giving the probability distribution of X. **(2)**

Find:

b $P(2 < X \leqslant 5)$ **(1)**

c the exact value of $E(X)$. **(2)**

d Show that $\text{Var}(X) = 1.97$ to 3 s.f. **(3)**

e Find $\text{Var}(2 - 3X)$ **(2)**

← Statistics 1 Sections 6.3, 6.4, 6.5

E **13** The random variable X has probability function:

$$P(X = x) = \begin{cases} kx & x = 1, 2, 3 \\ k(x + 1) & x = 4, 5 \end{cases}$$

where k is a constant.

a Find the value of k. **(2)**

b Find the exact value of $E(X)$. **(2)**

c Show that, to 3 significant figures, $\text{Var}(X) = 1.47$ **(3)**

d Find, to 1 decimal place, $\text{Var}(4 - 3X)$ **(2)**

← Statistics 1 Sections 6.3, 6.4, 6.5, 6.6

E/P **14** The random variable X has probability distribution given by:

x	1	2	3	4	5
$P(X = x)$	0.1	p	0.20	q	0.30

a Given that $E(X) = 3.5$, write down two equations involving p and q. **(3)**

Find:

b the value of p and the value of q **(2)**

c $\text{Var}(X)$ **(3)**

d $\text{Var}(3 - 2X)$ **(2)**

← Statistics 1 Sections 6.3, 6.4, 6.5

E/P **15** The random variable X has probability distribution given by:

x	1	3	5	7	9
$P(X = x)$	0.2	p	0.2	q	0.15

a Given that $E(X) = 4.5$, write down two equations involving p and q. **(3)**

Find:

b the value of p and the value of q **(2)**

c $P(4 < X \leq 7)$. **(1)**

Given that $E(X^2) = 27.4$, find:

d $Var(X)$ **(2)**

e $E(19 - 4X)$ **(1)**

f $Var(19 - 4X)$. **(2)**

← Statistics 1 Sections 6.3, 6.4, 6.5, 6.6

E/P **16** The discrete random variable X has probability distribution given by:

x	−2	−1	0	1
$P(X = x)$	0.2	0.3	a	b

The random variable Y is defined as $Y = 2 - 3X$. Given that $E(Y) = 2.9$,

a find the values of a and b **(5)**

b calculate $E(X^2)$ and $Var(X)$ **(3)**

c write down the value of $Var(Y)$ **(1)**

d find $P(Y + 1 < X)$. **(2)**

← Statistics 1 Sections 6.3, 6.4, 6.5, 6.6

E/P **17** A fair five-sided spinner has sectors numbered from 1 to 5. The spinner is spun and the number showing, X, is recorded.

a State the distribution of X. **(1)**

The spinner is spun four times and the number of spins taken to get an odd number, Y, is recorded.

b Write down, in table form, the probability distribution of Y. **(3)**

c Find $P(Y > 2)$. **(2)**

← Statistics 1 Sections 6.1, 6.6, 6.7

E/P **18** The measure of intelligence, IQ, of a group of students is assumed to be normally distributed with mean 100 and standard deviation 15.

a Find the probability that a student selected at random has an IQ less than 91. **(1)**

The probability that a randomly selected student has an IQ of at least $100 + k$ is 0.2090

b Find, to the nearest integer, the value of k. **(2)**

← Statistics 1 Sections 6.1, 6.6, 6.7

19 The heights of a group of athletes are modelled by a normal distribution with mean 180 cm and standard deviation 5.2 cm. The weights of this group of athletes are modelled by a normal distribution with mean 85 kg and standard deviation 7.1 kg.

Find the probability that a randomly chosen athlete:

a is taller than 188 cm **(1)**

b weighs less than 97 kg. **(1)**

c Assuming that for these athletes height and weight are independent, find the probability that a randomly chosen athlete is taller than 188 cm and weighs more than 97 kg. **(2)**

d Comment on the assumption that height and weight are independent. **(1)**

← Statistics 1 Sections 7.1, 7.4

E/P **20** From experience, a high jumper knows that he can clear a height of at least 1.78 m once in five attempts. He also knows that he can clear a height of at least 1.65 m on seven out of 10 attempts.

Assuming that the heights cleared by the high jumper follow a normal distribution,

a find, to 3 decimal places, the mean and the standard deviation of the heights cleared by the high jumper **(3)**

b calculate the probability that the high jumper will clear a height of 1.74 m. **(1)**

← Statistics 1 Sections 7.1, 7.4

E/P **21** A company makes dinner plates with an average diameter of 22 cm. The diameter, D cm, can be modelled using a normal distribution. Given that 32% of the plates are less than 21.5 cm in diameter, find:

a the standard deviation of the diameter **(2)**

b the proportion of plates with diameter between 21 cm and 22.5 cm. **(2)**

A plate can be used in a restaurant if the diameter is between 21 cm and 22.5 cm. A sample of 30 plates is taken.

c Find the probability that at least 10 of these plates can be used. **(2)**

← Statistics 1 Sections 7.1, 7.4

22 The random variable $X \sim N(14, 9)$.
Find:

a $P(X \geqslant 11)$

b $P(9 < X < 11)$

← Statistics 1 Section 7.4

23 The random variable $X \sim N(20, 5^2)$.
Find:

a $P(X \leqslant 16)$

b The value of d such that $P(X < d) = 0.95$

← Statistics 1 Section 7.4

E **24** The lifetime of lithium batteries are normally distributed.

A company, Strong Batteries, sells these batteries with a mean lifetime of 850 hours and a standard deviation of 50 hours.

a Find the probability of a battery from Strong Batteries having a lifetime less than 830 hours. **(3)**

b In a box of 500 batteries, sold in bulk, from Strong Batteries, find the expected number having a lifetime of less than 830 hours. **(2)**

A rival company, Power Batteries, sells batteries with a mean lifetime of 860 hours and 20% of these batteries have a lifetime of less than 818 hours.

c Find the standard deviation of the lifetimes of the batteries from Power Batteries. **(4)**

Both companies sell the batteries for the same price.

d State which company you would recommend. Give a reason for your answer. **(2)**

← Statistics 1 Sections 7.3, 7.4, 7.5

E **25** The time it takes in minutes, T, for a computer engineer to service a laptop follows a normal distribution with a mean of 25 minutes and a standard deviation of 4 minutes.

Find:

a $P(T < 28)$ **(3)**

b $P(|T - 25| < 5)$ **(4)**

One afternoon the computer engineer has three laptops to service.

c Find the probability that she will take less than 23 minutes on each of the three laptops. **(4)**

← Statistics 1 Sections 7.3, 7.4, 7.5

Challenge

1 The table below shows data collected from a scientific experiment:

x	1	3	4	5	7	8
y	1.5	3.3	5.3	7.5	13.8	16.8

a Use your calculator to find the following regression models for these data:

i Linear ($y = a + bx$)

ii Quadratic ($y = a + bx + cx^2$)

iii Exponential ($y = ae^{bx}$ or $y = ab^x$)

b By calculating the residuals for each model, determine which model is most suitable.

← Statistics 1 Sections 5.2, 5.3

2 Three fair four-sided dice are rolled. The discrete random variable X represents the difference between the highest score and the lowest score on the three dice.

a Write down the probability distribution of X.

b Show that $E(X) = \frac{15}{8}$

← Statistics 1 Sections 6.1, 6.2, 6.3

Exam practice

Mathematics International Advanced Subsidiary/ Advanced Level Statistics 1

Time: 1 hour 30 minutes
You must have: Mathematical Formulae and Statistical Tables, Calculator
Answer ALL questions

1 Sudeshna is undergoing a training course which awards a certificate to each student who passes a test while taking the course. If she fails the test she can retake the test up to three more times, and if she passes she will be awarded a certificate.

The probability of passing the test on the first attempt is 60%, but the probability of passing reduces by 10% on each attempt.

a Complete the tree diagram below to show this information. **(2)**

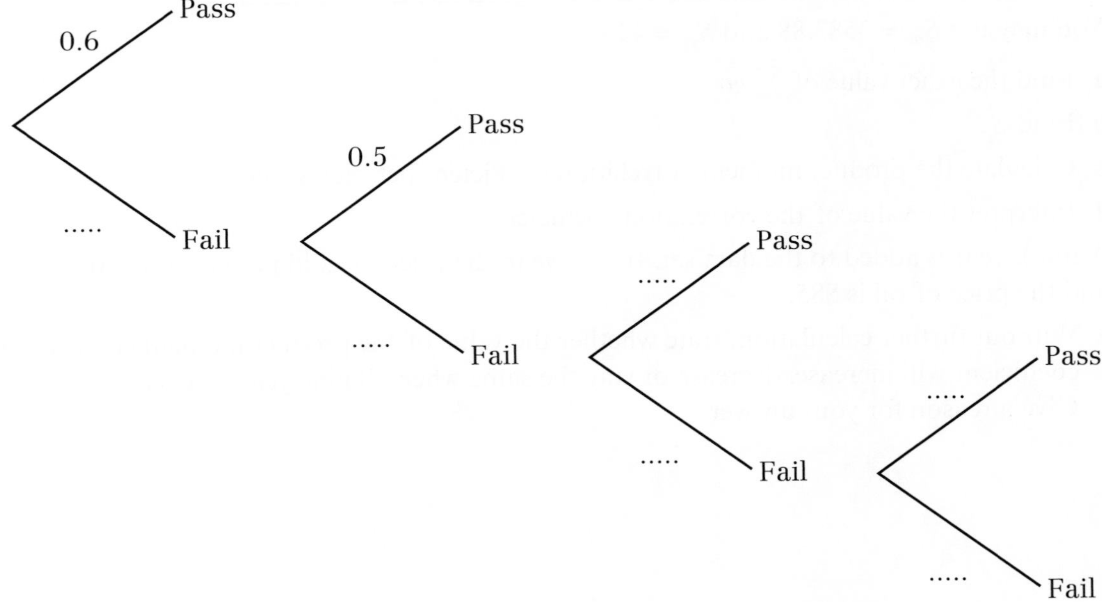

b Given that the probability of Sudeshna being awarded a certificate is 91.6%, find the probability that she passed on the first or second attempt. **(3)**

2 Zaynab works for a motorbike insurance company. She randomly selects eight people and records the price of their motorbike insurance, p (€), and time, t years, since they passed their driving test. The data are shown in the table below.

t	12	13	15	17	20	24	25	23
p	720	650	430	495	510	390	270	285

$\bar{t} = 18.63$, $p = 468.75$, $S_{tp} = -5023.75$, $S_{tt} = 181.88$, $S_{pp} = 179\,337.50$

a Draw a scatter diagram for these data. **(2)**

b Comment on the relationship between p and t. **(1)**

c Find the equation of the regression line of p on t. **(4)**

d Use your regression equation to estimate the price of motorbike insurance for Asaad who passed his driving test 22 years ago. **(2)**

Ali passed his test 39 years ago and decides to use Zaynab's data to predict the price of his motorbike insurance.

e Comment on Ali's decision. Give a reason for your answer. **(2)**

3 The table below shows the price of gold per gram, g, and the price of oil, o, (both in \$) for 8 different years.

g	29	31	36	41	43	46	48	50
o	130	128	126	123	121	91	83	75

You may use $S_{oo} = 3583.88$ and $S_{gg} = 426$

a Find the exact value of $\sum go$ **(1)**

b Find S_{go} **(3)**

c Calculate the product moment correlation coefficient between g and o. **(2)**

d Interpret the value of the correlation coefficient. **(1)**

A ninth year is added to the data set. In this year, the price of gold per gram is \$40 and the price of oil is \$85.

e Without further calculation, state whether the value of the product moment correlation coefficient will increase, decrease or stay the same when all nine years are used. Give a reason for your answer. **(2)**

4 A supervisor records the number of hours of overtime claimed by 450 employees in a month. The histogram below represents the results.

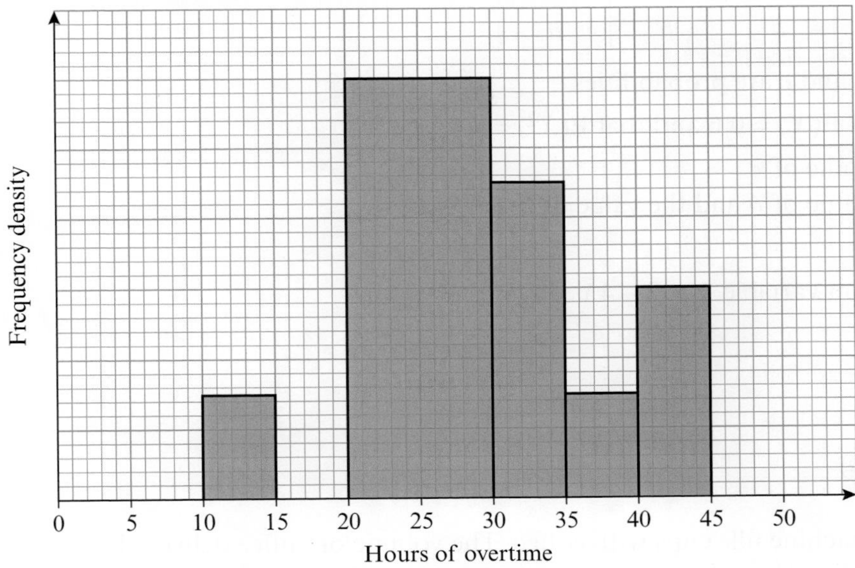

a Calculate the number of employees who have claimed more than 35 hours of overtime in the month. **(4)**

b Estimate the mean number of hours, to the nearest hour, of overtime claimed by these 450 employees in the month. **(2)**

c Estimate, to the nearest hour, the median number of hours of overtime claimed by these 450 employees in the month. **(2)**

The manager wants to compare these data with overtime data he collected earlier to find out if the overtime claimed by employees has decreased.

d State, giving a reason, whether the manager should use the median or the mean to compare the overtime claimed by employees. **(2)**

5 100 students are asked if they like tennis, football or basketball.

All students who like tennis also like football
No students like both football and basketball
75 students do not like basketball
12 students who like football do not like tennis
30 students like tennis

a Draw a Venn diagram to illustrate this information. **(4)**

b State two of these types of sport that are mutually exclusive. **(1)**

Find the probability that a randomly chosen student:

c does not like tennis, football or basketball **(1)**

d likes football **(1)**

e likes tennis or basketball. **(1)**

Given that a randomly chosen student likes football,

f find the probability that he or she also likes tennis. **(2)**

6 The discrete random variable X has the following probability distribution:

x	-2	0	2	4
$\mathrm{P}(X = x)$	a	b	a	c

where a, b and c are probabilities.

Given that $\mathrm{E}(X) = 0.6$ and that $\mathrm{E}(X^2) = 4$ find:

a **i** the value of c

ii the value of a and the value of b. **(6)**

b $\mathrm{Var}(X)$ **(2)**

The random variable $Y = 7 - 4X$

Find:

c $\mathrm{E}(Y)$ **(1)**

d $\mathrm{Var}(Y)$ **(2)**

e $\mathrm{P}(Y \geqslant 0)$ **(4)**

7 A coffee machine fills cups with coffee. The volume of coffee delivered by the machine to a cup is X ml, where $X \sim \mathrm{N}(\mu, \sigma^2)$.

One of these cups of coffee is selected at random.

Given that $\mu = 505$ and $\sigma = 1.8$,

a find:

i $\mathrm{P}(X > 507)$

ii $\mathrm{P}(501 < X < 505)$ **(5)**

Following adjustments to the machine, the mean volume of coffee delivered to each cup is 503 ml, with a standard deviation of 1.6

b Find w such that $\mathrm{P}(1006 - w < X < w) = 0.9426$ **(3)**

The coffee machine is further adjusted, and now the mean volume of coffee per cup is $\mu = r$, with a standard deviation of $\sigma = q$.

Given that $\mathrm{P}(X < 499) = 0.01$ and $\mathrm{P}(X > 505) = 0.05$

c find the value of r and the value of q. **(7)**

TOTAL FOR PAPER: 75 MARKS

The Normal Distribution Function

The function tabulated below is $\Phi(z)$, defined as $\Phi(z) = \dfrac{1}{\sqrt{2\pi}} \displaystyle\int_{-\infty}^{z} e^{-\frac{1}{2}t^2}\, dt$

z	$\Phi(z)$	z	$\Phi(z)$	z	$\Phi(z)$	z	$\Phi(z)$	z	$\Phi(z)$
0.00	0.5000	0.50	0.6915	1.00	0.8413	1.50	0.9332	2.00	0.9772
0.01	0.5040	0.51	0.6950	1.01	0.8438	1.51	0.9345	2.02	0.9783
0.02	0.5080	0.52	0.6985	1.02	0.8461	1.52	0.9357	2.04	0.9793
0.03	0.5120	0.53	0.7019	1.03	0.8485	1.53	0.9370	2.06	0.9803
0.04	0.5160	0.54	0.7054	1.04	0.8508	1.54	0.9382	2.08	0.9812
0.05	0.5199	0.55	0.7088	1.05	0.8531	1.55	0.9394	2.10	0.9821
0.06	0.5239	0.56	0.7123	1.06	0.8554	1.56	0.9406	2.12	0.9830
0.07	0.5279	0.57	0.7157	1.07	0.8577	1.57	0.9418	2.14	0.9838
0.08	0.5319	0.58	0.7190	1.08	0.8599	1.58	0.9429	2.16	0.9846
0.09	0.5359	0.59	0.7224	1.09	0.8621	1.59	0.9441	2.18	0.9854
0.10	0.5398	0.60	0.7257	1.10	0.8643	1.60	0.9452	2.20	0.9861
0.11	0.5438	0.61	0.7291	1.11	0.8665	1.61	0.9463	2.22	0.9868
0.12	0.5478	0.62	0.7324	1.12	0.8686	1.62	0.9474	2.24	0.9875
0.13	0.5517	0.63	0.7357	1.13	0.8708	1.63	0.9484	2.26	0.9881
0.14	0.5557	0.64	0.7389	1.14	0.8729	1.64	0.9495	2.28	0.9887
0.15	0.5596	0.65	0.7422	1.15	0.8749	1.65	0.9505	2.30	0.9893
0.16	0.5636	0.66	0.7454	1.16	0.8770	1.66	0.9515	2.32	0.9898
0.17	0.5675	0.67	0.7486	1.17	0.8790	1.67	0.9525	2.34	0.9904
0.18	0.5714	0.68	0.7517	1.18	0.8810	1.68	0.9535	2.36	0.9909
0.19	0.5753	0.69	0.7549	1.19	0.8830	1.69	0.9545	2.38	0.9913
0.20	0.5793	0.70	0.7580	1.20	0.8849	1.70	0.9554	2.40	0.9918
0.21	0.5832	0.71	0.7611	1.21	0.8869	1.71	0.9564	2.42	0.9922
0.22	0.5871	0.72	0.7642	1.22	0.8888	1.72	0.9573	2.44	0.9927
0.23	0.5910	0.73	0.7673	1.23	0.8907	1.73	0.9582	2.46	0.9931
0.24	0.5948	0.74	0.7704	1.24	0.8925	1.74	0.9591	2.48	0.9934
0.25	0.5987	0.75	0.7734	1.25	0.8944	1.75	0.9599	2.50	0.9938
0.26	0.6026	0.76	0.7764	1.26	0.8962	1.76	0.9608	2.55	0.9946
0.27	0.6064	0.77	0.7794	1.27	0.8980	1.77	0.9616	2.60	0.9953
0.28	0.6103	0.78	0.7823	1.28	0.8997	1.78	0.9625	2.65	0.9960
0.29	0.6141	0.79	0.7852	1.29	0.9015	1.79	0.9633	2.70	0.9965
0.30	0.6179	0.80	0.7881	1.30	0.9032	1.80	0.9641	2.75	0.9970
0.31	0.6217	0.81	0.7910	1.31	0.9049	1.81	0.9649	2.80	0.9974
0.32	0.6255	0.82	0.7939	1.32	0.9066	1.82	0.9656	2.85	0.9978
0.33	0.6293	0.83	0.7967	1.33	0.9082	1.83	0.9664	2.90	0.9981
0.34	0.6331	0.84	0.7995	1.34	0.9099	1.84	0.9671	2.95	0.9984
0.35	0.6368	0.85	0.8023	1.35	0.9115	1.85	0.9678	3.00	0.9987
0.36	0.6406	0.86	0.8051	1.36	0.9131	1.86	0.9686	3.05	0.9989
0.37	0.6443	0.87	0.8078	1.37	0.9147	1.87	0.9693	3.10	0.9990
0.38	0.6480	0.88	0.8106	1.38	0.9162	1.88	0.9699	3.15	0.9992
0.39	0.6517	0.89	0.8133	1.39	0.9177	1.89	0.9706	3.20	0.9993
0.40	0.6554	0.90	0.8159	1.40	0.9192	1.90	0.9713	3.25	0.9994
0.41	0.6591	0.91	0.8186	1.41	0.9207	1.91	0.9719	3.30	0.9995
0.42	0.6628	0.92	0.8212	1.42	0.9222	1.92	0.9726	3.35	0.9996
0.43	0.6664	0.93	0.8238	1.43	0.9236	1.93	0.9732	3.40	0.9997
0.44	0.6700	0.94	0.8264	1.44	0.9251	1.94	0.9738	3.50	0.9998
0.45	0.6736	0.95	0.8289	1.45	0.9265	1.95	0.9744	3.60	0.9998
0.46	0.6772	0.96	0.8315	1.46	0.9279	1.96	0.9750	3.70	0.9999
0.47	0.6808	0.97	0.8340	1.47	0.9292	1.97	0.9756	3.80	0.9999
0.48	0.6844	0.98	0.8365	1.48	0.9306	1.98	0.9761	3.90	1.0000
0.49	0.6879	0.99	0.8389	1.49	0.9319	1.99	0.9767	4.00	1.0000
0.50	0.6915	1.00	0.8413	1.50	0.9332	2.00	0.9772		

Percentage Points Of The Normal Distribution

The values z in the table are those which a random variable $Z \sim \mathrm{N}(0, 1)$ exceeds with probability p; that is, $\mathrm{P}(Z > z) = 1 - \Phi(z) = p$.

p	z	p	z
0.5000	0.0000	0.0500	1.6449
0.4000	0.2533	0.0250	1.9600
0.3000	0.5244	0.0100	2.3263
0.2000	0.8416	0.0050	2.5758
0.1500	1.0364	0.0010	3.0902
0.1000	1.2816	0.0005	3.2905

GLOSSARY

anomaly a value that is different from what is normal or expected

bivariate data data for two variables

box plot used to represent important features of data. It shows the quartiles, minimum and maximum values and the median

class a set or category of things having some property or attribute in common and differentiated from others by kind, type, or quality

class boundary the range of each group of data

class width the difference between the upper or lower **class** limits of classes that follow one after the other in a series

coding used to simplify calculations in statistics

complement (of an event) for event *A*, the complement of *A* is that event *A* does not occur

conditional probability the probability of one event occurring given that another event has occurred

continuous variable a **variable** that can take any value in a given range

correlation how strongly two sets of data are linked

cumulative distribution adding together all the probabilities for the outcomes that are equal to or less than x

dependent (or response) variable a variable whose values are determined by the values of the **independent variable**. It is plotted along the y-axis

discrete data that can take only certain values in a given range

discrete random variable only takes values on a **discrete** scale

discrete uniform distribution a symmetric probability distribution whereby a finite number of values are equally likely to be observed; every one of the n values has equal probability $\frac{1}{n}$

discrete variable a **variable** that can take only certain values in a given range

estimate to find something close to the correct answer, but not exact

event a collection (or set) of one or more outcomes

expected value the **mean** of a **random variable**

experiment a repeatable process that may lead to a number of outcomes

extrapolation used to **estimate** a value outside the range of the data

grouped frequency grouping data in a table to make it easier to read

histogram a graphical way to show how continuous data is distributed

independent (or explanatory) variable a variable that is set independently of other variables. It is plotted along the x-axis

independent events when one event has no effect on another

interpolation used to **estimate** the value of a dependent **variable** within the range of the data

interpercentile range the difference between the values for two given percentiles

interquartile range the range from lowest quartile to highest quartile

mathematical model a simplification of a real world situation. It can be used to make predictions about a real world problem

mean the sum of all the observations divided by the total number of observations

measures of spread how spread out (separated to cover an area) a set of data is

measures of location a set of data can be summarised by giving a single number to describe its centre. This is often described as or referred to as an average

median the middle value when the data is put in order

midpoint the point in the middle of something

modal class the **class** with the highest frequency

mode the value that occurs the most in a data set

model (noun) a thing used as an example to follow or imitate

model (verb) (**modelled/modelling**) a system or procedure as an example to follow or imitate

mutually exclusive when events have no outcomes in common

normal distribution data that has been distributed or spread out in the shape of a bell curve

outlier a value that 'lies outside' most of the other values in a set of data

percentile split the data into 100 parts

prediction to forecast an item in the future

probability the likelihood of an event occurring

probability distribution a table to show the **probability** of each outcome of an **experiment**

product moment correlation coefficient an indication of how weak or strong the **correlation** between two **variables** is

qualitative variables variables associated with non-numerical observations

quantitative variables variables associated with numerical observations

quartiles split the data into four equal parts

random variable when the value of a variable is the outcome of a random event

range the limits between which something varies, from lowest value to highest value

refine to improve something by making small changes

regression predicting the value of Y when we know the value of X

regression line used to **estimate** the value of the **dependent variable** for any value of the **independent variable**

sample space the set of all possible outcomes of an **experiment**

scatter diagram a graph of plotted points that shows the relationship between two sets of data

skew the shape of a data set

simplification the process of making something easier to understand

standard deviation a measure of how spread out numbers are

standard normal variable a normally distributed random **variable** with expected value 0 and variance 1

stem and leaf diagram a diagram where each data value is split into a 'stem' and a 'leaf'

tree diagram a graphical way to calculate probabilities, showing the outcomes of two (or more) events happening one after the other

variable able to be changed. Represented by a symbol (x, y, a, b, etc.) and able to take on any of a specified set of values

variance a measure of how spread out numbers are

Venn diagram a graphical way to show the relationship between sets

ANSWERS

CHAPTER 1

Prior knowledge check

1 I. Quantitative data is information that can be measured and written down with numbers
  II. Qualitative data is information that can't actually be measured

2 Can include but not limited to;
  I. Finance industry – to predict financial markets
  II. Sport – to compare different players and teams
  III. Scientists – to model, measure and predict about future health trends

Exercise 1A:

1 The statistical tests provide a clear and objective means of deciding the differences between the model's prediction and experimental data. These tests will show if and how the model can be refined even further.

2 Predictions based on the model are compared with the experimental data. By analysing this, the model and is adjusted and refined. The process is repeated.

3 Stage 1: The recognition of a real-world problem
  Stage 4: Experimental data is collected from the real world
  Stage 6: Statistical concepts are used to test how well the model describes the real-world problem

Chapter review 1

1 • Cheaper to use
  • Easier to use
  • They enable predictions to be made
  • Help improve the understanding of our world
  • Help to see how certain changes in variables will affect the outcomes
  • Help simplify complex situations

2

Advantages	Disadvantages
They are relatively quick and easy to produce	Simplification of a real-world situation may cause errors as the model is too simplistic
They help enable predictions to be made	The model may work only in certain conditions

3 The answer could be, but is not limited to: 'Climate data can sometimes be too large to investigate thoroughly as it can be too time consuming, too expensive and logistically difficult to investigate. As a result, mathematical modelling can be used to simplify the model, but still give meaningful results.'

4 1. Some assumptions need to be made to ensure the model is manageable. These include that birth and death rates.
  2. Plan a mathematical model which will include mathematical models and diagrams
  3. Use this model to predict the population over a period of years
  4. Include and collect new data that match the conditions of the predicted values. Historical data may be used in this scenario
  5. Analyse the data and compare the predicted data with the experimental data
  6. Use statistical tests that will provide an objective way of deciding if the differences between the model's predictions and experimental data are accurate enough for the study
  7. Refine the model

CHAPTER 2

Prior knowledge check

1 Mean = 25.56
  Median = 23
  Mode = 38
2 61 km per hour
3 Mean: 5.33, Median: 6, Mode: 6, Range: 4

Exercise 2A

1 a Quantitative as it is numerical
  b Qualitative as it is a descriptive word
  c Quantitative as it is numerical
  d Quantitative as it is numerical
  e Qualitative as it is a descriptive word
2 a Not True b True
  c True d Not True
3 a 5.95 and 6.95 b 9.45
4 a 1.4 and 1.5 b 1.35

Exercise 2B

1 a 700 g b 600 g c 700 g
  d The mean will increase; the mode will remain unchanged; the median will decrease.
2 a 42.7
  b The mean will increase.
3 a May: 23 355 m, June: 21 067 m
  b 22 230 m
4 a 8 minutes b 10.2 minutes c 8.5 minutes
  d The median would be best. The mean is affected by the extreme value 26.
5 a 2 b 1 c 1.47 d the median
6 6.31 petals
7 $p = 1$

Exercise 2C

1 a €351 to €400 b €345 c €351 to €400
2 a 82.3 decibels
  b The mean is an estimate as we don't know the exact noise levels recorded.
3 a $16 \leqslant t < 18$
  b 16.5 °C (correct to 3 s.f.)
4 Shop B (mean 51 years) employs older workers than shop A (mean 50 years).

Exercise 2D

1 a 1020 hPa b $Q_1 = 1017$ hPa, $Q_3 = 1024.5$ hPa
2 $Q_1 = 37$, $Q_2 = 37$, $Q_3 = 38$
3 1.08
4 a 432 kg b 389 kg c 480 kg
  d Three-quarters of the cows weigh 480 kg or less.

5 a 44.0 minutes b 48.8 minutes
c 90th percentile = 57.8 minutes so 10% of customers have to wait longer 57.8 minutes, not 56 minutes as stated by the firm.
6 a 2.84 m. 80% of condors have a wingspan of less than 2.84 m.
b The 90th percentile is in the $3.0 \leqslant w$ class. There is no upper boundary for this class, so it is not possible to estimate the 90th percentile.

Exercise 2E

1 a 71 b 24.6 c 193.1 mm d 7
2 a $81.87 b 22
3 a 6.2 minutes b 54
4 a Median 11.5 °C, Q_1 = 10.3 °C, Q_3 = 12.7 °C, IQR = 2.4 °C
b On average, the temperature was higher in June than in May (higher median). The temperature was more variable in May than June (higher IQR).
c 24 days

Exercise 2F

1 a 3 b 0.75 c 0.866
2 3.11 kg
3 a 178 cm b 59.9 cm^2 c 7.74 cm
4 Mean 5.44, standard deviation 2.35
5 a Mean OMR10.22, standard deviation OMR1.35
b 18
6 1.23 days
7 Mean 16.1 hours, standard deviation 4.69 hours
One standard deviation below mean 11.41 hours.
41 parts tested (82%) lasted longer than one standard deviation below the mean. According to the manufacturers, this should be 45 parts (90%), so the claim is false.
8 a Mean 8.1 knots, standard deviation 3.41 knots
b 12 days
c The wind speeds are equally distributed throughout the range.

Challenge
Mean = 81.8 cents, standard deviation = $1.03

Exercise 2G

1 a 11, 9, 5, 8, 3, 7, 6 b 7 c 70
2 a 7, 10, 4, 10, 5, 11, 2, 3 b 6.5 c 48.5
3 365
4 2.34
5 a

Battery life (b years)	Frequency (f)	Midpoint (x)	$y = \frac{x-14}{2}$
11–21	11	16	1
21–27	24	24	5
27–31	27	29	7.5
31–37	26	34	10
37–43	12	40	13

b Coded mean = 7.495
Actual mean – 28.99 or 29 hours to the nearest hour
6 a 1.2 hours b 25.1 hours c 1.76 hours
7 22.9

8 416 mm
9 Mean 1020 hPa, standard deviation 6.28 hPa

Chapter review 2

1 69.2
2 a 10, 12, 9, 2, 2.5, 9.5 b 7.5 c 607
3 a Group A: 63.4; group B: 60.2
b The method used for group A may be better.
4 a 21 to 25 hours b 21.6 hours
c 20.6 hours d 20.8 hours
5 37.5
6 a 20.5 b 34.7 c 14.2
7 a 13.1
b Variance 102, standard deviation 10.1 minutes
8 a 98.75 mm b 104 mm c 5.58 mm d 4.47 mm
9 a Mean 27.2, standard deviation 1.36
b 4.0 °C c 5 days
10 a Mean 3.42, standard deviation 1.61
b Mean 9.84 knots, standard deviation 3.22 knots
11 a Mean 15.8 cm, standard deviation 2.06 cm
b The mean wingspan will decrease.
c Mean 57 cm, standard deviation 3 cm

Challenge
Mean 3.145 cm, standard deviation 1.39 cm

CHAPTER 3

Prior knowledge check

1
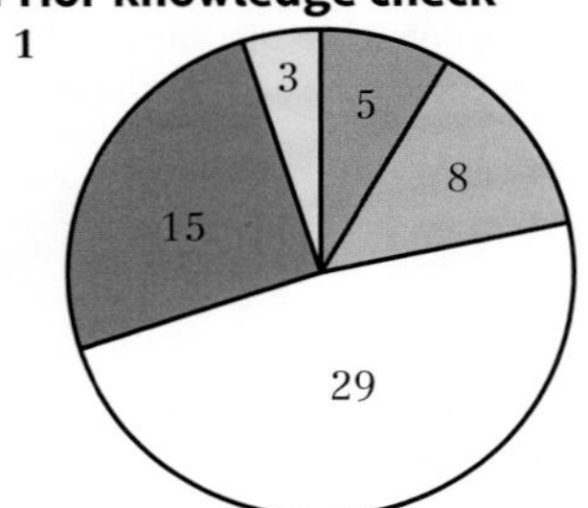

2 11
3 Mean 28.5, standard deviation 7.02

Exercise 3A

1
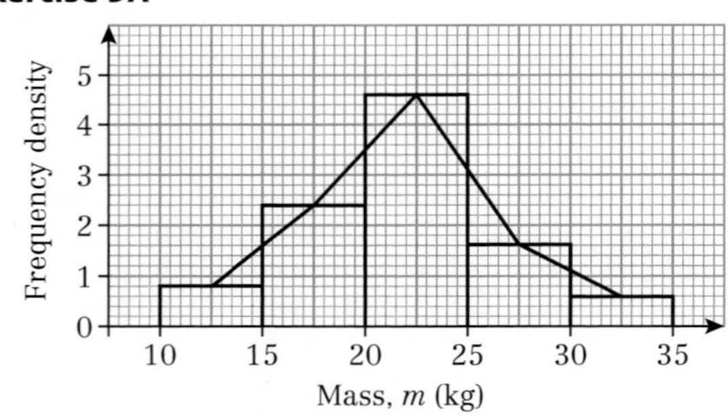

2 a The quantity (time) is continuous.
b 150 c 369 d 699
3 a The quantity (distance) is continuous.
b 310 c 75 d 95 e 65
4 a 32 lambs is represented by 100 small squares, therefore 25 small squares represents 8 lambs.
b 32 c 168 d 88

5 a i

Time, t (min)	Frequency
$0 \leqslant t < 20$	4
$20 \leqslant t < 30$	10
$30 \leqslant t < 35$	15
$35 \leqslant t < 40$	25
$40 \leqslant t < 50$	7
$50 \leqslant t < 70$	6

ii

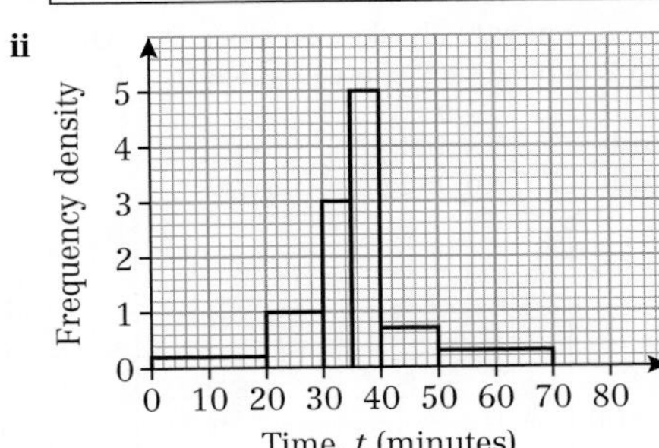

b 35

6 a 12.5 and 14.5

b i 6 cm ii 3 cm

7 a Width 0.5 cm, height 12 cm

b Mean €10.4, standard deviation 2.4

c €9 d 4.7 employees (rounded to 5)

Challenge

1:10

Exercise 3B

1 a 7 is an outlier b 88 is not an outlier

c 105 is an outlier

2 a No outliers b 170 g and 440 g

c 760 g

3 a 11.5 kg

b Smallest 2.0 kg, largest 10.2 kg

4 a Mean 10.2, standard deviation 7.36

b It is an outlier as it is more than 2 standard deviations above the mean.

c e.g. It could be the age of a parent at the party.

d Mean 7.75, standard deviation 2.44

Exercise 3C

1

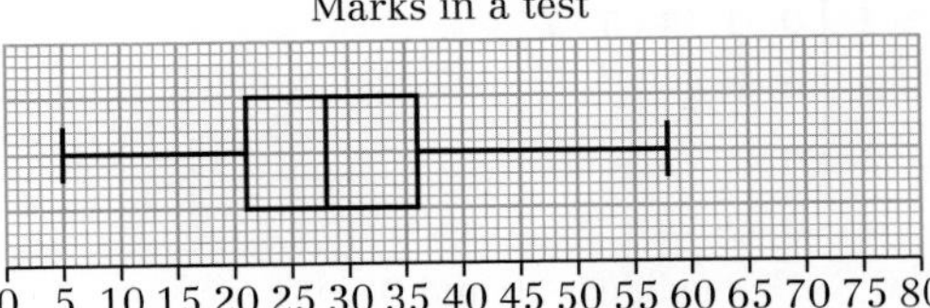

2 a 47, 32 b 38 c 15 d 64

3 a The male turtles have a higher median mass, a greater interquartile range and a greater total range.

b It is more likely to have been female. Very few of the male turtles had a mass this low, but more than a quarter of the female turtles had a mass of more than this.

c 500 g

4 a $Q_1 = 21.5$, $Q_2 = 26$, $Q_3 = 30$

b $Q_3 + 1.5(30 - 21.5) = 22.75$, and both 46 and 48 are above this value.

c

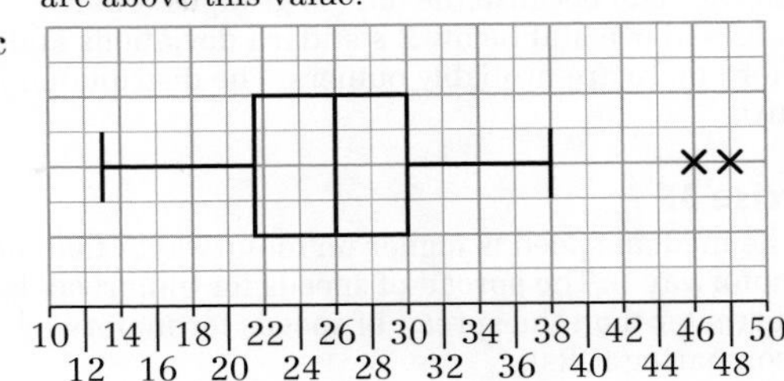

Exercise 3D

1 Ordered **Key 1 | 2 means 12 movies**

0	6 9
1	2 2 2 5 5 5 7 8 9
2	0 2 3 5 5 5 6 6 7 7 9 9
3	2 2 4 4 5
4	2 5

a 25 b 15 c 29

2 a 49 b 8 c 3 d 37

e 34 f 21 g 37

3 a Ordered **Key 2 | 6 means 26**

Boys		Girls
9 8	**2**	4 6 8
4 2 2	**3**	2 3 4 4 9
8 7 5 5 4	**4**	5 6 7
7 6 6 4 4	**5**	2 4
0	**6**	

b Girls gained lower marks than boys

4 a 19

b IQR = 3 and outliers are 27, 34, 34 and 41

Exercise 3E

1 $Q_2 - Q_1 > Q_3 - Q_2$

2 a Skew = 0.46 therefore a positive skew

b Median and quartiles because of the skew

3 a 64

b Median =65, Lower quartile = 56 and Upper quartile = 81

c

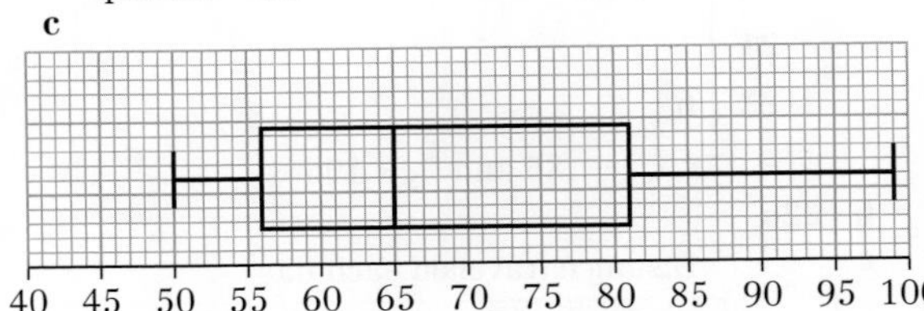

d Positive skew

e Mean = 68.72 and standard deviation = 13.73

f $Q_2 - Q_1 = 65 - 56 = 9$ and $Q_3 - Q_2 = 81 - 65 = 16$

$Q_2 - Q_1 < 65 - Q_3 - Q_2 \Rightarrow$ Positive skew

$\frac{3(Q_3 - Q_1)}{Q_2} = \frac{3(81 - 56)}{65} = 1.15 \Rightarrow$ Positive skew

g b – because of the skew

Challenge

Mean = 82.08 and standard deviation = 8.44

It is an estimate because the data is grouped. There are values above and below 2 standard deviations and therefore there are probably outliers. The distribution is negative.

Exercise 3F

1 The median speed is higher on motorway A than on motorway B. The spread of speeds for motorway B is greater than the spread of speeds for motorway A (comparing IQRs).

2 Class 2B: mean 32.5, standard deviation 6.6
Class 2F: mean 27.2, standard deviation 11.4
The mean time for Class 2B is higher than the mean time for Class 2F. The standard deviation for Class 2F is bigger than for Class 2B, showing that the times were more spread out.

3 a Median = 26.5
IQR (in complete years) is 17

b Any of the following:
- The median for both groups is similar but the median for females is higher
- Both males and females have most of their members in their 20s
- Male range is greater
- Generally, females are younger than the males

4
- Median marks for students taking their exam for the first time are lower than students retaking their exam.
- Interquartile range of marks for students taking their exam for the first time is smaller than students retaking their exam.
- The range of marks for students taking the exam for the first time is lower than that for students retaking the exam.
- Both groups marks are positively skewed.

Chapter review 3

1 a **Key: 15|5 means 155 kilometres**

Stem	Leaf
15	5
16	4 8 9
17	3 5 7 8 8 8 9 9 9
18	4 4 5 5 8
19	2 3 4 5 5 6
20	4 7 8 9
21	1 2
22	6

$Q_1 = 178$, $Q_2 = 185$ and $Q_3 = 196$

b 226

c Distance travelled each day

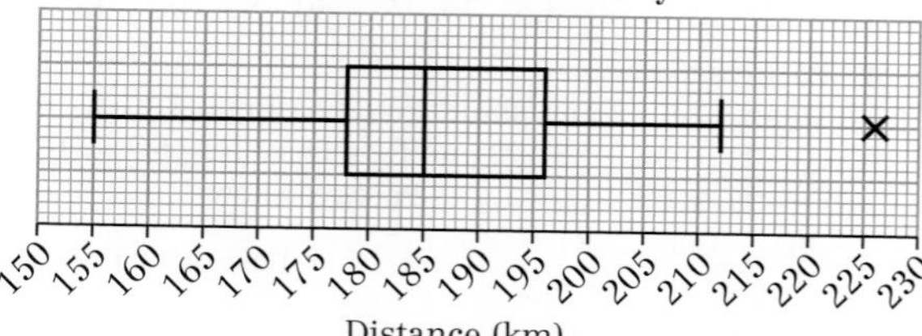

d The distribution has a positive skew

2 a 45 minutes **b** 60 minutes

c This represents an outlier.

d The Runners Club has a higher median than the Marathon Club.
The interquartile ranges were about the same.

e The Marathon Club had the faster runners.

f Advantages: easy to compare quartiles, median and spread. Disadvantages: cannot compare mean or mode.

3 a Median = 39, $Q_1 = 31$ and $Q_3 = 55$

b For Zoo 2 the outlier is 99 year old tortoises

c Zoo 1 is negatively skewed since $Q_2 - Q_1 > Q_3 - Q_2$
Zoo 2 is positively skewed since $Q_2 - Q_1 < Q_3 - Q_2$

4 a 26 **b** 17

5 a width = 1.5 cm, height = 2.6 cm

b width = 7.5 cm, height = 0.3 cm

6 a

b Mean 19.8 kg, standard deviation 0.963 kg

c 20.1 kg

d −1.06

e The distribution of the weights of bags of compost is negatively skewed

7 a 22.3

b Number of bags **Key: 1|1 = 11 bags**

0	5
1	0 1 3 5 7
2	0 0 5
3	0 1 3
4	0 2

$Q_1 = 13$, Median = 20 and $Q_3 = 31$

c No outliers.

d Bags of potato crisps sold each day

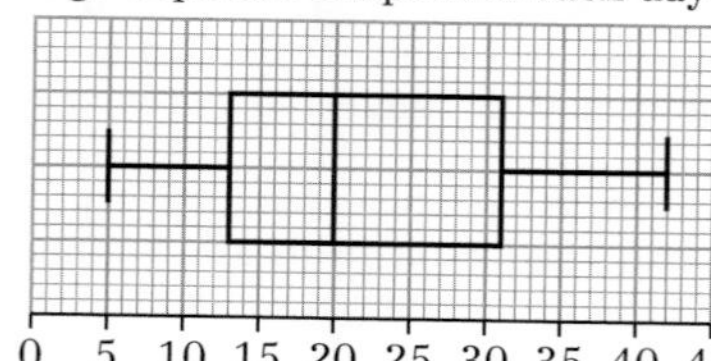

e Positive skew because $Q_2 - Q_1 < Q_3 - Q_2$

Online Worked solutions are available in SolutionBank.

8 a 22
b $X = 11, Y = 27, Z = 22$
9 a 1987: 11.9 °C, 2015: 12.1 °C
b The mean temperature was slightly higher in 2015 than in 1987. The standard deviation of temperatures was higher in 1987 (2.46 °C) than in 2015 showing that the temperatures were more spread out.
c 15 days, assuming that the temperatures are equally distributed throughout the range.

Challenge:
0.6 cm

CHAPTER 4

Prior knowledge check

1 a $\frac{2}{9}$ **b** $\frac{4}{9}$ **c** $\frac{2}{3}$ **d** 0
2 HHH, HHT, HTH, HTT, THH, THT, TTH, TTT
3 a $\frac{25}{216}$
b $\frac{11}{36}$
c $\frac{125}{216}$

Exercise 4A

1 $\frac{1}{2}$
2 a

		Second roll					
		1	2	3	4	5	6
First roll	1	1	2	3	4	5	6
	2	2	4	6	8	10	12
	3	3	6	9	12	15	18
	4	4	8	12	16	20	24
	5	5	10	15	20	25	30
	6	6	12	18	24	30	36

b i $\frac{1}{18}$ **ii** $\frac{2}{9}$ **iii** $\frac{3}{4}$
3 a $\frac{2}{5}$
b $\frac{5}{7}$
c Less likely; frequency uniformly distributed throughout the class.
4 a $\frac{19}{40}$ **b** $\frac{109}{240}$ **c** $\frac{71}{240}$
d $\frac{2}{15}$; distribution of lengths of koalas between 70 and 75 cm is uniform.
5 a $\frac{16}{35}$
b $\frac{32}{35}$

Challenge:
5, 7 or 9

Exercise 4B

1 a
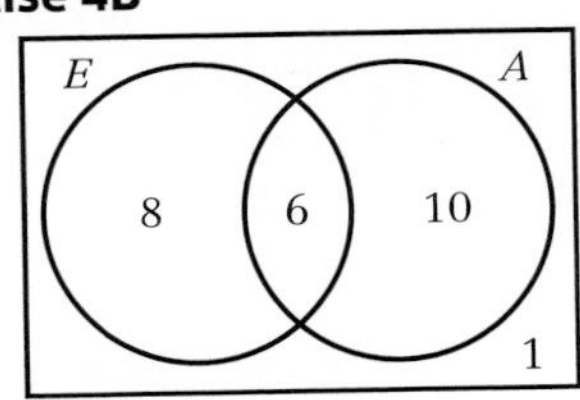

i $\frac{14}{25}$ **ii** $\frac{6}{25}$ **iii** $\frac{8}{25}$ **iv** $\frac{1}{25}$
2 a
G B C
7 10 10
15
11 5
13 54

b i $\frac{3}{25}$ **ii** $\frac{2}{25}$ **iii** $\frac{2}{25}$ **iv** $\frac{54}{125}$
3 a i
G P D
20 64 15
1
29 9
35 102

b i $\frac{89}{275}$ **ii** $\frac{103}{275}$ **iii** $\frac{14}{55}$ **iv** $\frac{102}{275}$
4 a 0.17
b 0.18
c 0.55
5 a 0.3
b 0.3
6 a 0.15
b 0.15
7 $p = 0.13, q = 0.25$

Challenge
$p = 0.115, q = 0.365, r = 0.12$

Exercise 4C

1 a
A B
0.2 0.5
0.3

b 0.7 **c** 0.3
2 P(sum of 4) + P(same number) ≠ P(sum of 4 or same number), so the events are not mutually exclusive.
3 0.15
4 0.3
5 a Bricks and trains; their curves do not overlap.
b Not independent.
6 a 0.25 **b** Not independent
7 a P(S and T) = 0.3 − 0.18 = 0.12
P(S) × P(T) = 0.3 × 0.4 = 0.12 = P(S and T)
So S and T are independent.
b i 0.12 **ii** 0.42
8 P(W) × P(X) = 0.5 × 0.45 = 0.225
P(W and X) = 0.25, so W and X are **not** independent.
9 a $x = 0.15, y = 0.3$
b P(F and R) = 0.15 ≠ P(F) × P(R) = 0.45 × 0.4 = 0.18
10 $p = 0.14$ and $q = 0.33$ or $p = 0.33$ and $q = 0.14$

Challenge

a Set P(A) = p and P(B) = q, then P(A and B) = pq
P(A and not B) = P(A) − P(A and B) = $p - pq$
P(not B) = $1 - q$
$\Rightarrow$ P(A) × P(not B) = $p(1 - q) = p - pq$ = P(A and not B)

b P(not A and not B) = 1 − P(A or B)
= 1 − P(A) − P(B) + P(A and B)
= $1 - p - q + pq = (1 - p)(1 - q)$
But P(not A) = $1 - p$ and P(not B) = $1 - q$, so
P(not A and not B) = P(not A) × P(not B)

Exercise 4D

1 a $A \cap B'$ b $A' \cup B$
c $(A \cap B) \cup (A' \cap B')$ d $A \cap B \cap C$
e $A \cup B \cup C$ f $(A \cup B) \cap C'$

2 a
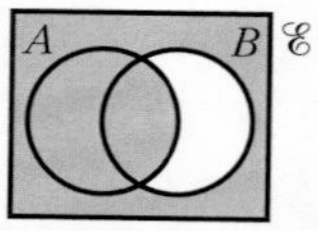

b
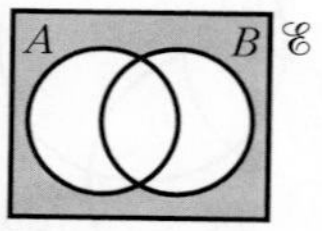

c
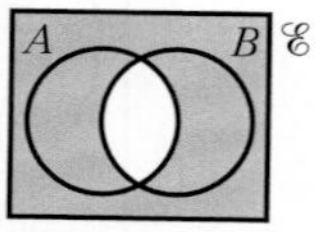

3 a
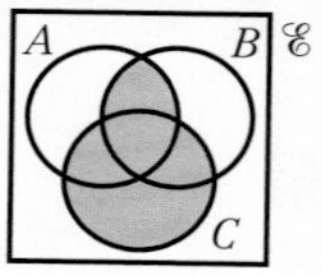

b
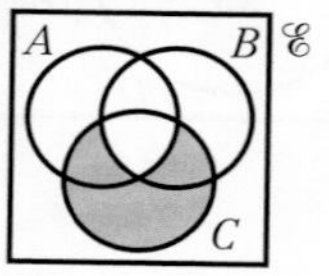

c
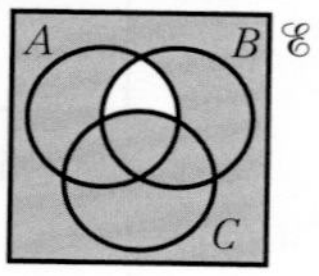

4 a 0.0769 b 0.25 c 0.0192
d 0.308 e 0.75 f 0.231

5 a 0.6 b 0.8 c 0.4 d 0.9

6 a 0.25 b 0.5 c 0.65 d 0.1

7 a
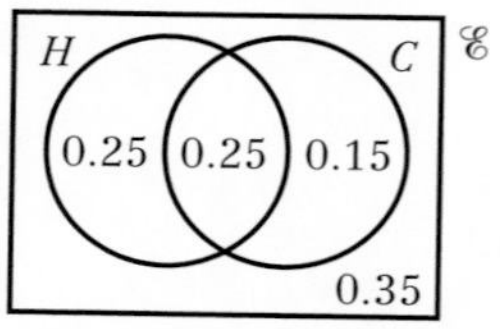

b i 0.65 ii 0.15 iii 0.85

8 a
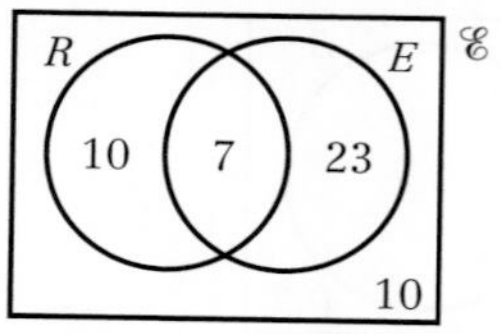

b i 7 ii $\frac{1}{5}$ iii $\frac{43}{50}$

9 a
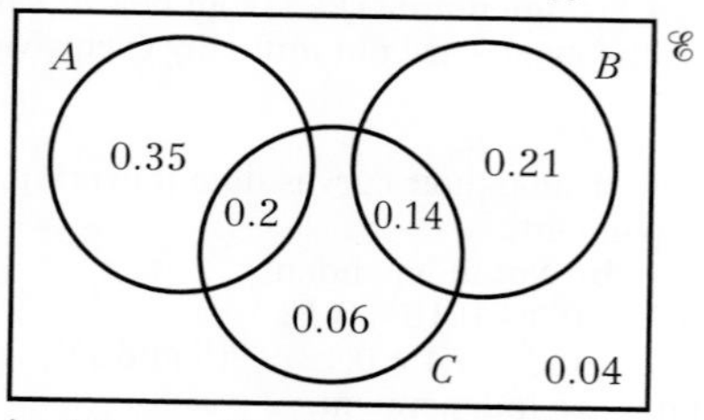

b i 0.1 ii 0.76 iii 1

10 a
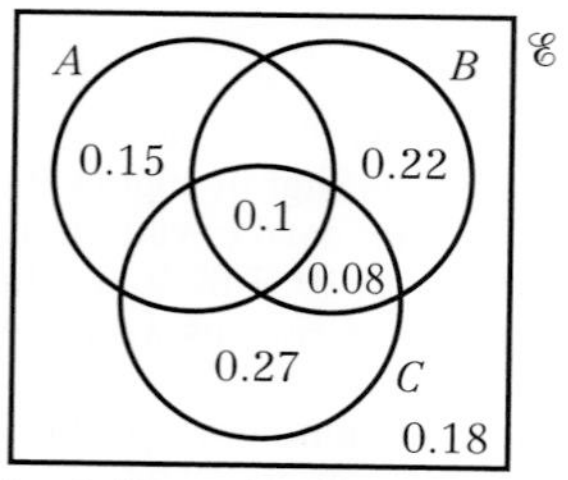

b i 0.53 ii 0.18
c Not independent.
$P(A' \cap C) = 0.35$, $P(A') \times P(C) = 0.75 \times 0.45$
$= 0.33765$

11 a
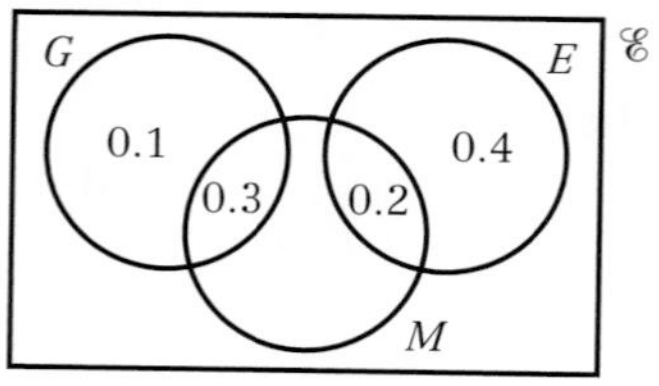

b i 0.6 ii 0.5
c Not independent.
$P(G' \cap M) = 0.2$, $P(G') \times P(M) = 0.6 \times 0.5 = 0.3$

12 a xy b $x + y - xy$ c $1 - y + xy$

Challenge

a xyz
b $x + y + z + xyz - xy - yz - xz$
c $z - yz + xyz$

Exercise 4E

1 a $\frac{29}{60}$ b $\frac{18}{29}$ c $\frac{18}{35}$ d $\frac{14}{31}$

2 a

	Badminton	Squash	Total
Teenager	21	22	43
Adult	15	17	32
Total	36	39	75

b i $\frac{22}{39}$ ii $\frac{15}{36}$ or $\frac{5}{12}$ iii $\frac{17}{32}$

3 a

	Girls	Boys	Total
Vanilla	13	2	15
Chocolate	12	10	22
Strawberry	20	23	43
Total	45	35	80

b i $\frac{23}{43}$ ii $\frac{13}{15}$ iii $\frac{10}{35}$ or $\frac{2}{7}$

4 a

Blue spinner

Red spinner	1	2	3	4
1	2	3	4	5
2	3	4	5	6
3	4	5	6	7
4	5	6	7	8

b i $\frac{1}{4}$ ii $\frac{1}{4}$ iii $\frac{1}{4}$

5 a

		Dice 1					
		1	2	3	4	5	6
Dice 2	1	1	2	3	4	5	6
	2	2	4	6	8	10	12
	3	3	6	9	12	15	18
	4	4	8	12	16	20	24
	5	5	10	15	20	25	30
	6	6	12	18	24	30	36

b $\frac{1}{6}$ **c** $\frac{1}{4}$

d All outcomes are equally likely.

6 0.0769 (3 s.f.) or $\frac{1}{13}$

7 a 0.333 **b** 0.667

c Assume that the coins are not biased.

8 a

	D	D'	Total
S	18	38	56
S'	59	5	64
Total	77	43	120

b i $\frac{43}{120}$ **ii** $\frac{5}{120}$ **iii** $\frac{18}{77}$ **iv** $\frac{38}{56}$

9 a

	Women	Men	Total
Stick	26	18	44
No stick	37	29	66
Total	63	47	110

b i $\frac{44}{110}$ or $\frac{2}{5}$ **ii** $\frac{26}{63}$ **iii** $\frac{18}{44}$ or $\frac{9}{22}$

10 a $\frac{6}{25}$ **b** $\frac{13}{30}$ **c** $\frac{29}{64}$ **d** $\frac{31}{90}$

Exercise 4F

1 a 0.7 **b** 0.3

c 0.483 (3 s.f.) **d** 0.571 (3 s.f.)

2 a

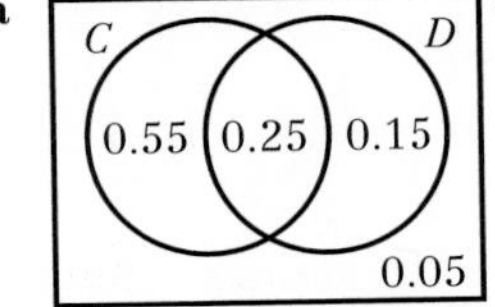

b i 0.95 **ii** 0.625 **iii** 0.313 (3 s.f.) **iv** 0.25

3 a

S, T, ℰ; 0.15, 0.35, 0.35; 0.15

b i 0.35 **ii** 0.5 **iii** 0.7 **iv** 0.231 (3 s.f.)

4 a $\frac{3}{8}$ **b** $\frac{2}{5}$ **c** $\frac{6}{11}$ **d** $\frac{13}{19}$

5 a $\frac{9}{80}$ **b** $\frac{9}{32}$ **c** $\frac{1}{5}$ **d** $\frac{12}{35}$

6 a 0.6 **b** 0.4

c 0.299 (3 s.f.) **d** 0.329 (3 s.f.)

7 a $\frac{9}{23}$ **b** $\frac{3}{23}$

c $P(B|C) = 0.111\ldots \neq P(B) = 0.345\ldots$ So B and C are not independent

8 a

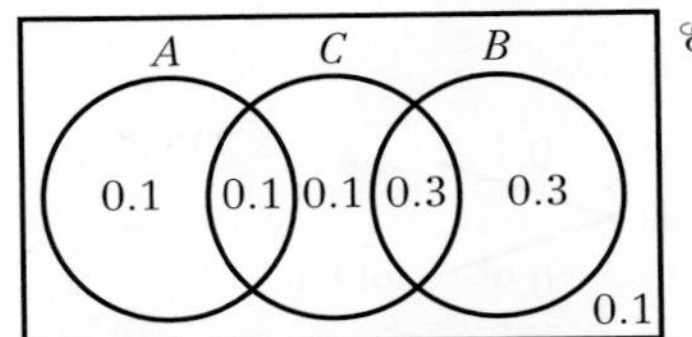

b i 0.2 **ii** 0.6 **iii** 0.5

9 a

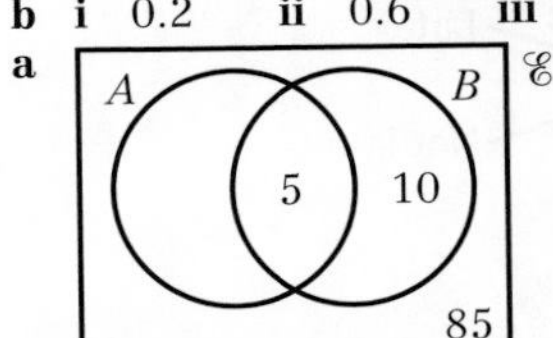

b $\frac{1}{3}$

c No one who doesn't have the disease would be given a false negative result. However, only $\frac{1}{3}$ of the people who have a positive result would have the disease.

10 a 0.7 **b** 0.7 **c** They are independent.

11 $x = 0.21$, $y = 0.49$

12 $c = \frac{7}{30}$, $d = \frac{4}{15}$

Exercise 4G

1 a 0.3 **b** 0.6 **c** 0.8 **d** 0.9

2 a 0.8

b i 0.2 **ii** 0.615 (3 s.f.) **iii** 0.429 (3 s.f.)

c $P(C \cap D) \neq P(C) \times P(D)$

3 a 0.9

b i 0.8 **ii** 0.2 **iii** 0.5

4 a 0.15 **b** 0.45 **c** 0.55 **d** 0.25 **e** 0.3

5 0.1

6 a 0.5 **b** 0.3 **c** 0.3

7 a 0.3 **b** 0.35 **c** 0.4

8 a 0.0833 (3 s.f.) **b** 0.15

c 0.233 (3 s.f.) **d** 0.357 (3 s.f.)

e 0.643 (3 s.f.) **f** 0.783 (3 s.f.)

9 a 0.67 **b** 0.476 (3 s.f.) **c** 0.126

d

A, C, B, ℰ; 0.174, 0.174, 0.126, 0.12, 0.25; 0.156

e 0.294

10 a 0.28 **b** 0.7

c 0.333 (3 s.f.) **d** 0.467 (3 s.f.)

11 a 0.1 **b** 0.143 (3 s.f.)

c $P(A) \times P(B) = 0.3 \times 0.7 = 0.21$, $P(A \cap B) = 0.15$
This suggests that the events are not independent. If Fatima is late, Gayana is *less* likely to be late and vice versa.

12 a 0.5 **b** 0.333 (3 s.f.) **c** 0.833 (3 s.f.)

d $P(C \mid J) = 0.833\ldots \neq P(C) = 0.7$. So J and C are not independent.

Exercise 4H

1 0.88 or $\frac{44}{50}$

2 a

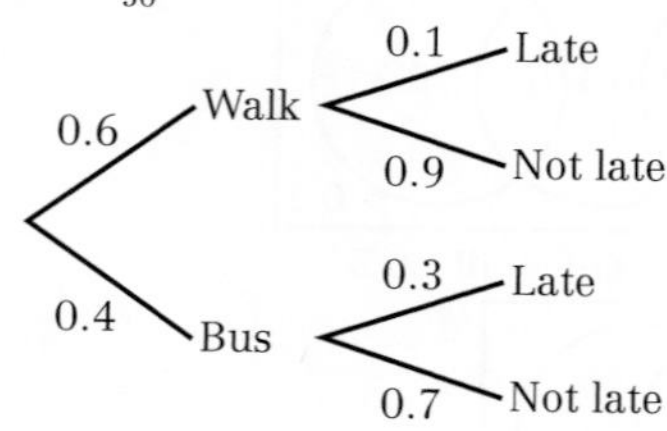

b 0.12

c 0.82

3 a $\frac{12}{380}$ or equivalent

b $\frac{90}{380}$ or equivalent

4 a

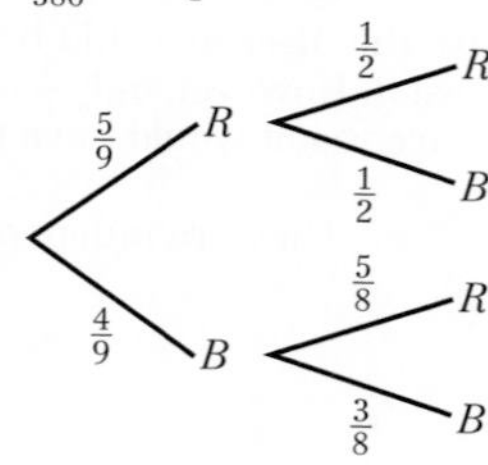

b $\frac{5}{8}$ **c** $\frac{5}{8}$ **d** $\frac{1}{2}$ **e** $\frac{1}{2}$

5 a

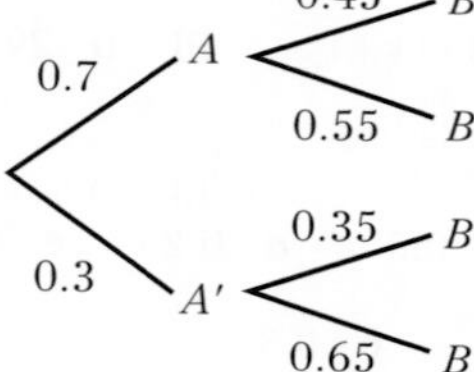

b i 0.315 **ii** 0.195 **iii** 0.75

6 a

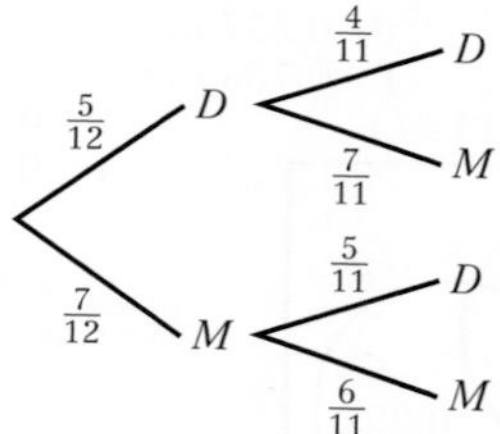

b 0.163 (3 s.f.) **c** 0.507 (3 s.f.) **d** 0.243 (3 s.f.)

7 0.36

8 a 0.25 **b** 0.333

9 a

B $\frac{4}{11}$: B $\frac{3}{10}$, G $\frac{7}{10}$

G $\frac{7}{11}$: B $\frac{4}{10}$, G $\frac{6}{10}$

b $\frac{7}{11}$ **c** $\frac{3}{5}$

10 a

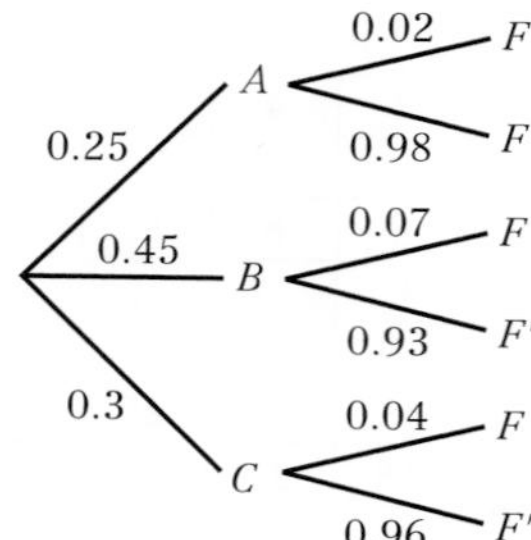

b i 0.0315 **ii** 0.0485 **c** 0.103 (3 s.f.)

11 a

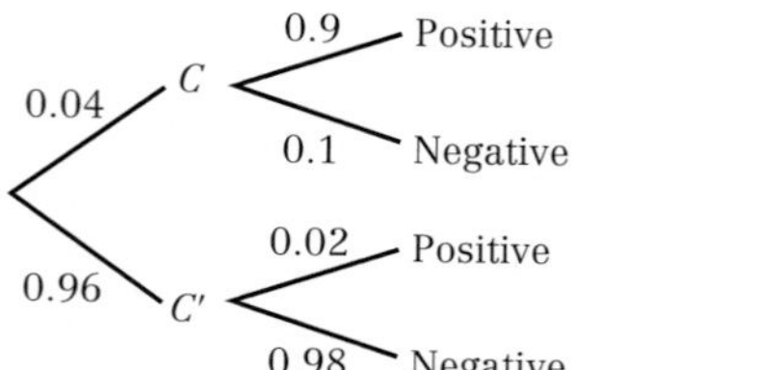

b 0.945 (3 s.f.) **c** 0.00423

d The probability that a positive result is a false positive (positive result for someone without the condition) is P(−|+) = 0.348. Over one third of positive results are false positives and 10% of people with the condition give negative results.

12 a

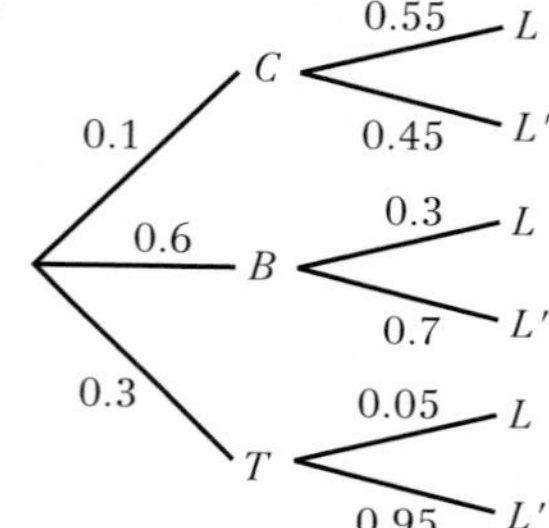

b i 0.015 **ii** 0.25 **c** 0.78

13 a

G $\frac{4}{7}$: G $\frac{1}{2}$ (G $\frac{4}{7}$, B $\frac{3}{7}$); B $\frac{1}{2}$ (G $\frac{3}{7}$, B $\frac{4}{7}$)

B $\frac{3}{7}$: G $\frac{2}{3}$ (G $\frac{3}{7}$, B $\frac{4}{7}$); B $\frac{1}{3}$ (G $\frac{2}{7}$, B $\frac{5}{7}$)

b $\frac{3}{7}$

c Adding together the probabilities on the 4 branches of the tree diagram where the counter from box B is blue: $\frac{12}{98} + \frac{16}{98} + \frac{24}{147} + \frac{15}{157} = \frac{27}{49}$

d Adding together the probabilities on the two branches of the tree diagram where events C and D both occur. $\frac{12}{98} + \frac{15}{147} = \frac{11}{49}$

e $\frac{37}{49}$ **f** $\frac{8}{13}$

14 Emilia has not taken into account the fact that the jelly bean is eaten after being selected. The correct answer is 0.5.

Chapter review 4

1 a

1st pick 2nd pick

Y ($\frac{4}{7}$): Y ($\frac{4}{6}$), B ($\frac{3}{6}$)

B ($\frac{3}{7}$): Y ($\frac{4}{6}$), B ($\frac{2}{6}$)

b $\frac{6}{42}$

c $\frac{24}{42}$

2 a $\frac{392}{3375}$ **b** $\frac{14}{75}$

3 a 0.0397 **b** 0.286 **c** 0.714

4 a $\frac{64}{125}$

b $\frac{8}{25}$

c $\frac{33}{250}$

d $\frac{74}{125}$, using interpolation and assuming uniform distribution of scores

5 a $\frac{44}{50}$ **b** $\frac{77}{100}$

6 a

T F S

18 5 35 4 8 10 40 30

b i 0.2 **ii** 0.82

7 a

A B

$\frac{1}{4}$ $\frac{1}{12}$ $\frac{1}{6}$ $\frac{1}{2}$

b $P(A) = \frac{1}{3}$, $P(B) = \frac{1}{4}$, $P(A \text{ and } B) = \frac{1}{12}$
$P(A) \times P(B) = P(A \text{ and } B)$, so A and B are independent.

8 a Cricket and swimming

b Not independent

9 a

J K S

0.25 0.05 0.2 0.5

b $P(J) = 0.3$, $P(K) = 0.25$, $P(J \text{ and } K) = 0.05$
$P(J) \times P(K) = 0.075 \neq P(J \text{ and } K)$, so J and K are not independent.

10 a 0.5

b

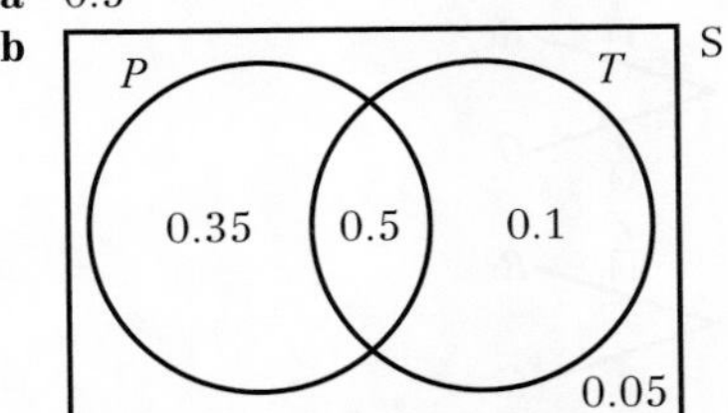

c 0.35

d No. $P(P) = 0.85$ and $P(T) = 0.6$, so $P(P) \times P(T) = 0.51 \neq P(P \text{ and } T)$

11 Not independent

12 a

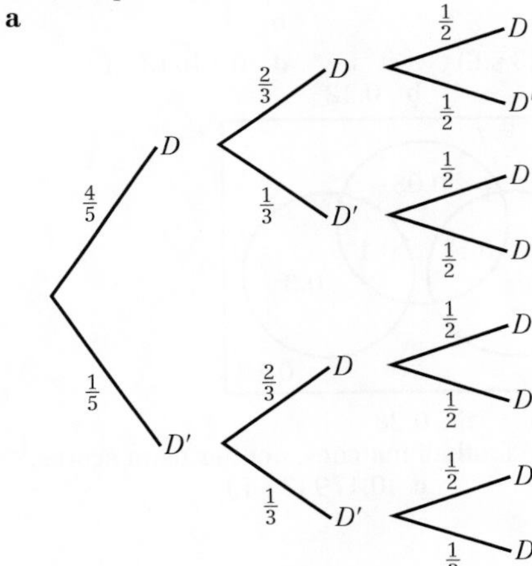

b i $\frac{4}{15}$ **ii** $\frac{7}{30}$

c $\frac{11}{15}$

13 a

A (0.16): F (0.04), F' (0.96)

B (0.5): F (0.03), F' (0.97)

C (0.34): F (0.07), F' (0.93)

b i 0.015 **ii** 0.0452

14 a 0.55 **b** 0.45 **c** 0.5 **d** 0.429 (3 s.f.)

15 a

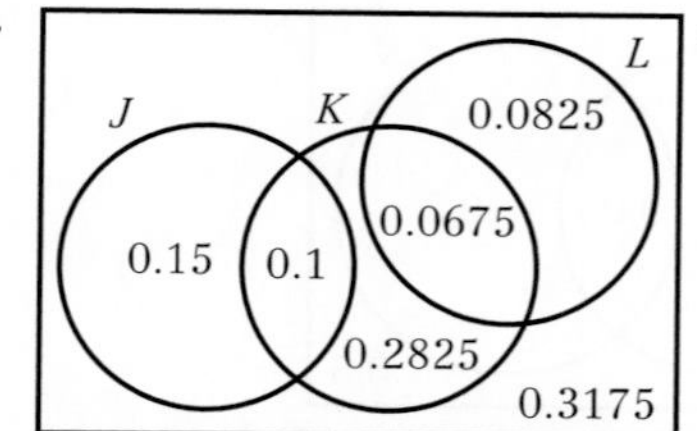

b **i** 0.6 **ii** 0.6 **iii** 0.222 (3 s.f.) **iv** 0.471 (3 s.f.)

16 a 0.433 (3 s.f.) **b** 0.6 **c** 0.72
d 0.25 **e** 0.577 (3 s.f.)

17 a

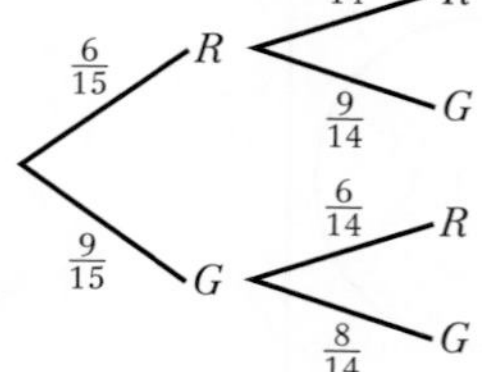

b **i** $\frac{12}{35}$ **ii** $\frac{18}{35}$
c $\frac{2}{5}$ **d** $\frac{6}{65}$

18 a 0.74 **b** 0.757 (3 s.f.) **c** 0.703

19 a $\frac{4}{15}$ **b** $\frac{15}{41}$
c 0.117 (3 s.f.) **d** 0.146 (3 s.f.)

20 a 0.3 **b** 0.42
c

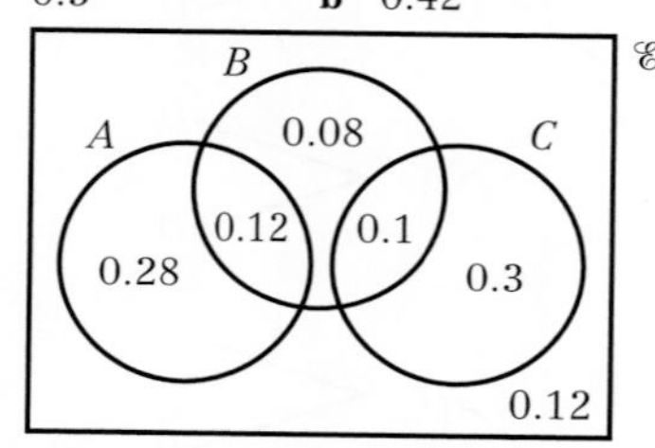

d **i** 0.25 **ii** 0.28

21 a In some football matches, neither team scores.
b 0.12 **c** 0.179 (3 s.f.)

Challenge

1 0.2016

2 a $0.4 \leqslant p \leqslant 0.6$ **b** $0.2 \leqslant q \leqslant 0.5$

3 a $\frac{1}{15}$ **b** $\frac{5}{12}$ **c** $\frac{2}{3}$

Review exercise 1

1 a Any 2 lines from:
- Used to simplify or represent a real world problem.
- Cheaper or quicker (than producing the real situation) or more easily modified.
- To improve understanding of the real world problem.
- Used to predict outcomes from a real world problem (idea of predictions).

b (3) Model used to make predictions.
(4) Experimental data collected.
(7) Model is refined. (Steps 2 (or 3) to 5 (or 6) are repeated).
You could put 3 and 4 the other way round.

2 Mean = 240 and standard deviation = 14

3 Mean = 57.7142 (58) and standard deviation = 4.71

4 Mean 3.06 hours, standard deviation 3.32 hours

5 USD 18,720

6 a $t = 0.8(m + 12)$ or $t = \frac{m + 12}{1.25}$
b Mean 54, standard deviation 0.64

7 a Missing values: 35 and 15
b 40
c 18.91
d 7.26
e Lower quartile = 13.75, Median = 18 and upper quartile = 23
f 0.376 therefore it is positively skewed.

8 a $15.3 + 2 \times 10.2 = 35.7$ so 45 is an outlier
b A temperature of 45 °C is very high so it is likely this value was recorded incorrectly.

9 a Positive skew **b** 26.7
c 29.6 **d** 0.520
e Yes it is as $0.520 > 0$
f Use median since data is skewed
g If the data is symmetrical or skewness is zero

10 a 56
b $Q_1 = 35$, $Q_2 = 52$ and $Q_3 = 60$
c Mean = 49.4 and standard deviation = 14.6
d −1.356
e For a negative skew
Mean < Median < Mode $(49.4 < 52 < 56)$
$Q_2 - Q_1\ (17) > Q_3 - Q_2$
$\frac{3(49.4 - 52)}{14.6} = -0.534$

11 a Distance is a continuous variable
b 0.8, 3.8, 5.3, 3.7, 0.75, 0.1
c Median = 58.8
Lower Quartile = 52.5
Upper Quartile = 67.1
d Mean =62.5 and standard deviation = 15.8
e 0.137 and it is positively skewed
f For positive skew Mean > median and $62.5 > 58.8$
or
$Q_3 - Q_2\ (8.3) > Q_2 - Q_1\ (6.3)$
or
$\frac{3(62.5) - 58.8)}{15.8} = 0.703 > 0$
Therefore positive skew.

12 a Time is a continuous variable
b Area is proportional to frequency
c 30

13 a

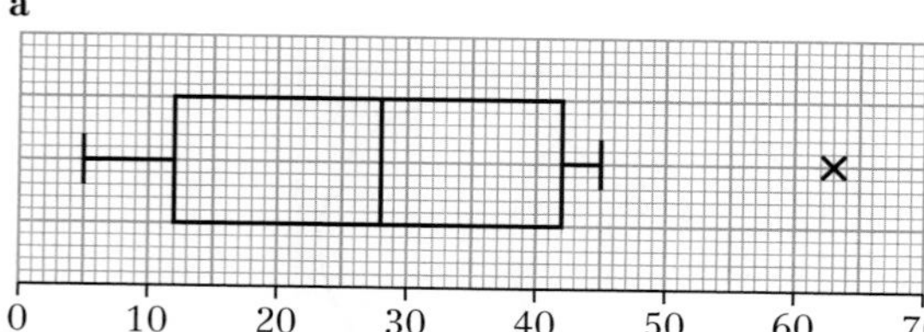

b The distribution is a slight negative skew because $Q_2 - Q_1\ (16) > Q_3 - Q_2\ (14)$
c The distribution is almost symmetrical meaning that passengers can expect an average delay on this flight of 28 minutes, and 50% of flights will be delayed between 12 and 42 minutes.

14 a 17 males and 15 females
b £48
c Males earned the most in general

15 a **i** 37 minutes
ii upper quartile, third quartile, 75 percentile

b Outliers – values that are much greater than or much less than the other values and need to be treated with caution.

c

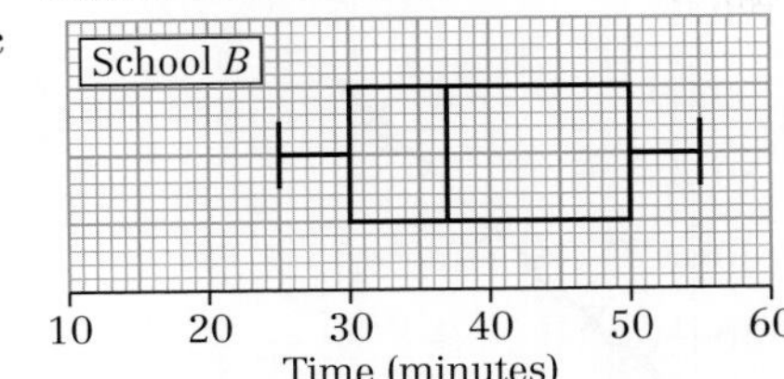

d The children from school A generally took less time than those from school B. The median for A is less than the median for B. A has outliers, but B does not. The interquartile range for A is less than the interquartile range for B. The total range for A is greater than the total range for B.

16 0.82

17 a

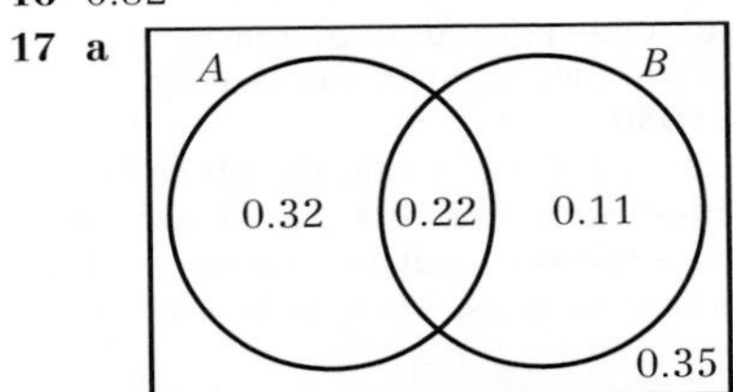

b P(A) = 0.54, P(B) = 0.33
c They are not independent.

18 a M and T
b P(M and B) = 0.34; P(M) × P(B) = 0.32 so the events are not independent

19 a

G, L, D, $\mathscr{E}$: 10, 7, 6, 10, 9, 5, 12, 41

b 0.1

c 0.41 **d** 0.21 **e** 0.667 (3 s.f.)

20 a 0.1 **b**

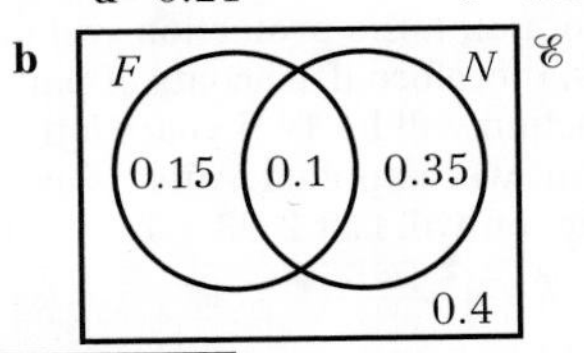

c 0.25

21 a

A, B, $\mathscr{E}$: 0.34, 0.15, 0.13, 0.38

b P(A) = 0.49, P(B) = 0.28
c $\frac{17}{36}$ or 0.472 (3 s.f.)
d No: P(A) × P(B) ≠ P($A \cap B$)

22 a 0.5 **b** 0.35
c

A, B, C, $\mathscr{E}$: 0.25, 0.15, 0.15, 0.1, 0.3, 0.05

d i 0.25 **ii** 0.4 **iii** $\frac{2}{3}$

23 a 0.338 (3 s.f.) **b** 0.46
c 0.743 (3 s.f.) **d** 0.218 (3 s.f.)

24 a 0.198 (3 s.f.) **b** $\frac{45}{79}$ or 0.570 (3 s.f.)

25 a

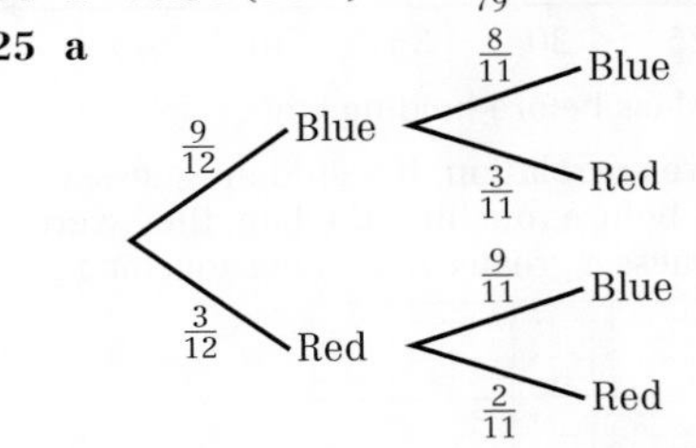

b 0.25 **c** 0.409

26 a

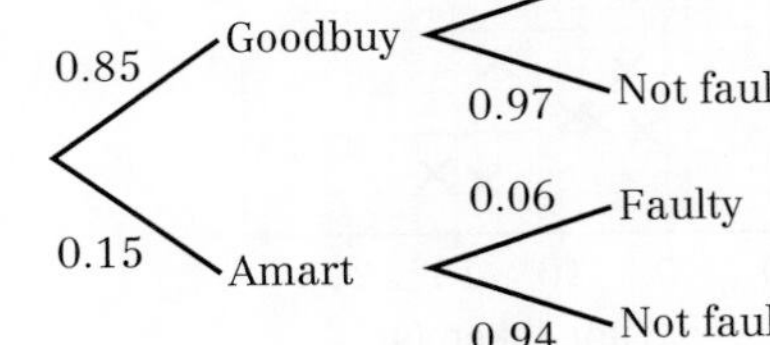

b 0.9655

27 a

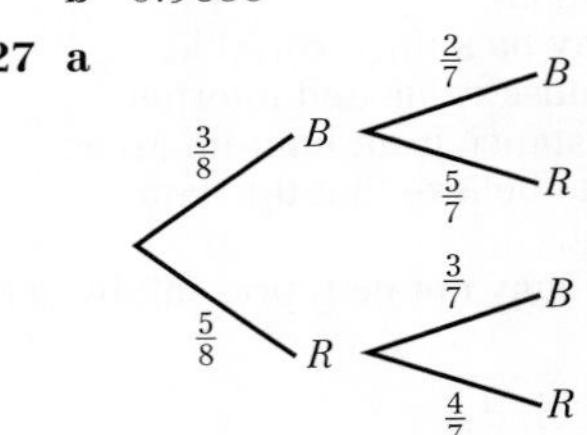

b i $\frac{21}{56}$ or $\frac{3}{8}$ **ii** $\frac{2}{7}$

Challenge

1 $x = 4, y = 6, z = 14$
2 a $0.4 \leqslant p \leqslant 0.7$ **b** $0 \leqslant q \leqslant 0.45$

CHAPTER 5

Prior knowledge check

1 a $y = 3x$
b $y = -6x + 24$
2 a −3.21
b 0.34

Exercise 5A

1 a Positive correlation.
b The longer the treatment, the more hair growth observed.

2 a No correlation.
b The scatter diagram does not support the statement that hotter cities have less rainfall.

3 a

Mass after holding bag

Mass before holding bag

b There is positive correlation. If a student guessed a greater mass before touching the bag, they were more likely to guess a greater mass after touching it.

4 a

House value (€1000s)

Time taken (s)

b Weak negative correlation.

c For example, there may be a third variable that influences both house value and internet connection, such as distance from built-up areas.

5 b i There is no reason to believe that the data collected is incorrect.

ii 22.3 is an outlier so may not be representative of the typical rainfall.

c

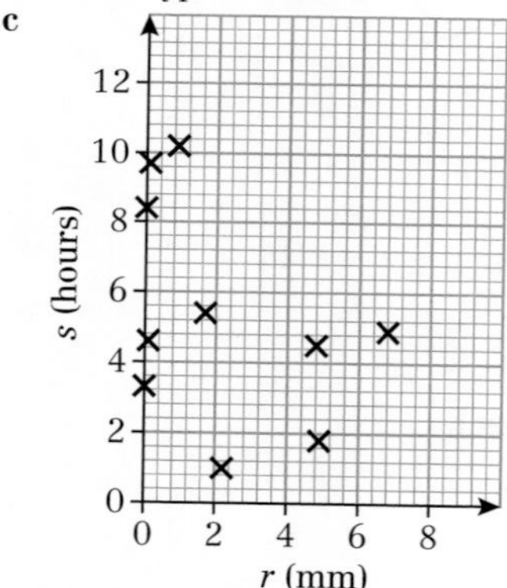

d No correlation

e For example, there could be a causal relationship as days with more rainfall will have more clouds, and therefore less sunshine.

Exercise 5B

1 a, b

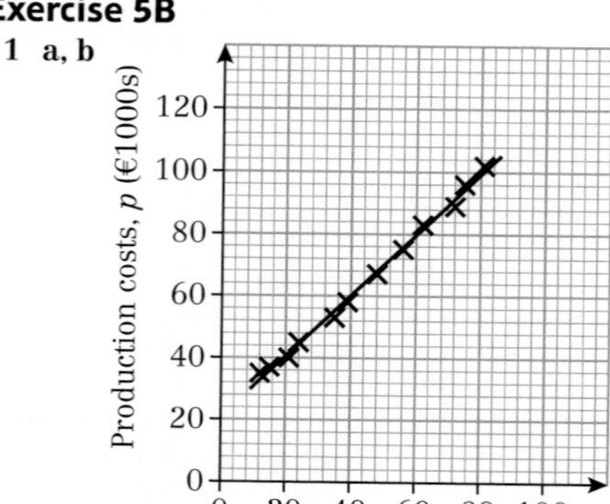

c If the number of items produced per month is zero, the production costs will be approximately €21,000. If the number of items per month increases by 1000 items, the production costs increase by approximately €980.

d The prediction for 74 000 is within the range of the data (interpolation) so is more likely to be accurate. The prediction for 95 000 is outside the range of the data (extrapolation) so is less likely to be accurate.

2 a

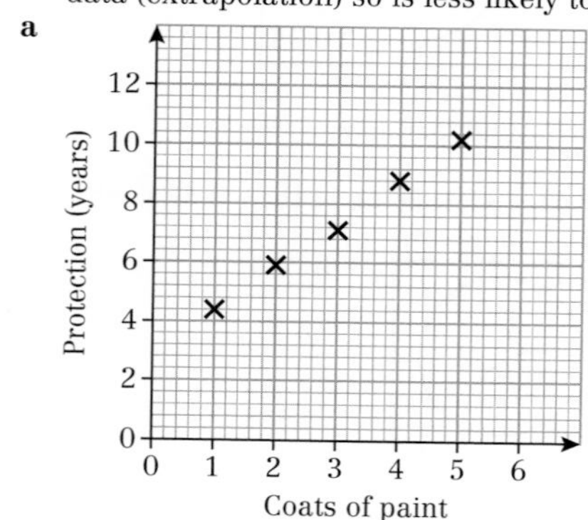

b A gradient of 1.45 means that for every extra coat of paint, the protection will increase by 1.45 years, therefore if 10 coats of paint are applied, the protection will be 14.5 years longer than if no coats of paint were applied. After 10 coats of paint, the protection will last 2.93 + 14.5 = 17.43 years.

3 a

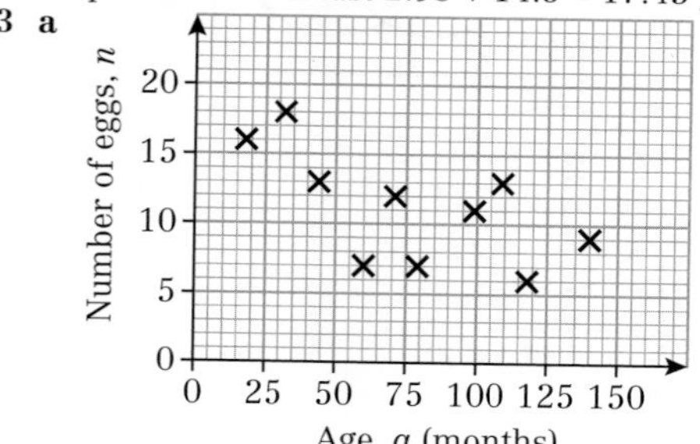

b The scatter diagram shows negative correlation, therefore the gradient in the regression equation should be negative.

4 This is not sensible as there are unlikely to be any houses with no bedrooms.

5 a Each visitor spends €740.

b €1161 million

c As this involves interpolation the value of money spent is reliable.

Exercise 5C

1 $a = -3, b = 6$
2 $y = -14 + 5.5x$
3 $y = 2x$
4 a $\bar{x} = 2.5, \bar{y} = 12, S_{xx} = 5, S_{xy} = 20$
b $y = 2 + 4x$
5 a $S_{xx} = 40.8, S_{xy} = 69.6$ b $y = -0.294 + 1.71x$
6 a $y = -59 + 57(6) = 283$
b For each dexterity point, productivity increases by 57.
c i No, because this is extrapolation as it is outside the range of data.
ii No, because this is extrapolation as it is outside the range of data.
7 $g = 1.50 + 1.44h$
8 a $p = 65.4 - 1.38w$
b $w = 47.4 - 0.72p$
c The gradient of the second regression line is calculated using different summary statistics rather than just the reciprocal of the summary statistics used for the first regression line.
d i The first one. ii The second one.
9 a $y = 78.0 - 0.294x$
b
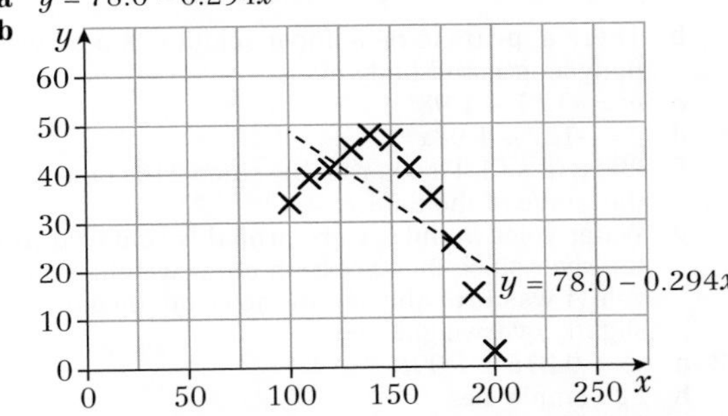

c Model is not valid since data does not follow a linear pattern.
10 a $S_{nn} = 6486, S_{np} = 6344$
b $p = 21.0 + 0.978n$
c €60,100 (3 s.f.)
d Reliable, as 40 000 items lies inside the range of the data.
11 a $S_{nn} = 589.6, S_{np} = 1474$
b $p = 20 + 2.5n$
c The increase in cost, in dollars, for every 100 leaflets printed.
d $t > 8$
12 a $y = -0.07 + 1.45x$
b Number of years protection per coat of paint.
c Unreliable, as 7 coats lies outside the range of the data.
d 10.08 years
e i $0.4779 + 1.247x$
ii 9.2 years (2 s.f.)
iii The answer now uses interpolation not extrapolation and the number of data points has increased, which increases accuracy in prediction.

Challenge

z = time available – time taken
$= (100 - x) - (a + bx)$
$= (100 - a) - (1 + b)x$

and

$z = 81.5 - 1.546x$

for $z = 0$

$x = \frac{81.5}{1.564} = 52$

The latest time is 8:52 am

Exercise 5D

1 $y = 6 - x$
2 $s = 88 + p$
3 $y = 32 - 5.33x$
4 $t = 9 + 3s$
5 a $y = 3.5 + 0.5x$ b $d = 35 + 2.5c$
6 a $S_{xy} = 162.2, S_{xx} = 190.8$; $y = 7.87 + 0.850x$ (3 s.f.)
b $c = 22.3 + 2.13a$ (3 s.f.)
c \$90.46 or \$90.56
7 a $p = 3.03 + 1.49v$ (3 s.f.) b 10.1 tonnes (3 s.f.)

Exercise 5E

1 0.985 (3 s.f.)
2 0.202 (3 s.f.)
3 a 9.71 (3 s.f.)
b 0.968 (3 s.f.)
c There is positive correlation. The greater the age, the taller the person.
4 a $S_{LL} = 30.3, S_{TT} = 25.1, S_{LT} = 25.35$
b 0.919 (3 s.f.)
c The value of the correlation coefficient is close to 1 and the points lie on an approximate straight line, therefore a linear regression model is suitable.
5 a 0.866 (3 s.f.)
b There is positive correlation. The higher the IQ, the higher the mark in the general knowledge test.
6 0.973
7 a

p	0	5	3	2	1
q	0	17	12	10	6

b 0.974 (3 s.f.) c 0.974 (3 s.f.)
8 a $S_{pp} = 10, S_{tt} = 5.2, S_{pt} = 7$
b 0.971 (3 s.f.)
c 0.971 (3 s.f.)
9 a $S_{xx} = 1601, S_{yy} = 1282, S_{xy} = -899$
b -0.627 (3 s.f.)
c The shopkeeper is wrong. There is negative correlation. Sweet sales actually decrease as newspaper sales increase.
10 a $S_{ff} = \Sigma f^2 - \frac{(\Sigma f)^2}{n} = \Sigma(10x)^2 - \frac{(\Sigma 10x)^2}{n}$
$= 100\Sigma x^2 - \frac{100(\Sigma x)^2}{n} = 100\left(\Sigma x^2 - \frac{(\Sigma x)^2}{n}\right)$
$= 100S_{xx} = 100 \times 111.48 = 11\,148$
b 0.934 (3 s.f.)
c The PMCC suggests strong linear correlation but the scatter diagram suggests non-linear fit so a linear regression model is not suitable.
11 a $S_{xx} = \Sigma x^2 - \frac{(\Sigma x)^2}{n} = 22.02 - \frac{12^2}{7} = 1.448\ldots$
$S_{xy} = \Sigma xy - \frac{\Sigma x \Sigma y}{n} = 180.37 - \frac{12 \times 97.7}{7}$
$= 12.884\ldots$
$S_{yy} = \Sigma y^2 - \frac{(\Sigma y)^2}{n} = 1491.69 - \frac{97.7^2}{7}$
$= 128.077\ldots$
$r = \frac{S_{xy}}{\sqrt{S_{xx}S_{yy}}} = \frac{12.884\ldots}{\sqrt{1.448\ldots \times 128.077\ldots}} = 0.946$ (3 s.f.)
b $-2.29345, 0.22765, 0.8382, 1.16985, 1.39095, 0.61205, -1.94575$
c Residuals are not randomly scattered about zero (they 'rise and fall') so this indicates that a linear model is not a good model for this data.

Chapter review 5

1 The data shows that the number of serious road accidents in a week strongly correlates with the number of fast food restaurants. However, it does not show whether the relationship is causal. Both variables could correlate with a third variable, e.g. the number of roads coming into a town.

2 a

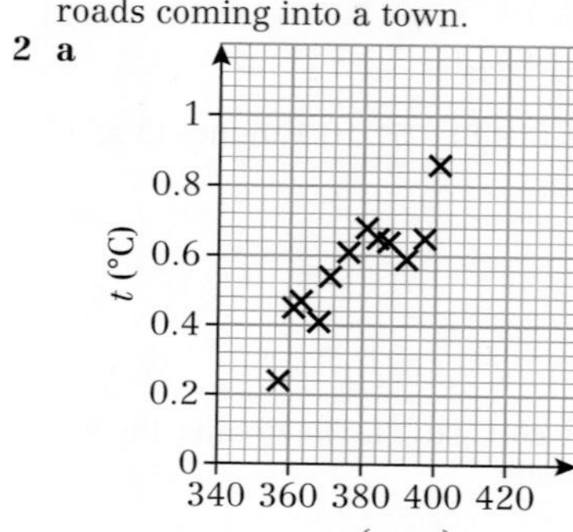

b Strong positive correlation.

c As mean CO_2 concentration in the atmosphere increases, mean global temperatures also increase.

3 a Strong positive correlation.

b If the number of items increases by 1, the time taken increases by approximately 2.64 minutes.

4 a Mean + 2SD = 15.2 + 2 × 11.4 = 38; 50 > 38

b The outlier should be omitted as it is very unlikely that the average temperature was 50 °C.

c If the temperature increases by approximately 1 °C, the number of pairs of gloves sold each month decreases by 0.18.

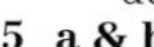

5 a & b

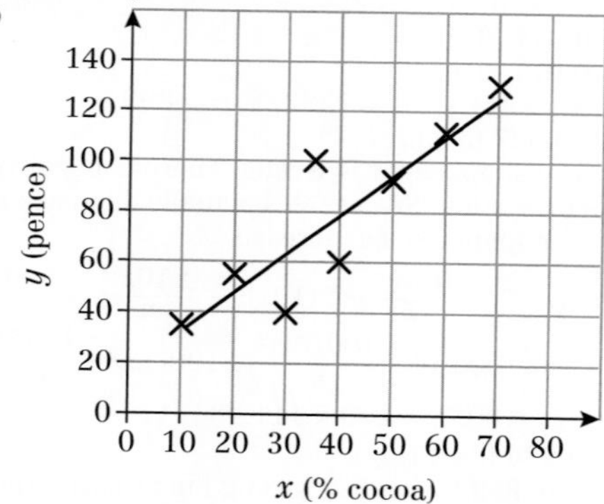

c Brand D is overpriced, since it is a long way above the line.

d The regression equation should be used to predict a value for y given x so the student's method is valid.

6 a $t = 1.96 + 0.95s$ b 49.5 (3 s.f.)

7 a $S_{xx} = 16\,350$, $S_{xx} = 210\,331$

b $y = 224.5 + 12.86x$

c 1511

d 255

e This answer is unreliable since a Gross National Product of 3500 is a long way outside the range of the data. Also, the regression equation should only be used to estimate values of y given x.

8 a $y = 0.343 + 0.449x$ b $t = 2.34 + 0.224m$

c 4.6 cm (2 s.f.)

9 a $S_{xy} = 78$, $S_{xx} = 148$ b $y = 7.311 + 0.5270x$

c $w = 816.2 + 210.8n$ d 5032 kg

e 100 items is a long way outside the range of the data.

10 a 0.79 kg is the average amount of food consumed in 1 week by 1 hen.

b 23.9 kg (3 s.f.) c €47.59

11 a & e

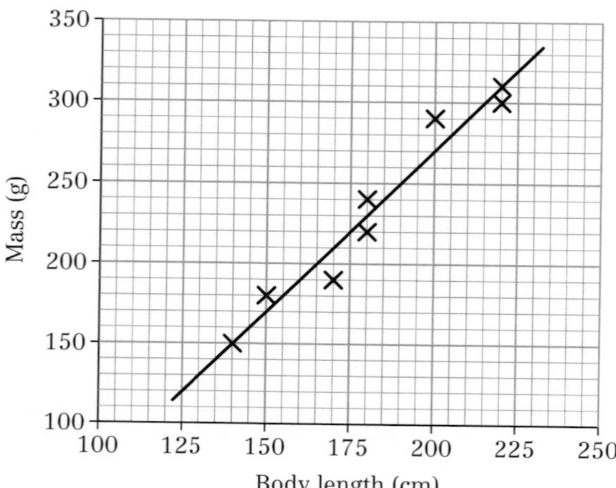

b There appears to be a linear relationship between body length and body mass.

c $w = -12.7 + 1.98l$

d $y = -127 + 1.98x$

f 290 g (2 s.f.). This is reliable since 210 cm is within the range of the data.

g Water voles B and C were probably removed from the river since they are both underweight. Water vole A was probably left in the river since it is slightly overweight.

12 a $s = -0.215 + 1.09t$

b 229 employees

13 PMCC = 0.375 (3 s.f.)

14 a −0.147 (3 s.f.) b −0.147 (3 s.f.)

c This is a weak negative correlation. There is little evidence to suggest that science marks are related to art marks.

15 a $S_{jj} = 4413$, $S_{pp} = 5145$, $S_{jp} = 3972$

b 0.834 (3 s.f.)

c There is strong positive correlation, so Nimer is correct.

16 a
$$S_{pp} = \Sigma p^2 - \frac{(\Sigma p)^2}{n} = \Sigma(x-10)^2 - \frac{(\Sigma x - 10)^2}{n}$$
$$= \Sigma(x^2 - 20x + 100) - \frac{((\Sigma x) - 10n)^2}{n}$$
$$= \Sigma x^2 - 20\Sigma x + 100n - \left(\frac{(\Sigma x)^2 - 20n\Sigma x + 100n^2}{n}\right)$$
$$= \Sigma x^2 - 20\Sigma x + 100n - \left(\frac{(\Sigma x)^2}{n} - 20\Sigma x + 100n\right)$$
$$= \Sigma x^2 - \frac{(\Sigma x)^2}{n} = S_{xx}$$

b −0.964 (3 s.f.) c −0.964 (3 s.f.)

d The PMCC suggests strong (negative) linear correlation but the scatter diagram suggests non-linear fit so a linear regression model is not suitable.

Challenge

a 1835.2 b 0.776

CHAPTER 6

Prior knowledge check

1 HHH HHT HTH HTT THH THT TTT

2 $k = \frac{12}{25}$

3 $x = 3$ and $y = 1$

Exercise 6A

1 a This is not a discrete random variable, since height is a continuous quantity.
b This is a discrete random variable, since it is always a whole number and it can vary.
c This is not a variable at all, since the number of days in a week is always 7.

2 0, 1, 2, 3, 4

3 a (2, 2) (2, 3) (3, 2) (3, 3)
b i

x	4	5	6
$P(X = x)$	0.25	0.5	0.25

ii $P(X = x) = \begin{cases} 0.25, & x = 4, 6 \\ 0.5, & x = 5 \end{cases}$

4 $\frac{1}{12}$

5 $k + 2k + 3k + 4k = 1$,
so $10k = 1$, so $k = \frac{1}{10}$.

6 a 0.125 b 0.875

7 a 0.3
b

x	−2	−1	0	1	2
$P(X = x)$	0.1	0.1	0.3	0.3	0.2

c 0.7

8 0.25

9 a 0.02 b 0.46 c 0.56

10 a 0.625 b 0.375 c 0

11 a

s	1	2	3	4
$P(S = s)$	$\frac{2}{3}$	$\frac{2}{9}$	$\frac{2}{27}$	$\frac{1}{27}$

b $\frac{1}{9}$

12 a

x	$P(X = x)$
0	0.07776
1	0.2592
2	0.3456
3	0.2304
4	0.0768
5	0.01024

b

y	$P(Y = y)$
0	0.32768
1	0.4096
2	0.2048
3	0.0512
4	0.0064
5	0.00032

c

z	$P(Z = z)$
1	0.4
2	0.24
3	0.144
4	0.0864
5	0.1296

13 a The sum of the probabilities is not 1.
b $2\frac{22}{61}$

Challenge
0.625

Exercise 6B

1 a

x	1	2	3	4	5	6
$F(x)$	0.1	0.2	0.35	0.60	0.9	1

b 0.9
c 0.2

2 a

x	1	2	3	4	5	6
$P(X = x)$	0.1	0.1	0.25	0.05	0.4	0.1

b 0.5
c 0.4

3 a $k = \frac{1}{18}$
b

x	1	2	3	4	5	6
$P(X = x)$	$\frac{1}{18}$	$\frac{1}{18}$	$\frac{1}{5}$	$\frac{1}{5}$	$\frac{5}{18}$	$\frac{5}{18}$

c $\frac{7}{18}$
d $\frac{4}{9}$
e $\frac{1}{18}$

4 a $\alpha = 0.3$
b

x	−2	−1	0	1	2
$P(X = x)$	0.1	0.1	0.25	0.25	0.3

c 0.45

5 a $\frac{5}{6}$
c

x	1	2	3	4	5
$P(X = x)$	$\frac{2}{6}$	$\frac{1}{6}$	$\frac{1}{6}$	$\frac{1}{6}$	$\frac{1}{6}$

6 a $k = 1$
b

x	1	2	3
$P(X = x)$	$\frac{4}{16}$	$\frac{5}{16}$	$\frac{7}{16}$

Exercise 6C

1 a $E(X) = 4.6$, $E(X^2) = 26$
b $E(X) = 0.3$, $E(X^2) = 2.5$

2 $E(X) = 4$, $E(X^2) = 18.2$

3 a

x	2	3	6
$P(X = x)$	$\frac{1}{2}$	$\frac{1}{3}$	$\frac{1}{6}$

x	2	3	6
$P(X = x)$	$\frac{1}{4}$	$\frac{1}{9}$	$\frac{1}{36}$

b $E(X) = 3$, $E(X^2) = 11$
c $(E(X)^2) = 9$, therefore $(E(X)^2) \neq E(X)^2$

4 a

x	1	2	3	4	5
$P(X = x)$	$\frac{1}{2}$	$\frac{1}{4}$	$\frac{1}{8}$	$\frac{1}{16}$	$\frac{1}{16}$

b $E(X) = 1.9375$, $E(X^2) = 5.1875$
c $(E(X)^2) = 3.754$, therefore $(E(X)^2) \neq E(X)^2$

5 $a = 0.3$, $b = 0.3$

6 $a = 0.1$, $b = 0.4$

7

x	1	2	3	4	5	6
$P(X = x)$	$\frac{1}{8}$	$\frac{1}{8}$	$\frac{1}{8}$	$\frac{1}{8}$	$\frac{3}{20}$	$\frac{7}{20}$

8 $2.78

Challenge
$\frac{119}{24}$

Exercise 6D

1 a 1 b 2

2 a $E(X) = \frac{11}{6} = 1.83$, $Var(X) = \frac{17}{36} = 0.472$

b $E(X) = 0$, $Var(X) = 0.5$

c $E(X) = -0.5$, $Var(X) = 2.25$

3 $E(Y) = 4.5$, $Var(Y) = 5.25$

4 a

s	$P(S = s)$
2	$\frac{1}{36}$
3	$\frac{2}{36}$
4	$\frac{3}{36}$
5	$\frac{4}{36}$
6	$\frac{5}{36}$
7	$\frac{6}{36}$
8	$\frac{5}{36}$
9	$\frac{4}{36}$
10	$\frac{3}{36}$
11	$\frac{2}{36}$
12	$\frac{1}{36}$

b 7

c 5.833

d 2.415

5 a

d	0	1	2	3
$P(D = d)$	$\frac{1}{4}$	$\frac{3}{8}$	$\frac{1}{4}$	$\frac{1}{8}$

b 1.25

c $\frac{15}{16} = 0.9375$

6 a $P(T = 1) = P(\text{head}) = 0.5$

$P(T = 2) = P(\text{tail, head}) = 0.5 \times 0.5 = 0.25$

$P(T = 3) = 1 - P(T = 1) - P(T = 2) = 0.25$

b $E(T) = 1.75$, $Var(T) = \frac{11}{16} = 0.688$.

7 a $E(X) = 4a + 2b$

b $a = 0.375$, $b = 0.25$

Exercise 6E

1 a

y	−1	1	3	5
$P(Y = y)$	0.1	0.3	0.2	0.4

b $E(Y) = 2.8$

c $E(X) = 2.9$ and $2E(X) - 3 = 5.8 - 3 = 2.8 = E(Y)$

2 a

y	−8	−1	0	1	8
$P(Y = y)$	0.1	0.1	0.2	0.4	0.2

b $E(Y) = 1.1$

3 a 8 b 4 c 2 d 18

e 8 f 3

4 a 6 b −9 c −2 d 1

e 9

5 a 4μ b $2\mu + 2$ c $2\mu - 2$ d $4\sigma^2$

e $4\sigma^2$

6 a 3.5

b $Y = 200 + 100X$

c $E(Y) = 550$

7 726.5 cm³

8 a $E(X) = 1.25$, $Var(X) = 0.9375$

b $E(Y) = \frac{1}{4} \times 1 + \frac{3}{8} \times 2 + \frac{1}{4} \times 4 + \frac{1}{8} \times 8 = 3$

$E(Z) = 2E(X) + \frac{1}{2} = 3$

c $Var(Z) = 4Var(X) = 3.75$

Challenge

$E((X - E(X))^2) = E(X^2 - 2E(X)X + (E(X))^2)$
$= E(X^2) - 2E(X)E(X) + (E(X))^2 = E(X^2) - E(X)^2$

Exercise 6F

1 a $E(X) = 2$ b $Var(X) = 2$ c 1.414

2 a $E(X) = 2$ b $Var(X) = 4$ c $E(X^2) = 8$

3 $a = 0.1$, $b = 0.4$

4 a $-0.3 \leqslant E(Y) \leqslant 0.4$

b $a = 0.5$, $b = 0.2$

Exercise 6G

1 $E(X) = 3$, $Var(X) = 2$

2 a 4

b 4

3 a Expectation = 3.5 and variance = $2\frac{11}{12}$

b $\frac{2}{3}$

4 a $\frac{3}{10}$

b Expectation = 11 and Variance = 33

5 A discrete uniform distribution is not likely to be a good a model for this distribution. The game depends on the skills of the player. The points are likely to cluster around the middle.

6 a Discrete uniform distribution

b $E(X) = 4.5$

c $Var(X) = 5.25$

d The expected winnings are less than the 5 cents stake.

Chapter review 6

1 a

x	$P(X = x)$
1	$\frac{1}{15}$
2	$\frac{2}{15}$
3	$\frac{3}{15}$
4	$\frac{4}{15}$
5	$\frac{5}{15}$

b $\frac{9}{15}$

2 a $q = 0.1$ b 0.6

3 a

x	1	2	3	4
$P(X = x)$	0.0769	0.1923	0.3077	0.4231

b $\frac{19}{26}$

4 a The probabilities must be the same.

b i 0.0625 ii 0.375 iii 0.5

5 a 15

b

y	1	2	3	4	5
$P(Y = y)$	$\frac{1}{15}$	$\frac{2}{15}$	$\frac{3}{15}$	$\frac{4}{15}$	$\frac{5}{15}$

c $\frac{9}{15}$ or $\frac{3}{5}$

6 a

t	0	1	2	3	4
$P(T = t)$	0.316	0.422	0.211	0.0469	0.00391

b 0.949

c

s	1	2	3	4	5
$P(S = s)$	0.25	0.188	0.141	0.105	0.316

d 0.562

7 a

x	$P(X = x)$
1	$\frac{1}{21}$
2	$\frac{2}{21}$
3	$\frac{3}{21}$
4	$\frac{4}{21}$
5	$\frac{5}{21}$
6	$\frac{6}{21}$

b $\frac{12}{21}$ or $\frac{4}{7}$ **c** $\frac{91}{21}$ or $\frac{13}{3}$ **d** $\frac{20}{9} = 2.22$
e $\frac{80}{9} = 8.89$ **f** $\frac{325}{3} = 108.3$

8 a 0.2 **b** 0.7 **c** 3.6 **d** 8.04
9 a 0.3 **b** $E(X) = 0 \times 0.2 + 1 \times 0.3 + 2 \times 0.5 = 1.3$
c 0.61 **d** 0.5
10 a $k + 0 + k + 2k = 1$, so $4k = 1$, so $k = 0.25$
b $E(X) = 2$
$E(X^2) = 0^2 \times 0.25 + 1^2 \times 0 + 2^2 \times 0.25 + 3^2 \times 0.5 = 1 + 4.5 = 5.5$
c 6
11 a $\frac{1}{8}$ **b** $\frac{9}{8}$ **c** $\frac{19}{8}$ **d** $\frac{55}{64}$
e 0.2854
12 a 0.3 **b** 2.3 **c** 1.61 **d** 0.35
e 1.46 **f** 0.281
13 a $p + q = 0.5$, $2p + 3q = 1.3$
b $p = 0.2$, $q = 0.3$
c 1.29
d 5.16
14 a $\frac{1}{9}$ **b** $\frac{31}{9}$
c $\text{Var}(X) = E(X^2) - E(X)^2 = \frac{125}{9} - \left(\frac{31}{9}\right)^2 = 2.02$ (3 s.f.)
d 8.1 (1 d.p.)
15 a $a = 0.4$, $b = 0.2$
b $E(X^2) = 1.3$, $\text{Var}(X) = 0.81$
c $\text{Var}(Y) = 7.29$
d $P(Y + 2 > X) = P(3X - 1 + 2 > X) = P(X > -0.5) = 0.9$
16 a Discrete uniform distribution
b Any distribution where all the probabilities are the same. An example is throwing a fair dice.
c $E(X) = 2$
d $\text{Var}(X) = 2$

Challenge

$$E(X) = \sum_{i=1}^{n} \frac{i}{n} = \frac{n(n+1)}{2n} = \frac{n+1}{2}$$

$$E(X^2) = \sum_{i=1}^{n} \frac{i^2}{n} = \frac{n(n+1)(2n+1)}{6n} = \frac{(n+1)(2n+1)}{6}$$

$$\text{Var}(X) = E(X^2) - (E(X))^2 = \frac{(n+1)(2n+1)}{6} - \frac{(n+1)^2}{4}$$

$$= \frac{4n^2 + 6n + 2 - 3n^2 - 6n - 3}{12} = \frac{(n+1)(n-1)}{12}$$

CHAPTER 7

Prior knowledge check

1 a $\frac{1}{8}$ **b** $\frac{5}{8}$ **c** $\frac{3}{8}$
2 a 0.211 (3 s.f.) **b** 0.599 (3 s.f.)

For Chapter 7, answers may differ slightly from those shown here when calculators are used rather than table values.

Exercise 7A

1 a Continuous – lengths can take any value
b Discrete – scores can take only certain values
c Continuous – masses can take any value
d Discrete – shoe sizes can take only certain values
2

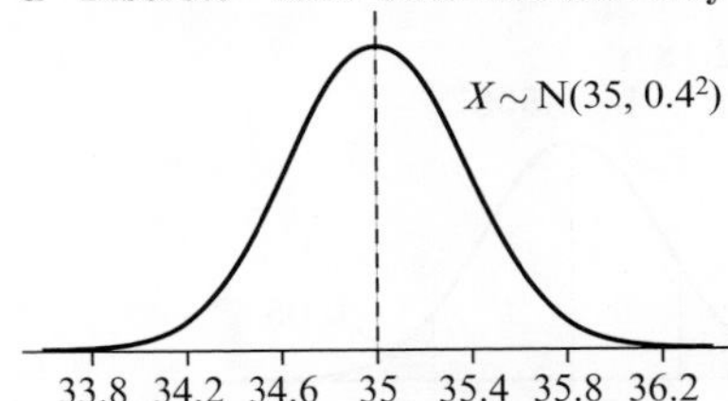

3 The distribution is not symmetrical.
4 a 0.68 **b** 0.95
5 49
6 60 g
7 $\mu = 56.7$ (3 s.f.), $\sigma^2 = 4.69^2$ (3 s.f.)
8 a 0.5 **b** 0.683 (3 s.f.) **c** 0.954 (3 s.f.)
d Incorrect: although $P(X > 100) > 0$, it is very small since 100 is more than 3 standard deviations away from the mean, so the model as a whole is still reasonable.
9 a 36 **b** Between 2 and 3

Exercise 7B

1 a 0.102 **b** 0.9515 **c** 0.0113
d 0.4049 **e** 0.0674 **f** 0.0522
2 a 0.9830 **b** 0.9131 **c** 0.2005
d 0.352 **e** 0.4893 **f** 0.0516
g 0.1823 **h** 0.8836

Exercise 7C

1 a −0.43 **b** −0.489
c 1.22 **d** −0.81 and 0.81
2 a 1.33 **b** 1.86 **c** 1.0364
d −1.6449 **e** 1.06 **f** 2.55
g 1.2816 **h** 0.5244

Exercise 7D

1 a 0.9332 **b** 0.0062 **c** 0.7734
2 a 0.264 **b** 0.171
3 a 0.9522 **b** 0.7475 **c** 0.0038
4 32.6
5 18.1
6 a 70.6 **b** 80.8 **c** 0.075
7 a i 81.0 **ii** 80.6 **b** 0.0364
8 a 0 **b** −0.16 **c** 0.2 **d** 0.74
9 a $\Phi(0)$ **b** $\Phi(0.5)$ **c** $1 - \Phi(-0.25)$
d $\Phi(0.0833) - \Phi(-1.17)$
10 a 1.96 **b** 87.8 (3 s.f.)
11 a −1.0364 **b** 54.9 cm
12 a $-1.2816 < z < 1.2816$ **b** 1103–1247 hours

Exercise 7E

1 11.5
2 3.87
3 31.6
4 25
5 $\mu = 13.1, \sigma = 4.32$
6 $\mu = 28.3, \sigma = 2.59$
7 $\mu = 12, \sigma = 3.56$
8 $\mu = 35, \sigma = 14.8$ or $\sigma = 14.9$
9 4.75
10 $\sigma = 1.99, a = 2.18$
11 **a** 0.1299 mm **b** 0.5587
12 **a**

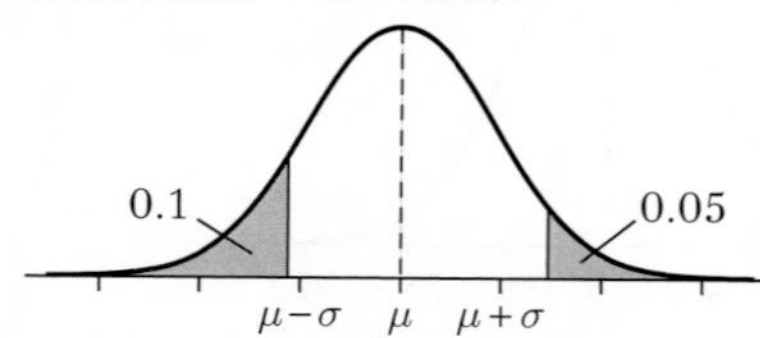

b $\mu = 23.26, \sigma = 4.100$
13 **a** $\mu = 16.79, \sigma = 0.9421$ **b** 1.27

Challenge

a Let z be such that $\Phi(z) = 0.75$, then upper quartile $= \mu + z\sigma$ and lower quartile $= \mu - z\sigma$, so $q = (\mu + z\sigma) - (\mu - z\sigma) = 2z\sigma$.
Calculate that $z = 0.674$, then $q = 1.348\sigma$ and thus $\sigma = 0.742q$ (3 s.f.).
b Since $q = (\mu + z\sigma) - (\mu - z\sigma) = 2z\sigma$ (the μs cancel), q is not dependent on μ and vice versa, and it is not possible to write μ in terms of q.

Chapter review 7

1 **a** 0.0401 **b** 0.3307 **c** 188 cm
2 **a** 12.7% or 12.8% **b** 51.1% or 51.2%
3 **a** 0.0668 **b** 0.0521
4 **a** 3.65 **b** 0.1357 **c** 32.5
5 **a** 8.60 ml **b** 0.123 **c** 109 ml
6 **a** $\mu = 30, \sigma = 14.8$ or $\sigma = 14.9$ **b** 38.03
7 Mean 10.2 cm, standard deviation 3.76 cm
8 **a** 0.3085
b 0.370 or 0.371
c The first score was better, since fewer of the students got this score or more.
9 **a** 4.25 or 4.26 **b** 0.050 (2 d.p.)
10 **a** 8.54 minutes **b** 0.1758
11 Mean 6.12 mm, standard deviation 0.398 mm

Challenge

1 27 800 televisions
2 **a** Unchanged at 5.2
b Decreases, as average deviation from the mean is less
c The shape of the curve changes and $P(Z = 5.2) > 0$

Review exercise 2

1 Diagram A corresponds to −0.79, since there is negative correlation.
Diagram B corresponds to 0.08, since there is very weak or no correlation.
Diagram C corresponds to 0.68, since there is positive correlation.
2 **a** $15.3 + 2 \times 10.2 = 35.7$ so 45 is an outlier
b A temperature of 45 °C is very high so it is likely this value was recorded incorrectly.
c When the temperature increases by 1 °C, the number of ice creams sold per month increases by 2810.
d Outside the range of the data (extrapolation)
3 **a**

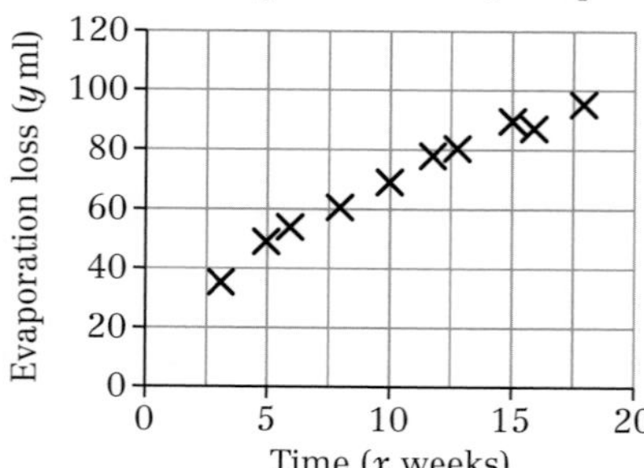

b The points lie close to a straight line.
c $a = 29.02, b = 3.90$
d 3.90 ml of the chemicals evaporate each week.
e **i** 103 ml **ii** 166 ml
f **i** This estimate is reasonably reliable, since it is just outside the range of the data.
ii This estimate is unreliable, since it is far outside the range of the data.
4 **a & d**

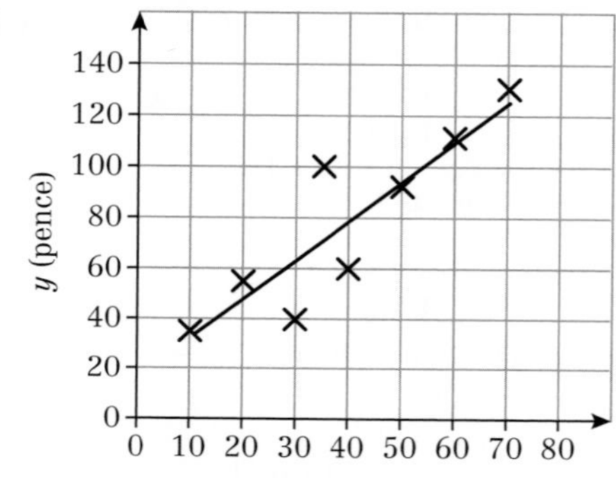

b $S_{xy} = \sum xy - \frac{\sum x \sum y}{n} = 28\,750 - \frac{315 \times 620}{8} = 4337.5$
$S_{xx} = 2821.875$
c $a = 17.0, b = 1.54$
e **i** Brand D is overpriced, since it is a long way above the regression line.
ii 69p or 70p since this is the predicted price for a bar of chocolate with 35% cocoa.
5 **a** $y = -0.425 + 0.395x$ (3 s.f.)
b $f = 0.735 + 0.395k$ (3 s.f.)
c 93.6 litres (3 s.f.)
6 **a** $S_{xy} = 71.4685$, $S_{xx} = 1760.459$
b $y = 0.324 + 0.0406x$ (3 s.f.)
c 2461.95 mm (2 d.p.)
d $l = 2460.324 + 0.0406t$
e 2463.98 mm (2 d.p.)
f This estimate is unreliable, since it is outside the range of the data.
7 **a** −0.816
b Houses are cheaper the further away they are from the railway station.
c −0.816
8 **a** $17
b $S_{tt} = 983.6, S_{mm} = 1728.9, S_{tm} = 1191.8$
c 0.914 (3 s.f.)
d 0.914. Linear coding does not affect the correlation coefficient.

e 0.914 suggests a relationship between the time spent shopping and the money spent.
0.178 suggests that there was no such relationship.
f e.g. Shopping behaviours may be different on different days of the week.

9 a

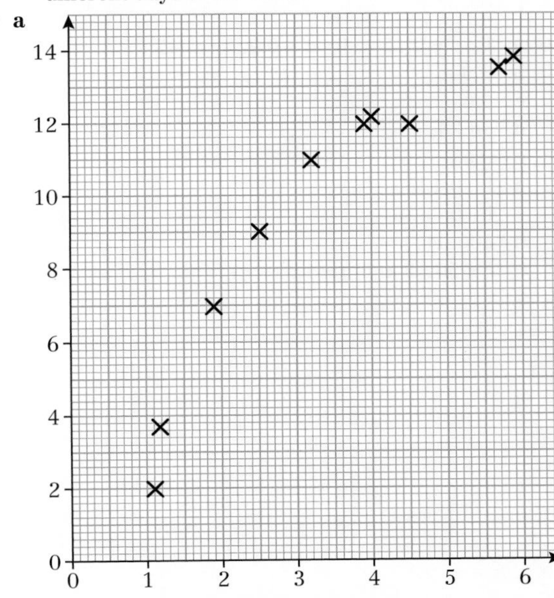

b The strength of the linear relationship between two variables.
c $S_{tt} = 26.589$; $S_{pp} = 152.444$; $S_{tp} = 59.524$
d 0.93494…

10 a 0.375 **b** 0.125 **c** 0.125

11 a

x	−3	−2	0	1	3
$P(X = x)$	0.1	0.2	0.2	0.1	0.4

b 0.9

12 a

x	$P(X = x)$
1	$\frac{1}{36}$
2	$\frac{3}{36}$
3	$\frac{5}{36}$
4	$\frac{7}{36}$
5	$\frac{9}{36}$
6	$\frac{11}{36}$

b $\frac{7}{12}$ or 0.583 **c** $\frac{161}{36}$ or 4.47
d $\text{Var}(X) = E(X^2) - (E(X))^2 = \frac{791}{36} - \frac{25921}{1296} = 1.97$ (3 s.f.)
e 17.7

13 a $\frac{1}{17}$ or 0.0588 **b** $\frac{64}{17}$ or 3.76
c $\text{Var}(X) = E(X^2) - (E(X))^2 = \frac{266}{17} - \frac{4096}{289} = 1.47$ (3 s.f.)
d 13.3

14 a $p + q = 0.4$, $2p + 4q = 1.3$
b $p = 0.15$, $q = 0.25$
c 1.75
d 7.00

15 a $p + q = 0.45$, $3p + 7q = 1.95$
b $p = 0.3$, $q = 0.15$
c 0.35 **d** 7.15 **e** 1 **f** 114.4

16 a 0.1, 0.4 **b** 1.5, 1.41 **c** 12.69 **d** 0.4

17 a $P(X = x) = 0.2$
b

y	1	2	3	4
$P(Y = y)$	0.6	0.24	0.096	0.064

c 0.16

18 a 0.2743 **b** 12

19 a 0.0618 **b** 0.9545
c 0.00281 **d** This is a bad assumption.

20 a Mean 1.700 m, standard deviation 0.095 m
b 0.337

21 a 1.07 (3 s.f.) **b** 0.505 (3 s.f.) **c** 0.981 (3 s.f.)

22 a 0.8413 **b** 0.1112

23 a 0.2119 **b** 28.2

24 a 0.3446 **b** 172.3 **c** 49.9
d Power Batteries, as the mean is greater than Strong Batteries. They also have approximately the same standard deviation

25 a 0.7734 **b** 0.7888 **c** 0.3307

Challenge

1 a i Linear model: $y = -2.63 + 2.285x$
ii Quadratic model: $y = 1.04 + 0.1206x + 0.2353x^2$
iii Exponential model: $y = 1.1762e^{0.3484x}$
b Linear residuals: 1.845, −0.925, −1.21, −1.295, 0.435, 1.15
Quadratic residuals: 0.1041, −0.2195, 0.0128, −0.0255, 0.3861, −0.264
Exponential residuals: −0.16644, −0.04507, 0.560703, 0.785369, 0.321593, −2.29619
Hence quadratic model is most suitable as the residuals are smaller and are randomly scattered around zero.

2 a

x	0	1	2	3
$P(X = x)$	$\frac{1}{16}$	$\frac{9}{32}$	$\frac{12}{32}$	$\frac{9}{32}$

b $E(X) = \sum xP(X = x)$
$= 0 \times \frac{1}{16} + 1 \times \frac{9}{32} + 2 \times \frac{12}{32} + 3 \times \frac{9}{32}$
$= \frac{15}{8}$

Exam practice

1 a

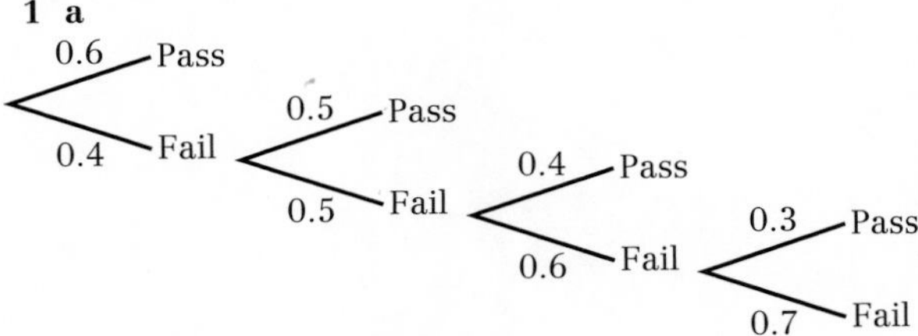

b 0.873 or (87.3%)

2 a

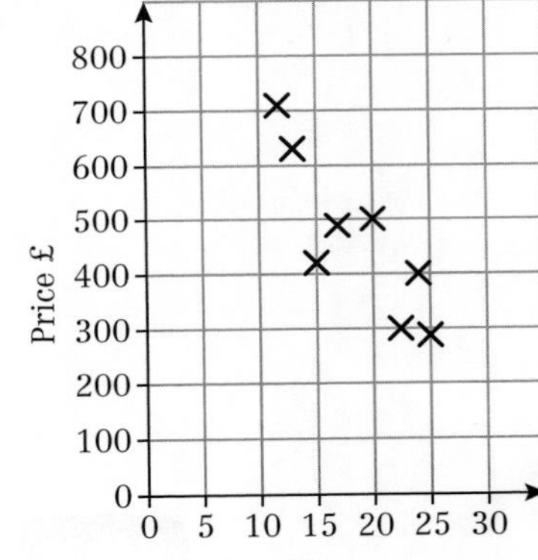

b Negative correlation or 'as t increases, p, decreases' or 'points close to a straight line' or linear correlation or words to that affect.
c $p = 938.21 - 27.6t$
d €375.53
e Not a good decision as 39 years is outside the range.

3 a 34440
b −1078.5
c −0.87285
d As the price of gold increases the price of oil decreases.
e The price of oil decreases and the price of oil increases which goes against the correlation. As a result, the PMMC will decrease (get weaker).

4 a 90 employees
b 29 hours
c 28 hours
d Median, since the data is skewed and therefore not affected by extreme values.

5 a

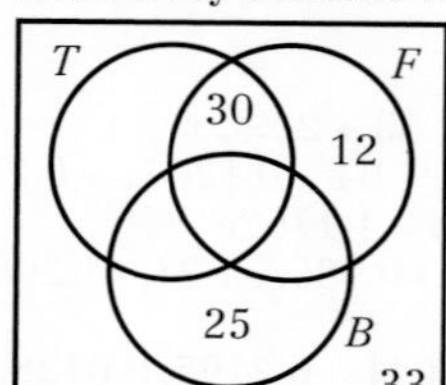

b tennis and basketball or football and basketball
c 0.33
d 0.42
e 0.55
f $\frac{30}{42}$ or $\frac{5}{7}$

6 a i $c = 0.15$, **ii** $a = 0.2$, $b = 0.45$
b 3.64
c 4.6
d 58.24
e 0.65

7 a i 0.1335
ii 0.7335
b 506.04
c $r = 502.5$ and $q = 1.51$

INDEX